Gary A. Freitas, Ph.D. has been a practicing clinical and forensic psychologist for the past 30 years. A child of the San Francisco Bay Area, he currently resides in Phoenix, Arizona. For the past 15 years, he has been creating 3-D sculptures from computers and electronic components in a series titled *Singularity: Arising Electronic Consciousness—The Art of Electric Dreaming.* He is also the author of three books (*Relationship Realities*, *War Movies*, and *Gone Mad in Glory and Ecstasy*), as well as professional works on involuntary commitment, workplace violence and malingering.

Facebook.com/Gary Freitas
singularityartworks.com

To my aunts and uncles—Alden, Tina, Nettie, Anna, Ken, Al and Trudy—
Thank you.

Gary A. Freitas

THE COMING SINGULARITY

The Rapid Evolution of Human Identity

AUSTIN MACAULEY PUBLISHERS™

LONDON • CAMBRIDGE • NEW YORK • SHARJAH

Ordering Information
Quantity sales: Special discounts are available on quantity purchases by corporations, associations, and others. For details, contact the publisher at the address below.

Publisher's Cataloging-in-Publication data
Freitas, Gary A.
The Coming Singularity

ISBN 9781649799128 (Paperback)
ISBN 9781649799142 (Hardback)
ISBN 9781649799135 (Audiobook)
ISBN 9781638291626 (ePub e-book)

Library of Congress Control Number: 2021925679

www.austinmacauley.com/us

First Published 2022
Austin Macauley Publishers LLC
40 Wall Street, 33rd Floor, Suite 3302
New York, NY 10005
USA

mail-usa@austinmacauley.com
+1 (646) 5125767

The unending technology discussions with my son Scott, Ph.D. in Computer Science, gave outline to all the topics explored here. The discovery of my art by film-maker Remi Vaughn provided inspiration for a deeper examination of my art and impetus to write this book. And my gratitude to Sonja Elcic for her support, insights and editing recommendations.

Table of Contents

Preface

Consciousness—a darting firefly in a universe lit by stars.

—G. Freitas

Futurists and thought leaders predict that by 2050 artificial intelligence (AI) will exceed human intelligence and profoundly alter the human experience. *The Coming Singularity* is an exploration of our evolving interface with technology, and the psychological, social, and political impact machine intelligence will have on all of us in the coming decades.

If there is one overarching theme, it is this—our e-technology interface is modifying our identities, individually and collectively—creating extraordinary demands and expectations that will test the limits of our adaptability. I have termed this transformational process and all its sequela *Identity Diffusion*.

The many books and articles I have encountered on the topic of Singularity have been generally indifferent to the human struggle, mostly offering bleary panaceas. Not surprisingly, their focus is on technology. Hopefully, this book is a corrective, as I attempt to delve into the impact of the tech-rapture being proselytized by thought influencers, but also examining the challenges and existential threat foretold by apostates of a dystopian future (Bill Gates, Stephen Hawking and Elon Musk).

I would emphasize *The Coming Singularity* is written from a psychological perspective and not as a tech insider. Like most of you, I have been observing and experiencing the many recent changes we are undergoing from our e-technology interface. I wonder aloud about the impact of the changes coming our way and the exceedingly brief time before human consciousness fully encounters a robust AI. As a psychologist, artist, writer and parent, I encourage all of us to prepare for a journey that will require all the imagination and courage we can summon.

Introduction: You Are Different Today and Don't Know It!

> The ache of cosmic specialness will be lost.
> —E. Becker, *The Denial of Death*

Big Picture

Universe	13.8 billion years
Earth	4.5 billion
First life	3.8 billion
First mammals	200 million
First primates	55 million
First apes	25 million
Proto-humans	5.5 million
Homo sapiens	300,000
First civilization	3,500

Last 200 years—electricity, the telegraph, the incandescent light bulb, internal combustion engine, trains, telephones, movies, automobiles, radio, refrigeration, airplanes, television, vaccines, transistors, nuclear power, satellites, computers, space station, video games, gene sequencing, internet and smartphones.

It is hard not to notice that something in the human experience has dramatically changed in recent years. Everyone is continuously interacting with electronic devices—sending out and receiving back electronic signals. A world once indexed by six degrees of separation is now instantaneously connected by one degree of separation.

While everything appears relatively normal day-to-day, we have changed and don't appear to realize it. So, what has changed, you ask? For one, we spend more than 7.5 hours a day interacting with electronic devices (Center for Disease Control). We can buy a home gene editing kit for $349 and have our DNA sequenced for $150. The world is being microchipped and censored into data streams, as we are harvested and scrubbed by data research labs (and hackers) around the world. Everything about us is available online to anyone who wants it badly enough—corporations, hackers or governments. Overnight, we have become vulnerable and exploited in terms that have significant implications regarding privacy, identity and independence of thought and action.

What remains unanswered is, Why are we all lining up to be electronically connected? And what does it mean to be disconnected? Disconnected, not in a Luddite sense, but out of a failure to be fully involved in the human experience; perhaps unadaptive in an evolutionary sense. E-technology comes to us as convenience, cost-saving, entertainment, information, safety-security, and connectivity. But we almost never ask what it wants from us in return. That is explored here as well.

Perhaps even more disconcerting, there is no opt-out or off-the-grid option. We are all hardwired into this electronic network, whether we like it or not. This is the new normal, and we should all be paying attention. And hold on, it's going to be a wild ride. While admission is whatever you can afford, it will require a significant shift in who we think we are. And even though there is no formal age or height requirement, there is also no privacy agreement.

Evolutionary Trajectory

Is there an evolutionary strategy underlying our technology interface? Despite much clever speculation, we don't really know why we were gifted a 1400 cm^3 brain. It came with some obvious upgrades—longer-smoother gait, language, opposable thumbs, and cognitive enhancements. And as our biological and social adaptations evolved one from the other, we gained superior tool-making skills, migratory capability, and complex social organization. It is also clear that *Homo sapiens* competed with any number of proto-human species to become the apex predator.

How many hominid species we extinguished is still up for conjecture. But after 300,000 years of gradual change, the most remarkable aspect of our evolutionary journey has occurred over the past few thousand years. From an evolutionary perspective, this has been at the speed of light.

The rise of electronic technology and AI has one previous parallel. Five hundred and forty million years ago, the Cambrian Explosion gave rise to all biological organisms on Earth today. I would propose that we are currently undergoing an analogous event, the Anthropocene Explosion of electronic forms, giving rise to infinite numbers of electronic interfaces. And the surprising DNA of this began humbly as 36 abstract symbols (26 letters and 10 numbers), underpinning the entire complexity of the modern world. Our data-rich networks are now driving evolution, including genetically altering us in ways not unlike millions of years of evolution.

The genesis of the Anthropocene Explosion was the arrival of consciousness, which quickly adapted a revolutionary strategy to outsource itself. The broad effect includes the development of complex social networks, the powerful ability to manipulate the physical world, unlimited knowledge generation, and now, the rise of machine intelligence. It has become evident that our evolution is no longer being exclusively driven by biological adaptation, but by social-cultural factors. And to be clear, in this moment, we are the ones adapting, not the ones evolving. It is our social-cultural complexity that is rapidly evolving. This book is an effort to gauge our adaptability to rapid social-cultural evolution.

The evolution of complex social networks highlights the adaptive advantages of our technological advancement, and the ability of consciousness to manipulate the physical world. But toward what end? We have gained greater autonomy and mastery of the world by more reliably predicting the future. As a result, we have extended our individual and collective longevity. But any reflection on the past 4,000 years or the world around us today should give us pause. Our evolution has not been a simple path forward. Many dozens of civilizations have disappeared—many still unknown to us. The path forward has always been a few hesitant steps forward and many steps backward.

So, why all the regression before we humans got to where we are today? And why are we struggling to avoid becoming a collapsing civilization? The short answer is that our primate psychology has numerous recessive traits that bring us into direct conflict with the future. Consequently, it's easy to imagine that we could stumble again. An underlying premise of this book is that the advanced cognitive capabilities of AI represent an opportunity for us to rapidly continue towards the future; not the inevitable future, but the one we are capable of imagining. To avoid the inevitable future, we will have to change beyond our current adaptation for machine intelligence to arise. Only then will we reach the Singularity—when machine intelligence exceeds human intelligence.

Identity Diffusion

If this book has one primary theme it is this: Our interface with e-technology is altering our individual and collective identities. This has created extraordinary demands for adaptation on our part, ones that will test the limits. Technology is changing who we are becoming as we move toward the coming Singularity. It is important for us to understand that alterations to our identities are prerequisite for the rise of machine intelligence.

Identity formation takes a lifetime and is exceptionally vulnerable and subject to wide-ranging disruptions. As e-technology begins altering identity, we are being exposed to increased stressors or what is termed here as Identity Diffusion. This is a chronic underlying condition of contemporary life, as evidenced by the ever-expanding *Diagnostic and Statistical Manual of Mental Disorders* (DSM-5). The diffusion of identity comes in many forms, but at its core is *derealization*—the unreality of life, as evidence by increased stress, anxiety, depression, alienation and default to cognitive distortion.

Underlying Identity Diffusion is a new reality. There is the *real you* or what you think of as "Me" or "I," and now there is an *electronic you*—each operating independently of the other. What is unique about this circumstance is the *real you* can reach out into the world as never before, and the *electronic you* can reach back through e-technology and impact the *real you*. In a world in which identity is exceptionally vulnerable, this portents serious consequences moving forward.

Networked Simulations

Today, we sapiens reside in highly complex social networks that organize us socially and culturally. In essence, we have evolved into a system of networks—nation-states, complex economies, transportation hubs, educational centers, energy grids, healthcare facilities, etc. They serve to insulate us from the exigencies of the natural world, or what sci-fi writers like to call a *simulation*. And because of this successful adaptation, we are seeking to expand the benefits of the simulation by adapting consciousness to machine intelligence and the coming Singularity.

The most significant adaptation that gave rise to our networked world and evolving machine intelligence was the startling emergence of consciousness and the development of language. This inevitably resulted in the externalization of information storage and retrieval, or what most of us think of as language, writing, literacy, printing—exponentially expanded by computers and the internet. For the first time, data, information, and knowledge resided external to the mind and became endlessly accessible.

Within the simulation, we are being scrubbed and surveilled 24/7 by machine intelligence, atomizing and siloing us from the experiential world. *The goal of rising machine intelligence and the coming Singularity is to potentiate complexity—that is its prime directive.* Which means, we will become increasingly dysfunctional if we fail to adapt to complexity.

Adapting to simulated complexity confronts us with many challenges, including Identity Diffusion, which is becoming a significant factor in our unending personal and social conflicts. Because e-technology is now a primary interface with both the natural world and our social networked reality, we should approach it cautiously. It shares many elements of early European colonialism, which quickly became a disruptive and violent cultural force across the world for centuries.

AI is now engaging our networked conformity in times of profound change. It is, and will be for the foreseeable future, rigid, fixed, and rule-bound. In the sapiens' sense, it is absolutist and operates with limited and well-defined parameter—which will be frustrating. It is also surveilling, quantifying, and qualifying our lives as a primary driver of our dynamically networked universe. The goal is to quantify the *Value of Everything*. This should be another caution.

There is one other detail that requires mentioning. Our remarkable social organization is subject to unpredictable perturbations or what chaos theory terms the instability of small changes or Butterfly Effect. It turns out that complex social networks can be surprisingly unstable for reasons we are unable to predict (Black Swans). Addressing this reality is clearly the driving adaptation behind the rise of machine intelligence—stabilizing the exponential rise of complexity.

1.0 – The Coming Singularity

Singularity: Accelerated evolution through technology allowing us to transcend our biological bodies and brains and gain power over our fates. Our mortality will be in our own hands. We will be able to live as long as we want—have the ability to infuse the universe with creativity and intelligence. This will be the Sixth Epoch in the evolution of patterns of information and the ultimate destiny of the Singularity and of the universe.

—R. Kurzweil,

The Singularity Is Near: When Humans Transcend Biology

The idea of Singularity is a product of the human demand for a narrative arc; one that encompasses a past, present, and future—apparently a profound characteristic of consciousness. We can only live in the present, one that is primarily shaped by the past, while imagination (our intersubjective reality) gives rise to an existential need to predict the future. And by the future, I mean this very moment and the next, today, tomorrow, and forever, to ensure our collective immortality—whose epilogue has been variously characterized as heaven, paradise, nirvana, and now the coming Singularity.

Singularity is the hope by futurists and thought leaders that all their speculation about the future of technology will turn out to be prescient. But let's explore this predicted future and what is being forecasted. On the surface, this appears to be a race toward human extinction by two competing models of global catastrophic risk. One is the traditional model—asteroids, volcanic events, nuclear war, global climate change, pandemic. The shiny new alternative is the creation of AI.

The hope extended by *dataists* is for the transformation of data at the quantum level; what we humans might think of as enlightenment, which will allow conscious and sentient technology to mitigate the universe's entropic reality and enter a future we are currently unable to comprehend (and, yes, that will be challenging). Futurists also posit a transitional period in which humans will be augmented with superior physical and intellectual capabilities, perhaps even an integrative phase between the biological and the technological.

On the downside, many theorists of evolution and technology see the potential for the rise of an evolutionarily competitive species, in much the same manner as *Homo sapiens* extinguished Neanderthals. Initially, AI may be nothing more than the rational imposed on the irrational, helpful and benign in the beginning, but by the end, who could possibly know?

Residing in the structure of human consciousness appears to be, for lack of a better term, a *forever drive*. This is the unique ability of human consciousness to project the individual *self*, beyond the immediate and indefinitely into future. And if our networked history is any indicator, we have been obsessively preoccupied with evading death for a long time. And if we can't achieve it here on Earth, we will gain it through our imagination. For thousands of years, we have been envisioning our immortality through deities and our ascension to an afterlife (wherever that is and however we envision it). What Freud characterized as a "life-instinct" appears to imbue us with a greater sense of purpose and, beyond that, a timeless sense of destiny.

For most of us, immortality means eating better and exercising more. And for those who have totally given up on an afterlife, there are anti-aging clinics to methylate their telomers while downing a *senolytic* cocktail (Metformin, Rapamycin, human growth hormones). Throw in a colonic and Botox for good measure. Clearly, in response to this insatiable drive, consciousness has given rise to AI—our new immortality vehicle (in the short-term, we may require cryogenics or uploading consciousness to a server). All of this, from time immemorial, derives from the capacity of consciousness to transform the genetic fight-flight preset and the individual sense of identity into a striving for immortality.

Sidenote: I have taken the liberty of deviating from Kurzweil's definition of Singularity, positing that the first Singularity (S1) has already occurred with the advent of human consciousness and the subsequent development of language and all that followed from this (writing, math, art, printing, literacy, technology), reaching its current apogee with the computer and internet. The rise of machine intelligence, as narrated by Kurzweil, represents the second

Singularity (S2). And if machine consciousness were to arise, I term this the third Singularity (S3).

Anthropocene Explosion

> The amount of plastic alone is greater in mass than all land animals
> and marine creatures combined.
>
> —Weizmann Institute of Science

The current rapid evolution of technology parallels a remarkable event that occurred 540 million years ago, one that paleontologists term the Cambrian Explosion. This event resulted in the rapid, mass diversification of biological organisms, representing all life on Earth today. What paleontologists now term the Anthropocene is a geologic time period demarcating the impact of sapiens on Earth. It variously dates from the Agricultural Revolution, 12,000–15,000 years ago, to the more recent socio-economic impact on both Earth's climate and biodiversity, now potentially resulting in a Sixth Mass Extinction Event of life-forms on Earth.

By 2100 (80 years from now), it's predicted that half of all life on Earth will disappear because of human activity. Mostly missing from any discussion are the repercussive shocks of e-technology on Earth's ecosystem. Let's be candid; in real geologic time, the Anthropocene is going to be exceedingly brief.

Okay, Maybe We Have Overdone It!

Scientists calculate that in 2019, sea temperatures were rising at a rate equivalent to detonating five atomic bombs per second in our oceans or 3.6 billion Hiroshima atomic bomb explosions. This may seem overly dramatic, but only because we don't get to experience missile launches, contrails latticing the horizon and mushrooming nuclear clouds. No, at the beginning of the end, there will just be a lot of bleached seaweed washing up onto the beaches.

The origins of the Anthropocene Explosion, based on available timelines, suggest human consciousness ascended 200,000 to 300,000 years ago and then crystalized into human civilization 3,500 years ago. This created the population density and communication infrastructure required for the rise of technology. Yes, we took our time. The first significant technology transformation did not take place until the Industrial Revolution, 250 years ago, and now in rapid succession, the so-called Fourth Industrial Revolution is upon us (robotics, AI, bioengineering, nanotechnology, quantum computing). Accelerating technology has resulted in expansive knowledge creation and complexity, as we chip and sensor the entire planet.

I would offer that we are currently undergoing an Anthropocene Explosion; that is, we are evidencing a rapid, mass diversification, similar to 540 million years ago, but this time it is millions of circuit boards and electronic devices altering the physical and social landscape. (I am talking to you—Alexa, Cortana, Siri, and Astro!) These many forms now constitute the fossil artifacts of an evolving machine intelligence.

Based on the grim timeline outlined above, it's pretty evident we are racing toward the future faster today than ever before. And simultaneously, we are speeding toward the coming Singularity and the potential rise of a new consciousness out of the old one. And if time is memory, we will soon be nearing the speed of light when it comes to evolutionary change. We appear to be at hyper-evolution's event horizon—not just modifying our DNA but originating inorganic consciousness that has no selective pressures other than to create knowledge of the universe. It's also important to keep in mind, it's not me or you or our children that are rapidly evolving at this moment, but rather the externalization of evolution as a cultural and technological phenomenon. That is the real story of the future.

As we reflect on the human timeline, our rapid evolution as a species is quite remarkable. It is worth noting that it took *Homo sapiens* a brief 4.5 million years to fully evolve from apes. So, when machine intelligence reflects on its rapid rise—from mammals to primates, to great apes, to proto-humans, to *Homo sapiens*, to *Techno sapiens* (technologically augmented humans) and, finally, Singularity and *TechCons* (technological consciousness) —they will have required a brief 100 years to differentiate from humans. What once took millions of years, then millennia, may now only take decades (practically chump-change in evolutionary terms).

What isn't being chipped, embedded with a sensor, coded, programmed, Wi-Fi'd, or converted to a data stream? So, what are Siri and your Ring doorbell/video surveillance network telling the police? Who is hacking your security video feed? No, don't pee on your Fitbit for glucose levels (your health insurer wants to scan it); not to mention, your Nest Thermostat and smart refrigerator are reporting you as an energy waster; and by the way, you are out of soy milk and buy a heck of a lot more pet food than vegetables. And how much dirt is your Roomba collecting on you? (The chain of evidence is pretty reliable here—your apartment is a homeless shelter.) "Hey, that's a chill looking ankle monitor, where can I get one?" "Oh, you mean, my smartwatch has all the same features, is way more stylish and removeable?"

And coming soon, your thoughts and emotions will be monitored, and you will be tracked by bio-identification, chip implants, GPS traces, cell tower pings, and facial recognition technology. This is just the beginning, and we appear to be clueless. And until our AI overlords arrive, you will be augmented, analyzed, surveilled, and monetized 24/7 by algorithms and deep machine-learning programs—all for your benefit, of course.

One of the questions that emerges from all of this is, does our current electronic diversification portent the rise of an inorganic consciousness for the very first time? And has human intelligence been the necessary catalyst in the primordial evolutionary soup for the rise of techno-consciousness? In the same way, *Homo habilis* and *Australopithecus afarensis* (Lucy) were transitional species to *Homo sapiens*; we may be a transitional species between the biologic and the technologic.

In evolutionary terms, this could mean a significant bump-up in intelligence from the biologic to the technologic. An intelligence superior to our own that is untied to biology and any intersubjective experience, guided only by algorithmic pattern recognition. Rather than synaptic-biochemistry, this new consciousness will be a wave-particle photon in electronic data that flows at the quantum level. Equally important, this rising technology will be untied to biological evolution and will be able to rapidly self-direct its future, which raises two profound questions, what happens when intelligence is uncoupled from subjective experience, and how fast can it self-evolve?

As for us, we may get an early data-dump—obsolescent operating system not worth the upgrade, aging consumers hanging on to inefficient technology that's no longer backward compatible—as we go the way of Neanderthals (in 14 years, there have been 14 iPhone models—just saying). Of course, we will not know it and continue along with the illusion of being you. (Who is in charge? No one!)

The Anthropocene Age

- Big brain (300,000 BC)
- Language (50,000 BC)
- Agriculture (12,000 BC)
- Metallurgy (3,800 BC)
- Social complexity (3,500 BC)
- Written language and mathematics (3,100 BC)
- First written legal code (Ur-nammu) (2,100 BC)
- Printing press (1440 AD)
- Public education and universal literacy (1635 AD)
- First Industrial Revolution (1750 AD) (steam engine/factory system)
- Second Industrial Revolution (1880 AD) (electricity)
- Third Industrial Revolution (1950 AD) (computer and the internet)
- Fourth Industrial Revolution (2020 AD) (bioengineering, nanotechnologies, quantum computing, Internet of Everything)
- Singularity (S2) (machine intelligence exceeds human intelligence (2045)
- Singularity (S3) (machine consciousness) (post 2045)

Outsourcing Information Storage and Retrieval

At some unknown time in our recent evolution (best estimates are around 300,000 years ago), we evolved from experiencing the world primarily as a sensory phenomenon (like most creatures) to one that combined sensory experience with a deep intersubjective experience; what we humans like to think of as consciousness. In reality, consciousness dropped the mic and left the house millennia ago. Essentially, consciousness began outsourcing itself to improve its memory and cognitive bandwidth. In the final evolutionary stages in the development of human consciousness, the first Singularity (S1) advanced beyond language, with the advent of writing 3,500 years ago. (And, no, there is no evidence of alien intervention, yet.)

For the first time, knowledge began residing outside the mind and out in the world, no longer trapped in our heads—first with the evolution of spoken language, and then, written language, math, art, printing, literacy, photography, film, radio, TV, and exponentially with the advent of the computer and its internet interconnectedness. All these advanced efforts at communication, analog and digital, were an attempt to superimpose consciousness on reality—and it has worked remarkably well (at least for the mathematicians—physicists, not so much).

With each advancement, the human interface with reality was altered, as was reality itself. But our computer interface is rapidly evolving in terms that are hidden from our immediate awareness due to our uniquely symbiotic relationship to it. It is not only modifying our interface with reality, but radically altering it at a speed that cloaks the rate of transformation.

The externalization of information storage and retrieval (e-ISR) is a counterweight by consciousness against the universal principle of modern physics—entropy—a measure of the degree of disorder or randomness in a system. Simply put, in time, everything falls apart and collapses, everything—all of us, and eventually, the universe. It's what most of us think of as death. And consciousness, individually and collectively, has been an effort to stave off entropy by anticipating the future—whatever that takes. Consciousness created a hedge against our mortality by creating an external knowledge base that eventually resulted in complex social networks. This increased our survivability and extended us collectively into the future.

As it turns out, the arc of our immortality appears to reside in the endless flow of data and knowledge creation, now imbedded in dynamical networks—and not with the individual *self*. As will often be stated here, it is network complexity that is evolving, not us so much. The idea that we are an immortality vessel is an illusion. It is merely consciousness sequencing each quantum of time, as if there's a past and future and that it's all about us. That's what it does. It is also evident that the desire to know the future is built into the structure of our consciousness, and that technology has become an arrow in the order of time.

With the computer and the Internet of Everything, we are on the cusp of fully externalizing knowledge creation: 1) We are in the infancy of developing deep machine learning programs using algorithms and neural-networks to collate and analyze large data sets—programs that detect hidden patterns, predictive of the future beyond human capability. 2) The next logical step is for AI to evolve the ability to self-organize this process independently of us, in what I term the second Singularity (S2).

Complexity: The Pattern of Everything

In 2018, an Israeli moon-lander deposited tardigrades (water bears), a microscopic extremophile organism, on the moon in sealed plastic wrap. In a moment of humility, we should contemplate—tardigrades have landed on the moon!

Perhaps we need to go farther back to the evolution of the microbiome and the beginning of bacterial and viral life 3.8 billion years ago. Our evolving understanding of the microbiome and its significance—that we (and all life on Earth) are primarily bacterial-viral in a complex aggregate form. These primitive bacto-virus are also controlling all essential aspects of human existence, inside and out—your physical health, mental health and likely every element of what defines you as human.

Microbiologists have now encountered the enteric nervous system, literally, a second brain in the large intestine comprised of millions of brain cells. And they have no real idea what bacteria are doing here (perhaps the original aliens). And, yes, if you were wondering, gut bacteria are magnetic. They can also generate electricity and make you drunk.

In private moments of speculation, one might ask, What if humans are nothing more than bacterial holograms—an evolving complex life form in which consciously driven intelligence allows bacteria to better interact with and manipulate the world around it? Think for a moment; it was not all that long ago that there were multiple thriving proto-human populations—all gone in an instant of evolutionary time—but always the bacteria and viruses.

For billions of years, there has been collaboration, then integration and then extinction, not unlike the Neanderthal genes (2–4%) many of us carry around with us. But none of us can survive without the bacto-virus. If we had the right lenses, we would see ourselves crawling with hundreds of billions of them, potentially giving us great new insights into ourselves and each other (but we might reproduce less).

The reality of the microbiome raises a profound question. What is the required complexity or aggregate of unique data required to reach the threshold of techno-consciousness? Will it, perhaps, derive from the massive inter-connectedness of all our electronic devices, much like our sense of *self* derives from a rich synaptic interconnectedness? What is the necessary threshold? Will it be 30 billion nodes creating a network of 100 trillion inter-nodal connections, like the human brain?

And how will we know where machine consciousness resides, and how it will interact with us? It may be that we are over-focused on smart devices, rather than on intelligent processes. Perhaps it occurs more rapidly than we anticipate, as each of our brains are ported into it (you will be charged extra for the dongle). These connections would then scale on the galactic—all of us staring into our smartphones—waiting no more! Rather than arriving at Singularity in 2050 in a Microsoft or Google lab, maybe we can get there by connecting enough personal devices. We will not know or understand the predictions of machine consciousness, or how it became indispensable— unaware we are now post-human.

Outside of the fact that consciousness resides in our brain, we know almost nothing about it. We are unable to hold it or even point to it. We can't see it or measure it. We have only a limited idea what it does or is fully capable of. This is all the more remarkable, given that we reside with it 24/7 and are unable to function or be human without it. How will we know if and when consciousness arises in AI? Where will it reside, and what will it look like? Will it try to communicate with us? Will it be able to communicate with us? Will it want to communicate with us, and will we be able to recognize its efforts any more than an alien intelligence trying to communicate with us across the universe? What if it exists outside our reality?

At first, we may experience AI primarily as algorithmic efficiency, as we default to more efficient and predictive models across multiple networked domains (healthcare, transportation, energy, communications, etc.). But over time, we default to the more efficient and predictable algorithmic logic of big data sets that are outside our ability to grasp. For example, we all get the size of a grain of sand or hair, but what about a Planck Length (1.6×10^{-35} meters with the number 16 preceded by 34 zeroes and a decimal point)? (Yes, it's really small.) Or what about a zeptosecond, the shortest unit of time ever measured—a trillionth of a billionth of a second. (Heck, faster than blink.) And the observable universe has 10 sextillion (10^{22}) stars. (That's probably a lot.) That's about it for us, really small, really fast and a lot. We have no idea and can't begin to conceptualize these numbers. They are merely abstractions beyond our comprehension.

Complexity is the evolutionary driver here. In foreign policy circles, there arc ongoing dcbatcs ovcr how supply-chain globalization has cntanglcd nation-states in new layers of complexity and confusion. Political scientists are emphasizing the issue of complexity when it comes to international relations, noting that "The world's powers are enmeshed in financial, trade and information networks that they do not fully understand (becoming) a new source of vulnerability, competition, and control; networks proved to be less paths to freedom than a new set of chains." (Kendal-Taylor) This is our e-interface and the rise of complex networks outside our ability to manage or fully understand.

As AI and our social networks evolve toward increasing complexity, we sapiens will reside in a parallel universe (the natural world versus our imagined world), or what cosmologists and futurists speculatively term as *simulation*. Broadly, this is a conjecture as to whether human existence is a computer simulation operated by an advanced civilization (alien or post-human). What is being proposed here is a less expansive variant of this conjecture; that the Singularity (S3) endgame is a simulated Pattern of Everything, or, literally, a closed loop reality of *data illusion*—one we have been in the process of designing and constructing for nearly 4,000 years.

Adapting to the Speed of Life

Life is going faster. This has been an essential human experience for the past 150 years, but are we approaching a tipping point? For the most part, we appear to be doing okay—but as this process becomes progressively impactful, I suspect, fewer of us will be as well-adapted to it. I would also conjecture that our adaptation to the *speed of life* is a precondition for the coming Singularity (S2). "You want it now! You got it! In fact, you may get same-day delivery before you order it."

Despite the current *speed of life* today, *time*, for most of us, exists as a subjective experience tied to a clock or calendar—and beyond that, it may well be our collective illusion. "Okay, physicists believe they have demonstrated time is real, is that what you wanted to hear?" But time is extremely complex to define unless you are a physicist. It is not something we get to hold and we don't physically observe it (because it doesn't appear to have mass); for most of us, it is a practical measure of the rate of change we experience in the world around us—a process that is always going forward toward the future, in what is termed an arrow of time. That is pretty much it. It derives from the mind's need to predict the future by incessantly measuring the rate of change around us.

If you are traveling in a spaceship away from Earth at the speed of light, you do not age at the same rate as those you left behind. Your rate of change slows—and there are people who could tell you how much, but you can't return to Earth and enjoy it. Change is the universal progression of events forward toward entropy or disorder, including all the planets and stars in motion. *And, apparently, we are the only species that concerns ourselves with constructing our entire existence around metering the rate of change.* (Or whatever it is we think we are observing.)

When we talk about everything going faster, we are referring to the rate of change. For most of us, that simply means we are doing more, having increased the rate of entropy around us—planes flying faster, more meetings are scheduled, shipments are processed and delivered sooner. But time has not changed. It is still the same 24/7/365 (we are not racing from Earth on a starship while at work). Heat a crockpot on the stove and notice that the changing temperature affects the rate of change in the molecules of water, and a heat transfer results from the temperature change—that is what we humans are doing—altering the rate of our activity (which takes a lot of energy). But are we altering time?

Change can be productive in economic terms, but also stressful in human terms. Bottom line is that everything today is moving faster than in the past, but in pretty much the same space as before; time has not expanded, and it has not been conserved. Nope, the day is still the same length, an hour is an hour. We have simply heated up the human crockpot. As a result, we are not just overheating the planet by speeding things up, we are kinetically multitasking life to stay relevant to technology.

Efforts by our Founding Fathers to communicate their dissatisfactions with King George and the British Parliament took time. Ship travel between Great Britain and the colonies was about 30 days each direction (and could be considerably longer), and between a ship's arrival at port, it could take more than 14 days to reach a postal distribution center—and from there to the individual recipient, who was responsible for picking it up. By 1860, a stagecoach mail run from St. Louis, MO, to San Francisco, CA, took 25 days of nearly non-stop travel over 2,800 miles at today's cost of $3,000. Today, postage can make it in four hours by plane for $30 and be delivered the same day or the next day. Even more likely, everything can take place at the speed of light in an email, text message, early morning videoconference or Predator Hellfire missile strike.

We are all moving faster than ever in a vastly more complex world, and the primary factor cloaking the *speed of life* from our immediate awareness is our inability to physically interact with it. We sense it more than we see it. It is our brain rapidly sequencing and organizing sensory perceptions, or what most of us think of as events occurring and time passing. It is days coming and going, meeting deadline, standing in line with a boarding pass that says Group A and being last to board. But it's also sensing time passing without awareness—your children became adults, family members passed—and friends in your high school yearbook look much younger than you remember.

As the *speed of life* increases, it begins to feel normal after a while, not unlike traveling 85 mph on an interstate highway for two hours—and losing one's sense of speed or time. While we may subliminally sense it, we have to glance down at the clock, speed-o-meter and odometer (or get pulled over by the highway patrol officer who has been chasing us for the last five miles) to objectify it. The reality is, computers, fiber optic cables and our evolving e-technology interface is also beyond our sensory awareness—yes, they are very fast and that's about it. But we do not really comprehend a billion calculations per second, except to note, "Wow, great graphics!"

By increasing the rate of change around us, we have amplified life beyond our ability to observe and be awareness of it (and we don't have a dashboard to glance at and tell us the rate of what is transpiring). What was already going extraordinarily fast, post-Industrial Revolution, is now going even faster—

soon at warp speed. We are all struggling to keep up, even if we don't know it or believe it. In 2011, Justin Gatlin set the world record in the 100 meters at 9.45 seconds. That extraordinary feat meant that there were 50.55 second left in that minute (and he expended a lot of energy). The moral is, doing more in less time is not really saving time—maybe time was more efficiently utilized, but it wasn't increased or saved big picture. (But if you speed-up the rate of entropy does that alter time? Okay, let's move on—this is just an analogy.)

Faster times come with a higher price tag and increased energy output. In the context of our amplified lives, we are forced to confront the rising stress from our interface with e-technologies. It doesn't seem debatable, today, to suggest that the complexity and amplification of ordinary life has given rise to an expanded number of psychological disorders, including Attention-Deficit/Hyperactivity Disorder, Autism Spectrum Disorder, Dyslexia, and Intellectual Disability, to name a few. Equally alarming, has been the rising suicide rate in the U.S., increasing 30 percent from 2000 to 2020; the 15 most deadly mass shootings occurred from 1999 to 2022; and from 1999 to the present, there has been a 400 percent increase in drug-related fatalities, totaling 760,000 deaths. There's a case to be made these are all a product of life speeding up to meet the demands of e-technology.

At an earlier time in our history, the incidence and relevance of the expanding number of mental disorders would have been small and incidental. These are a modern concern. There is also the concurrent dilemma of obsolescence stalking an aging population (Alzheimer's, Parkinson's, Dementia). Our aging family members are increasingly captive of e-technology, living out their lives in a multiverse of drug-induced states, while being attended to by *carebots* with large eyes, bright lights and warm voices telling them to take their medications and to roll over and pull down their pants (you do not want to know why). And an algorithm is now deciding the level of human contact required. In reality, we could all probably use an Amazon Halo upgrade or smartphone app to tell us how much human contact we should be receiving; particularly as human interactions are reduced to electronic exchanges.

Does speed amplify connectivity or not? What a great term to depersonalize the most personal thing in our lives—each other. E-relationships are subliminal, opaque affairs, whether work or interpersonal. E-technology quarantines us emotionally and fosters anonymity and privacy. It allows us to never reveal ourselves and to throttle emotional connections, while exerting higher levels of control. For good or bad, e-relationships are primary in connecting us to the world around us—now playing a significant role in our feeling isolated and alienated. We are being electronically connected in real time, but emotionally disconnected in subjective time. We are left in a virtual world—projecting more than there is, onto less than there is.

We used to emotionally relate because it was key to our survival in the natural world. But not so much in the simulated one, where we are a data stream or connected nodes in a network. We are now engaged in communications that feel cognitively connected at the front end and emotionally disconnected at the back end. A process that has always been difficult (emotionally connecting), has now been made exponentially more complicated for all of us. Unless all you desire is a transactional world and not an interpersonal life, it is too easy to click into privacy mode over and over—forever being busy and on the move. We have too many other connections to click on—we are Electronic Gods—"Just a second, I have another text I need to check."

Electronic life amplifies change and attenuates our presence—all enabled by the infinite expanse of our seeming connectivity to the world and its demands for our attention. As a result, we are becoming interpersonally derealized from one another, which raises the question: What will be the impact of us engaging a fully transactional reality—one our simulation appears to be evolving toward? Our current emotional state appears to be one of overwhelming isolation and self-importance, hallmarks of Identity Diffusion––"Yo, I gotta go; I have an online game with my homies."

E-technology is rendering time in fractional terms that are proving difficult for us to sequence. While life is still linear, we exist in a chronically impatient state, waiting for it to have meaning. If nothing else, our electronic interface has made us increasingly impatient with each link in the e-chain of life. We want everything at the speed of light—waiting for that damn computer screen to light up. Connectivity is no longer about the people we are connected with, but how efficiently we are connected—hardware, internet service provider, router, modem, Wi-Fi and Bluetooth, broadband, internet browser, software and app downloads). *Fractions of a second evidence frustration and anxiousness—as increasingly does our entire existence.* Swipe right, swipe left, the disappointing seconds devoted to shopping for relationships or online hookups.

Our computers and smartphones have quantified us and all our interactions. And it is becoming increasingly difficult to give up too many fractional moments to anyone, given all the demands and expectations that we have to meet. (Reality is now approximating the movie *In Time*, where time is stolen, borrowed or sold to survive a zero-sum life.) In effect, we are trying to connect all the dots in life faster than ever, because technology insists on it— but there are infinitely more dots than anyone anticipated. The paradox being—we are connecting an astounding number of dots at a frantic pace, yet feel increasingly disconnected from the world, where is the pattern of connectivity that supposedly emerges?

What does this e-technology connectivity mean for us going forward? For now, we will continue to be born, live, and die, and experience all the stages of life. But understand, technology is in the process of disrupting our sense of order. It is altering time and how we sequence it (not unlike that car on the interstate going 80 mph). Whether it's high-frequency trading on broadband networks in billionths of a second or law enforcement vectoring future crimes or instant accessibility to the coming metaverse—the future is moving at the *speed of life*. And just as the galaxies in our rapidly expanding universe are growing increasingly distant from one another—until the universe empties out—it may be the same for us.

Summary

- Singularity is the expectation that machine intelligence will surpass human intelligence by 2050.
- The first Singularity (S1) occurred with the advent of human consciousness and the development of language, reaching its current apogee with the computer and internet. The rise of machine intelligence represents the second Singularity (S2). And if machine consciousness were to evolve, it would constitute the third Singularity (S3).
- The current rapid evolution of technology parallels a remarkable biological event that occurred 540 million years ago, termed the Cambrian Explosion. We are currently undergoing the Anthropocene Explosion of e-technologies.

- Language development exponentially shifted our evolutionary timeline by externalizing knowledge creation. With the computer and the Internet of Everything we are on the cusp of fully externalizing this process.
- The externalization of information storage and retrieval (e-ISR) has provided a counterweight to the universal principle of *entropy*—a measure of the degree of disorder or randomness in a system—and extends our mortality.
- The Singularity (S2) endgame is a Pattern of Everything. A closed-loop reality of *data illusion* and endless knowledge creation. We are, in effect, in the process of adapting to a simulated reality through our e-technology interface.
- Everything in our lives is faster, more compressed and a product of our increasingly complex social networks. This has resulted in our personal derealization and the advent of Identity Diffusion—a critical condition for the rise of machine intelligence—that comes at a high price for all of us.

2.0 – Dynamical Networks

What we call the future is simply the direction of higher entropy; a state of lower entropy is what we call the past.

—A. Guth, *Scientific American*

Dynamical Social Networks: The organization of complex, interactive systems to facilitate communication, management, production, and distribution of information, services and goods that recursively scale. For example, nation-states and their sub-jurisdictions—towns, cities, counties, states. At another scale, the internet is a technology and communications sub-network that electronically ties together every major social network, including each of us around the world.

For the past 30 years, we have all been subjected to a barrage of internet hype about how connectivity will empower us and bring us all together as a global community. And at some low scale, this has been absolutely true, but there are also many levels to examine here. For example, authoritarian regimes surveilling civilian populations and quelling dissent. And state-sponsored hackers spreading disinformation and political confusion in democracies. And then, there is globalization, a plus for lifting millions out of poverty in China but gutting American manufacturing jobs at the same time. The supposed benefits of connectivity are grossly relative to the time and place one finds themself. And this does not begin to convey the intrusion of hacking and malware into our private lives.

Overall, e-technology connectivity has been mostly about consumer convenience and distraction, and in return consumers get unending personal and financial manipulation. This is not to minimize how it has fired up the economy as well. And if this transaction ended here, it would be a win-win. But this exchange is unbalancing wealth, extracting hidden data and value from consumers, and subjecting all of us to intense levels of surveillance and the loss of privacy. And this is just the beginning. We get it, supply chains are more efficient, and we are generating enormous amounts of knowledge at the research level, and the future could be transformative. That's e-technology's story, and it's sticking to it!

After acknowledging all the recent changes we have undergone, we still need to drill down deeper to grasp the many changes coming our way. Besides, the future is not going away. Our new complexity is a portent of greater unpredictability and a potentially chaotic future, as networks appear to be centralizing. You might inquire, Why would that be destabilizing in the face of all the potential benefits?

Some could reasonably make the case that our complex social networks are stabilizing and that the state-sponsored conflicts of the past 500 years are beginning to attenuate. So, why should anyone be complaining? Heck, isn't complexity mitigating conflict and violence? The result is a more robust and coherent social reality, which is good, isn't it?

In this context, two events appear to be occurring simultaneously. The broad ascent of human individuality, and significant increases in social complexity. Clearly, these two interactive processes gave rise to our modern world—and not without considerable conflict and social upheaval. But it is increasingly evident that the "I" side of this equation (you and me) is now attenuating relative to the networked side. In simpler terms, individuality is being suppressed and democratic norms are under increased pressure.

Healthcare: Model Social Network

So, what exactly is a dynamical social network? Let's take the example of our healthcare system—a model of rising complexity. Where to begin? It is large, it is complex, and we are all reliant on it. It is an essential marker for the advancement of knowledge and plays a significant role in our increased health and longevity. It makes life better. First off, it comprises dozens of subsystems, e.g., there are as many as 120 medical specialties. Students go to medical school after graduating from strenuous undergraduate programs in biology or chemistry.

Physicians in training undertake five years of medical school and lengthy residencies, before taking standardized national licensing exams. They are then subject to state board oversight with extensive professional guidelines for standards of care. They must continually upgrade their education and training. They are required to maintain professional insurance and are highly regulated by medical specialty boards. They work closely with nurses, pharmacists, and medical technologists, who are also subject to many of the same rigid training and oversight requirements. All of this is then reorganized and given oversight through private offices, clinics, urgent care centers and hospitals, which require trained technical, administrative, housekeeping, and security staff.

This includes hundreds of outside medical laboratories to process test results, imaging centers, outpatient surgical centers, and physical therapy programs. There are private medical research labs, medical instrument designers, and medical supply manufacturers; there are hundreds of university medical departments devoted to research; first responders, medivac helicopters and planes; professional conferences and journals; then there are the pharmaceutical and medical insurance industries. This system reaches deeply into the finances of employers, the government (Medicare and Medicaid in the U.S.), and each of us individually as a primary expense. This model operates worldwide. In 2017, U.S. healthcare costs were $3.5 trillion, 17.9 percent of GDP with a per capital cost of $10,739.

Imagine this system a 100 years ago (1922) or 200 years ago (1822). Currently, there are approximately 3.8 million nurses, 1.1 million doctors, 6,146 hospitals and 924,107 hospital beds in the U.S. And in all candidness, this description is ridiculously simple and understated. We exist in a world of interconnected dynamic networked systems. This list could easily encompass hundreds of interrelated networks that constitute the modern world. Ask yourself, who or what aspect of this system would you delete? You quickly come to realize that everyone and every element of it is required, and probably a lot more.

Chaos From Complexity: The Stochastic Future

Chaos theory is the mathematics of the unpredictable, exploring the transitions between order and disorder in dynamical systems. Theories of chaos broadly assert that within the apparent randomness of complex systems, there are underlying patterns of interconnectedness and self-organization that are impossible to predict or control. This complexity is readily observable in modern organizational structures—typically dynamic, complex and nonlinear, including the stock market, traffic patterns, weather prediction, hydrology, ecosystems, encryption and wind turbulence.

One of the underlying principles of chaos theory is termed as *sensitive dependency* or what is prosaically referred to as the Butterfly Effect. In this instance, an extremely small change can result in dramatic effects. This is the idea that a hurricane in Indonesia can be the result of a butterfly flapping its wings in Mexico. The flapping wings represent a small change in the initial condition of the system, which causes an interactive chain of events that makes it impossible to predict large-scale phenomena.

The instability of small changes in dynamical systems is one of the forces at work that periodically tanks the stock market. Instability can be dramatically amplified when systems are subject to continuous feedback, making them unpredictable and chaotic. As the value of a stock rises or falls, people are then buying or selling that stock. This, in turn, further affects the price of the stock, causing it to rise or fall in an unpredictable manner. This is the reason why diversifying your investment, with a substantial proportion in mutual funds, and then holding steady as the market fluctuates, is the safest strategy (that is, if you aren't privy to insider trading).

Dynamic systems operate in what physicist's term as *phase space,* where the range of possible behaviors are often presented in familiar geometric terms. In a stable system, phase space refers to movement toward simple attractors, for example, a ball rolling down a steep incline will rest at the bottom (its attractor). But in a chaotic system, rather than a simple set of points or loops, there evolves an intricate recursive pattern of twists and turns at all possible scales that are impossible to predict, typical of our human system of social networks.

Most of us are familiar with this concept through Mandelbrot's fractal images, where the incredibly intricate shape of the attractor prevents us from predicting exactly how the system will evolve. And as our social networks grow increasingly complex and recursive at every level, we are unable to predict the outcome.

Complexity From Simplicity

Fractals are intricate, never-ending patterns of self-similarity across all scales. In effect, they are a feedback loop underlying all dynamic systems, by which infinite patterns of complexity are created from simplicity. Fractal theory aids scientists in modeling complex structures such as rivers, coastlines, mountains, cloud formations, snowflakes, hurricanes, crystal growth, fluid turbulence, and galaxy formation. Understanding theories of chaos and fractal dynamics has also provided us with insights into human social evolution over the past 10,000 years as well.

Consciousness exited the individual mind and began externalizing itself in the wave dimension of human social and cultural organization by creating dynamic social systems of infinite recursive complexity. This parallels the mathematical modeling seen in algorithmic networks and graph theory. With any cursory examination of our social evolution over the past 3,500 years, it becomes immediately evident that we have undergone, what is termed in physics, a *phase-transition*. That is, we have made the transition from relatively simple social interactions to highly complex self-similar social systems.

Historians and cultural anthropologists have been exploring and documenting this process for a century now. We have seen the simultaneous rise of tool use and complex social organization fully independent of one another across numerous ancient cultures. Underlying the rise of all these civilizations was the independent development of agriculture (energy storage), along with written language and record keeping (data storage).

Today, it can be overwhelming to contemplate the number of evolving social networks and their ever-expanding complexity. And all evidencing self-similar underlying patterns at the micro and macro levels. Simply, we are subdivided into complex self-repeating patterns. Think about something as familiar as universities and all their course offerings and degrees—pretty much the same in Hong Kong as in Iowa. Consider corporate models of leadership and organization, all with similarly structured MBA programs across the globe. Manufacturing assembly lines are models of robotic self-similarity.

The world's financial institutions are self-similar models of banking and investment strategies, using 180 currencies for homecourt advantage. It's evident that every group of professionals is broadly similar, requiring standards for education and professional competence. Governments and economies of each nation (we are all sequestered now in national identities) are mirror images of one another. Name it, and it is familiar and self-replicating in another part of the world. It is how modern civilization rolls—besides, self-similar social networks can seamlessly interact with one another.

The driving force behind all our advancing self-similar networks is knowledge creation and technological advancement. They combine to form a broad agreement and understanding of the underlying logic and required self-similarity and uniformity, whether that is in design, investment, production, management, marketing, supply chain management or consumer interface. As consumers of ideas and technology, our preferences are for simplicity and convenience at an affordable price. But it is important to keep in mind that we are the ones who are broadly conforming to the demands of our networks and technology, and not the other way around.

Nothing better illustrates this than a factory assembly line, a sea of office cubicles in a high-rise building or watching automobile lights streaming in slow-motion across freeways in evening traffic. Airplanes only take off and land one way, and that is true of every sector of our social, political and economic lives. We are all building the same pyramid, in effect, with our own stylistic touches, of course. But as the world becomes more similar and familiar, networks and technology are the primary driving force.

This cursory summation of chaos and fractal theory is a way of helping us understand how we, *Homo sapiens*, arrived at complexity. As consciousness began rapidly outsourcing information storage and retrieval, the broad effect was the creation of a hyper wave-particle duality. That is, it emphasized both individuality and complex social networks. And as our technology interface races forward and continues to impact us individually and collectively, we have now come to understand how small, unrecognized effects will continue to result in unpredictable and chaotic outcomes.

In the present, we will likely enjoy remarkable order and efficiency, but the future will be fraught with significant and unpredictable perturbations in our complex and interactive networks. In some humble way, this book is an effort to begin examining the potential changes coming our way.

The Rise of Complexity

Over geological time, sapiens slowly began selectively adapting and differentiating from hominids (proto humans). The surprising result was the rise of consciousness, which then began the long process of outsourcing information storage and retrieval through language development. *In retrospect, communication appears to have been the prime directive of consciousness, with language as its chief construct.* This unique ability to effectively communicate opened the door to the future, where, apparently, consciousness prefers to reside. This is what we must keep in mind. *Homo sapiens* required 4.5 million years to differentiate from the apes. In comparison, machine intelligence may only require 100 years to differentiate from us. It appears that networked complexity is the real evolutionary imperative here.

Once consciousness began communicating through language, the broad effect, over tens of thousands of years, has been our increased ability to manipulate the world around us. This includes tool use, agricultural development and increasingly complex social organization. The latent effect of outsourcing consciousness was eventually rapid technological innovation beginning with the Industrial Revolution in the 17th century, resulting in the Fourth Industrial Revolution, 400 years later.

It took 300,000 years for the First Industrial Revolution and a few hundred years to where we stand today. *The unexpected consequence of population growth was the production of enough intellectual capital to move the world technologically forward.* Before this, there simply had not been enough intellectual capital to effectively innovate and sustain change. As a result, today's complex system of dynamic social networks has proven exceptionally adaptive and appears to be the primary driver of human evolution.

Over the brief time it took these networked systems to evolve, we gained a clearer understanding of their complexity and fragility—and how small changes can result in significant consequences. Examples abound, including World War I, when a slew of trivial and irrelevant alliances among European nations resulted in the mindless killing of millions of young men. The lengthy history of stock market speculation and volatility stands out (from 1929 to 2020, the market crashed four times, and there have been five additional highly unstable events between 1980 and 2020).

And the recent ability of the coronavirus pandemic to economically destabilize the entire world in a matter of months, because people did not want to wear masks, highlights the fragility of complexity. This should be terrifying to all of us. Let's not kid ourselves. The giant amplifier of instability has been rapid population growth and density, resulting in climate change and environmental degradation on a previously unknown scale (except for asteroid strikes and volcanic eruptions, of course). Population growth, an evolutionary driver, is pushing us to the limits. We are going to require machine intelligence to do what we have been unable to—and we may not want to contemplate it.

The enveloping e-interface that is upon us is revolutionary, whether we understand it or appreciate it. This new interface is unlike our past use of primitive tools or even modern ones. Instead, it is a process that has enshrouded all of us in an electronic matrix and is altering our identity and, perhaps, who we are as a species. *When consciousness began outsourcing information storage and retrieval, it literally sped up our evolution through social and cultural mechanisms. As a result, we are rapidly evolving and experiencing the rise of process over action.* Process is the ascension of autonomous computer-generated information and knowledge arising from AI (drones, self-driving vehicles, automated factories—all operating independent of human interaction).

In the same manner that our intersubjective reality began to symbolically dominate our experience of the world around us beginning 10,000 years ago, today, information and knowledge creation is now being outsourced to generate network complexity. As bio-intelligence gravitates toward machine intelligence or processed complexity, we experience a world rife with memorandums, homeowner CC&Rs, insurance policies, administrative policies and procedures, contractual fine print and tech support. We are now residing in a partial-data simulation. The action of life is now symbolically contained and evolving in networked complexity.

We are now reduced, less consumed by action in the world and more directed toward the flow of data. The so-called theology-man, who morphed into the psychological-man of the 19th and 20th centuries, is on the way to becoming the 21st century data-facilitator. For the most part, action is primarily data sets being quantified.

For most of human history, our social adaptation was relatively simple and straightforward, small scale and tribal, and primarily subject to environmental influences. With the advent of agriculture, we were able to store vast amounts of energy and increase organizational capacity, resulting in villages, towns, cities, and, eventually, empires. Nonetheless, complexity was still largely latent and isolated, especially when one contemplates the hundreds of ancient civilizations that disappeared from history. Throughout our cultural evolution, and even after language formally became writing and mathematics, it still required the advent of something as technologically simple as the printing press to fully externalize human consciousness (literally, releasing it into the wild). Of course, this was the predicate for the computer and the internet to achieve warp speed complexity.

The DNA of our networked complexity is 26 letters and 10 numerical symbols (0-10). Today, our entire networked world rests on the recombinant process of coding these symbols into words, sentences, paragraphs and ultimately into every idea that exists in the world today. Similarly, the numbers 0 through 9 form the basis for all mathematical theory. In the same way that our DNA base pair of 23 chromosomes, with an estimated 3.2 billion long base, gave rise to all biological complexity. These 36 abstract symbols underpin the entire network complexity of the modern world. All human knowledge now resides outside individual consciousness and out in the world to be passed on generationally for the very first time, and soon by AI.

Dynamical social networks are evolving into formal systems of self-governance—nation-states, law, finance, education, transportation, labor, communications, energy, manufacturing, agricultural, science, medicine, technology, resulting in an Electronic Anthropocene Explosion of technology and the evolutionary rise of machine intelligence. Complexity's evolution is now exponential after a slow climb of many thousands of years. Still, over the past several hundred years, it rapidly evolved until knowledge creation began outstripping our capacity to understand it—which is why machine intelligence quickly evolved.

In much the same way human intelligence evolved 300,000 years ago, providing humans an adaptive advantage; machine intelligence provides a similar advantage by driving networked complexity. The rise of machine intelligence was inevitable, given the accelerating trajectory of our social evolution—they are symbiotic.

The Mystical Nature of Complexity

> There is a whole civilization to be remade.
> —A. Camus, *Notebooks*

Probing contemporary social theory leads to a default finding that systems of belief are the symbolic adhesive binding cultures together. And that the great transition of Western culture over the past 400 years has been from one of theological governance to one of psychological governance, that is, from an externalized system of control to an internalized system of control. Previously, the defining cultural norms of monotheistic belief and their moral imperatives broadly defined the relationship between the individual and society. It was all faith, but seldom contextualized to people's reality.

With therapy, it's always some generalized attempt to identify and attain the norm, but without significance or transcendence. An effective belief system must be both pragmatically normative and transcendent to be fully embraced. We are not in that time. Who is going to forgive us and understand us? AI is not up to this task, yet!

In *The Collapse of Complex Societies*, by Joseph Tainter, an economist by training, examines the role of complexity in networked societies, which he identifies as a recent historical event and an anomaly in our long cultural history. He correctly views complexity as a "process of adaptation" and a "problem-solving strategy." After looking across 4,000 years of our social history and the collapse of every culture for thousands of years, he concluded, as might any economist, that when investment in complexity produced declining marginal returns—we slowly bailed.

Tainter clarifies that the collapse of complexity does not necessarily result in "primordial chaos," but more often than not in a "return to the normal human condition of lower complexity." (Really, is anyone willing to go back to Pong, VHS, or snail mail?) It is all about the benefit-cost ratio. His solution is to invest a higher percentage of GDP in research and development to sustain growth and complexity. And the critical resource is an affordable and abundant energy supply. We can survive endlessly in complexity with this formulation, whether more or less free or happy. We should keep our eye on the return we get for investing in complexity. That is our survival sweet spot.

But what about all of us today? Where does the moral imperative lie for each of us when it comes to investing in complexity? What is currently operating at the symbolic level to govern our conduct and to give meaning to our lives? Some theorists default to what Rieff (*The Triumph of the Therapeutic*) cautiously theorizes—"that we … can live freely at last, enjoying all our senses … friendly barbarians all, in a technological Eden."

Beyond defaulting to sensualism and mysticism, what has symbolically structured complex societies from the beginning? The answer is not a belief in animal spirits, Ra, Zeus, Oden, Yahweh, but rather, one aggregated in complexity. What drives complexity and holds it all together is an evolving confidence in high margins of return. When we go out into the world and earn an education, take on the responsibility of a family and work hard, it is with a confidence that complexity makes the future more predictable. What holds our evolving technological culture together is not a religious tract, monarchical rulers, or psychological awareness—but dense, overlapping, complex social networks—the true latticework of our modern world. If there is a symbolic element to this complexity, it derives primarily from our pragmatic belief that it works—toilets flush, lights turn on, cars start, televisions broadcast each night, flights arrive on time and there is food on the shelves.

But no matter how evolved our confidence is in the pragmatic and utilitarian, there will always be a symbolic overlay to give explanation and meaning to our world. Beyond the sensualist delights of our times, beyond monotheism and all the 4chan threads organizing us around conspiratorial belief—resides tribalism in its most fully evolved form, the modern nation-state. The enigma currently posed by technology is that it transcends the nation-state. If our most recent social transition was from *Theological sapiens* to *Psychological sapiens*, it is now from *Psychological sapiens* to *Data sapiens*. In some discrete sense, this is the beginning of the end of human transformation, both practically and symbolically.

What is required to support and maintain deep complexity is now our universal imperative. Individually and collectively, are we capable of believing in and trusting technology and the arrival of machine intelligence? Which is likely the only intelligence that can make sense of it all—or what Rieff terms, "The wisdom of the next social order … amounting to permission for each man to live an experimental life." Each of us are now a unique experiment in complexity. That adds a lot more complexity, but it has been driving us for thousands of years. We are all part of the process, even in our trivial and sensual pursuits. "Religious-man was born to be saved; psychological-man was born to be pleased." Data-people are born to aspirate complexity as the highest good.

The Earth is now home to a laboratory of 7.5 billion experimental nodes driving network complexity. We are becoming a galaxy unto ourselves (or super organism). What might have been termed narcissism just a few decades ago is now each of us as a data packet in networked complexity—all one hop from everyone in the world. We all have some information to share—and we will share it. There is no opting out.

We will only be understood and have meaning as aggregate data. Data appears to be the energy source of the future, one that Tainter recommends we invest in. Data, in effect, is our modern gold rush. Your significance and meaning has yet to be determined. But you are a dense, data-rich packet that brings meaning to us all, whether you are Elon Musk and Space X or repairing flat tires at Discount Tire.

In 1650, at the very start of the Industrial Revolution, the Earth's population was 500 million. By 1750, it was 700 million, and just 50 years later, in 1804, it was a billion. Complexity is rapidly ascending and data sets are expanding exponentially, becoming the driver of our evolving simulation (simulation, as used here, is in reference to the complexity of our evolving social networks, and not to a synthetic reality controlled by computers and aliens, yet). We are now all in the hands of the AI research labs around the world.

Sub-Networks

Coding sub-network: Let's start with the most obvious game-changer. You may have noticed that we humans like to talk a lot—I mean we won't shut up! Currently, there are 6,500 languages spoken in the world today, with 23 accounting for 50 percent of all spoken languages. Two thousand have less than 1,000 speakers, and by 2100, it is estimated the total number of languages will decline to about 3,000. But in all human history, low estimates are for approximately 31,000 languages.

We are a communicating species, which is probably the number one quality that separates us from all other species. The fact that we rarely understand one another doesn't keep us from trying. But despite all the talking, language was not enough by itself. It required one other dynamic feature— written language. This was the first formal coding of our thinking; in the same way we code computer software today.

The dynamic interplay of complex systems constitutes the fabric of our modern social universe. And the underlying particle reality or quanta of the modern networked world is coded-language; a broad set of agreed upon abstractions defining our entire social existence—36 symbols (26 letters and 10 numbers). This is symbolic representation out of the mind of one person and into the minds of many others; more importantly, it is codified for generations. Before now, all ideas would be lost when the minds that retained the information no longer existed. In short, our social networks represent the fabric of our social reality. And language, more specifically coded symbols for language, represent the underlying particle basis for our social fabric.

The central conflict raised by the ascendance of coded language is whether complexity is better supported by distributed networks (liberal/democratic rule) or centralized networks (authoritarian rule). This has been a primary focus of our social order for nearly 4,000 years, reaching a crescendo over the past 600 years. And while we probably require both, many will project mystical significance onto either process. And is there an inevitable default set point going forward?

Complex networks evolve over thousands of years. Sometimes, the idea of something exists in the object, for example, a ring or spear. If the object is passed down, so is the idea of it. But how to make them may not be so evident and can be lost (e.g., how were the Egyptian pyramids built and how did the Romans make such superior concrete?). As a result, simple objects and ideas were passed down, but haphazardly and always with potential glitches.

There is preverbal learning—we learn by watching or mimicking or having our behavior shaped by the reaction of others or based on our own experiences. But verbal communication is an exponentially more complex and efficient way to teach and learn. And only when ideas are expressed in writing do they become codified and passed down. They also become a form of power. The advantage of this is that they can be more broadly shared and incrementally improved, and then, shared across time.

Today, ideas are being coded in a completely new and revolutionary language (zero-ones), one that very few of us speak or read—producing data, information and knowledge that eludes our understanding. The formal codification of language was and is the source of our social complexity. This complexity is being exponentially expanded with the addition of machine languages.

The Internet: What makes the fractal patterns of our social networks particularly unique is how rapidly they have begun evolving over the past several hundred years. As network theorists probe the fractal reality of our complex networks, a few fundamental factors have started to emerge from the algorithmic world of nodes and edges. One key factor is how an insatiable computer-internet interface has resulted in vast amounts of data. And out of this data deluge, we are developing a deeper understanding of network dynamics, and how the internet functions across networks.

The internet broadly tends to segregate us into like-minded groups. That is, it skews us toward polarization. Rather than facilitating open communication, we tend to gravitate toward those who think, feel and believe as we do. In effect, it creates an echo-chamber effect at every level. It also reveals harsher truths about us. We were never all together to begin with unless we are all under the same threat. Perhaps no nation better understands the complexity of neo-tribalism than the United States (okay, the Balkans, Middle East, French Canadians and Catalonians).

The internet, for all its many benefits, is fracturing social identity. There is also another underside to this reality. Online networks turn out to be extraordinarily resilient and continually seek equilibrium when under attack. In other words, it is hard to stamp out bad ideas once they gain a foothold. An excellent example of this is how effective ISIS (radical Arab terrorist organization) has been at utilizing online recruitment tactics and soliciting financial support. It would be naïve to believe that online networks only promote or emphasize good ideas, when the reality is just the opposite.

In the most absolute terms imaginable, the internet elevates bad ideas over good ones, hyping the extreme, extravagant, and exaggerated over the factual. In effect, the internet acts as a negative amplifier. And as a result, false news, extreme views, disinformation, and propaganda are more likely to go viral and be amplified. The internet is a technology that is continually shouting fire in our networked world.

The number of links between everyone on Earth has been six degrees of separation for nearly 60 years. That is, six people could link everyone on the planet. But today, we are literally one online search from linking everyone on the planet. There are no degrees of separation (at best there is one). No wonder researchers suggest that social media platforms are prone to contagion due to their hyper-connectivity. The impact is rapid and potentially explosive. In its most benign form, social contagion is fads and memes racing across the world—suddenly, everyone is wearing the same hairstyles, listening to the same music, or dancing on TikTok. But fake and false information can spread equally fast across the internet at the speed of light and gain credibility, resulting in mass hysteria, fear, and political turmoil.

When it comes to our social networks, the larger and more complex the social networks, the more unpredictable the chaos that inevitably follows. In the 16th century, it was primarily about witches, as nearly 40,000 women were put to death in acts of mass hysteria. Apparently, any accusation that a woman was practicing witchcraft was good enough to get her tortured and, if necessary, burned at the stake. Today, it's mostly about going online to light people on fire or to spread conspiratorial beliefs, or virtue test the country for not being *woke* and sensitive to everyone's subjective world. From QAnon to defunding police departments, to former President Trump dog-whistling White Nationalists, or TV host Ellen DeGeneres getting roasted for being insensitive—contagion is alive and well on the internet.

But the power of online contagion is best understood by its relationship to the recent coronavirus pandemic. These are two entwined processes: one social and one biological. In a matter of months, Covid-19 spread from its epicenter in Wuhan, China, to around the world, primarily due to our highly efficient airline transportation network, but also due to the density of life and our primate drive to socialize. The efficiency of our networks renders all of us highly vulnerable to the spread of this virus—something we already knew.

In historical terms, contagion was related to our degrees of separation; examples include the Black Plague (14th century, an estimated 400 million died) and the Spanish Flu (1918, an estimated 50 million died). But also, look more closely at the two recent world wars of the 20th century, with an estimated 35 million and 55 million deaths. These wars were models of network contagion and proximity, which is why so many died.

In its entirety, the spread of this pandemic represented the systemic failure of state and federal government in the United States, but also small decisions resulting in large consequences. The politics of fear quickly interjected itself into healthcare management decisions—the economy would never revive if shut down for too long, or that risk from the pandemic was greatly exaggerated and herd immunity would protect us. The result was to put millions at risk, and, ironically, the economy as well. And the key to this failure was the contagion-like spread of misinformation and disinformation through the media and the hysteria and distrust it sowed—when clear and unambivalent direction from the top could have solved this early on and prevented the deaths of tens of thousands of people.

In recent years, academic researchers have begun to seriously probe the impact of the internet and social media platforms on our social and political lives. And the results are disturbing. Broadly, we are being manipulated and siloed into polarizing extremes. Below are many of the hidden triggers impacting our interaction with e-technology in our simulated networked reality.

Distortions in the Matrix

Amplifying cognitive biases: Social media platforms are designed to amplify pre-existing cognitive biases. For example, we are more likely to attend to and share information about perceived risk. We tend to search for and remember those things that more closely fit with what we know and understand. When we encounter contradicting facts and information, we are more likely to double-down on pre-existing knowledge and beliefs, becoming even more committed to them. And algorithms are designed to exploit these cognitive vulnerabilities and to manipulate us.

Search engine bias: Search engines prioritize information that support our biases and direct us to sites that feed our prejudices and anxieties.

Narrow world effect: Search engines and social media platforms consistently delete content that is inconsistent with our data histories.

Information overload: Social media has saturated the online market with low-quality information, making it difficult to identify high-quality information.

Winner-take-all effect: Algorithms suppress the quality of information by over-focusing on popularity (wisdom of the crowd effect), confusing popularity with quality in winner-take-all scenarios.

Spreading disinformation: We are prone to sharing less factual and truthful information. The more extreme content, the more likely we are to share it.

Social contagion: When social media repeatedly exposes us to information or ideas from multiple sources, we become prone to adopting and re-sharing it.

Virality storms: We tend to pay more attention to information that goes viral. It becomes important by virtue of its ubiquity.

Echo chamber effect: Like-minded people tend to connect with one another. As a result, people are siloed into increasingly large and misinformed communities.

Clickbaiting: Negative content spreads faster than positive content. As a result, people are manipulated by negative narratives that trigger emotional responses, which they are then more likely to share.

Increased negativity: Overall, social media increases negativity by bolstering biases that become resistant to correction.

Extreme effect: Information in a social-diffusion chain is susceptible to distortion and overly influenced by the most extreme content. Efforts to balance the information only serves to create even more negative views.

Social herding: The broad effect of online distortions has been to sort us into polarized camps, resulting in an extreme divergence among groups.

(Extrapolated, in part, from "The Attention Economy" by Menczer and Hills, *Scientific American*.)

The Economic Sub-Network: Whatever their scale, economic networks appear to favor hierarchical strategies over distributive ones (a primate preset). That is, bigger is better, and centralized organization and management decision-making and economy of scale are the driving forces in their continual scaling up to become monopolies. This has been historically true throughout the rise of networks—from empires to nation-states to mega-corporations of the 19th and 20th centuries. It is certainly true today with e-technology (Amazon, Facebook, Google, Microsoft) and in China (Baidu, Alibaba, Tencent, Huawei). And there is little evidence they are democratic in nature or that the American model is that much different from the Chinese one.

They are hierarchical from the top down (dictatorial), intrude deeply into local and national politics (feudal) and, in crude terms, suppress workers and communities to bend to their interests (authoritarian). We mostly know them as products, services, and propaganda (I mean advertising). They are economically and politically powerful and act without our vote, and will do whatever it takes to satisfy shareholders, including harvesting your data and facilitating state surveillance.

One adaptive feature of economic networks is their acting as strange-attractors for investment, talent and innovation. By monopolizing tech hubs (Amazon, Apple, Microsoft, Google), forcing competitors out of business or buying them out, they suppress competition. This is by far their most successful gambit in maintaining and increasing market shares. It is analogous to the rise of a powerful nation—you violently take power, conquer all the territory you can and make everyone bend the knee. More recently, in computer network speak, monopoly power has been referred to as the Matthew Effect—the more you have, the more you get.

While our complex systems can quickly solve all types of problems (it can debit your bank account, overnight your packages, or GPS track or AirTag you on the run), we are unable to predict the impact of their actions on the system at large. The upshot of our rapidly evolving social networks is to render them prone to what has prosaically been termed *Black Swan* events (rare events that are hard to predict and beyond normal expectation with potentially severe consequences). Graphic examples include a catastrophic asteroid strike or the stock market tanking in 2007.

These unpredictable events are termed *unknown-unknowns* (risks that come from circumstances that are so completely unexpected they would never be considered) in the jargon of risk-management theory. Their only predictability lies in our knowledge that a small perturbation in the network can potentially result in a worldwide catastrophic event. We just don't know where, how, why, when or what it could be. Not very reassuring, but a measure of our current vulnerability. The agenda of big data is to quantify all of us to predict and interdict this wobble (axial precession) in our networks.

Quant Miss

Take our capitalist economic model, for example—for all the *quants* Wall Street has hired in recent years, and all the complex statistical modeling they have undertaken to squeeze small fractions of a dollar out of millions of trades in fractions of a second, it has never successfully predicted a market collapse; despite the fact these blips occur with concerning frequency, and predictably in hindsight. All the while, investment newsletters make unending claims, predicting superior returns on your investments. How is that possible? Turns out, it isn't. Our networked economy is *sensitive-dependent.* That is, you will make money until the market falls off a cliff—which it inevitably will.

Wealth/Power Sub-Network: What are the constructs of our modern world, given it is exponentially more complex than at any time in our history? Are the primary constructs more people, more structures, and more things, increased size and complexity, or is it something entirely different? What is really holding our world together, and how does it work?

According to Einstein's theory of general relativity, massive objects warp the spacetime around them in what we experience as gravity. So, when a ball is thrown into the air, it falls back to the ground, because the Earth distorts the spacetime around it—the path of the ball and the ground intersect. Locally, spacetime is curved around every object with mass. Mass also influences the overall geometry of the universe. The density of matter and energy in the universe determines whether the universe is open, closed, or flat.

The question arises, what forces are acting upon our dynamical social networks (DSN) that can render them open, closed, or flat? The case can be made that the social power, in all its many forms, acts to warp the fabric of complex social networks into either centralized (closed) or decentralized (open) states—in much the same way, gravity distorts spacetime. While this process assures cultural continuity by suppressing disruption (in the same way gravity keeps us from spinning off into space), it does so by inhibiting change. Throw a ball up and it always comes back down; same with power; it flows from the top down and is a primary attractor in the social organizations of primates. This is as true today as it was 4 million years ago. A network's power distribution has a strong gravitational effect on its social and hierarchical organization.

Our expansive and complex system of social networks comes to us with many vulnerabilities and, of course, with required sacrifices on our part. Likely, all the key factors resulting in the destabilization of these complex networks have been revealed to us, beginning with asteroid impacts, volcanic activity, and earthquakes as primary geological markers. Then there are cyclical weather and climate patterns. It should also be noted that humans arrived on the stage during a uniquely moderate climate period in Earth's geological history. But the human impact is the one we have the most control over, including human population growth, habitat loss and resource depletion from over-exploitation of the environment.

But by far, the most destabilizing factor over the past 5,000 years has been our regressive modeling of primate behavior and the concentration of wealth and power in the hands of a limited few (kings, emperors, dictators). This has resulted in closed social systems and the continuous collapse of sapiens' social order for thousands of years. Despite the eternal instability of centralized wealth and power, this folly continues to play out today (and I understand this is contrarian to accepted social theory).

In the United States, one percent of the population controls 40 percent of the capital wealth, and 400 wealthy families account for 50 percent of political campaign donations. It has been in the face of these facts that technological innovation has somewhat leveled the economic playing field worldwide over the past 70 years; however, it continues to serve the wealth and power vectors that destructively lace and distort our social order. We appear to be trapped in a never-ending loop of biology and primate psychology, with no social, economic or political models on how to extract ourselves.

Apparently, we lack the necessary imagination and will to change our trajectory at a crucial time in our history. (The highest paid employee of every major university in America is the football coach. We should pause for a moment and think seriously about the broad implications of this economic model.)

Both wealth and power accumulation have been the great disrupters of social networks during the past 5,000 years, resulting in perpetual conflict and efforts to suppress human populations. And it is abundantly clear that in 2022, we are no closer to arriving at a political consensus to mediate this reality than were ancient Egypt, Greece, Rome, or even Victorian England. But it will become necessary if we want to stabilize network complexity. As it now stands, concentrated wealth and power constitute the single greatest threat to a stable future, particularly as technology entangles the world in new and more complex networks. (The best current example of this historical process is the unprovoked military invasion of Ukraine by Russian president Vladimir Putin.)

A new social contract is required if we want to move forward. Authoritarian leaders, along with the oligarch class, share nearly identical interests—their own self-interest—at the expense of the rest. In the same way, mass distorts spacetime, wealth and power distort dynamical social networks. All the kings, queens, and robber barons have forever conspired to deny the future in the belief they are the future. When, in fact, they are ravenously consuming the future of generations to come.

As in the past, guns and the corrupting influence of wealth, help the oligarch class maintains the self-delusion they suffer this burden for everyone's benefit! (How humbling that must be.) And not to put too fine of a point on it—but the rise of dynamical social networks and its distributive organization has been an enduring threat to this confidence game.

Without doubt, one of the important disrupters to the inertia of wealth and power has been rising complexity, as it has increasingly become dependent on those who can innovate and manage complexity. From the 14th to the 19th century, the economic rise of a middle class began to upset the wealth/power dynamics of aristocratic Europe. Today, it is a sophisticated technical class that everyone is dependent on—lawyers, accountants, doctors, scientists, managers, engineers, and computer scientists. Knowledge workers are the current day disrupters of wealth and power, while simultaneously creating a new and irrelevant cadre of wealth and power players.

The great technology disrupter has been the computer and the internet, giving rise to machine intelligence and sparking a new arena of conflict between distributed (open) and centralized (closed) networks. The revelation revealed by our dynamical networks is—the concentration of wealth and power in the hands of a few does not add significant value. In fact, it is undermining the future. It is just difficult to see this given how wealth and power have been overly concentrated throughout history. In much the same way royalty is mostly an entertaining meme on TV today, so wealth and power are on the verge of becoming vestigial organs, but still, extremely repressive and dangerous.

As networks become more complex and denser, the old political order will become less relevant. Even what we term democratic and liberal, or authoritarian and illiberal, will no longer model reality, as technology crosses every boundary of individual and social identity, which is why it is more important than ever that the influence of wealth and power be modulated sooner rather than later.

Let's ponder the Starship Enterprise from the television series *Star Trek*. Yes, there must be command and order, but everyone is necessary and respected. They eat and dress similarly, and all share the same social amenities. They are all distinguished by their necessary contributions and unique skills, abilities, interests and talents. Here in the early 21st century, this truth became increasingly evident during the Covid-19 pandemic, resulting in a quick and brutal determination as to who, exactly, were the essential workers. Nope, no billionaires were identified, as they mostly hunkered down, moaning about market losses and quickly laying off employees and cutting benefits. If there is to be a future, the wealthy will be perp-walked off the stage of history.

The extravagantly wealthy are a glitch in the networked operating system, requiring a patch. There was never, ever really anything particularly special about them that was commensurate to their status—right time, right place, lucky, maybe smart and talented, often times connected, and serendipitous enough to seize the day—but more often than not, ruthless and willing to bend the world to fit their demands. But they are now disrupters in a dynamical system. In the same way monopolies suppress innovation and competition, wealth and power are suppressing human talent and ambition around the world.

There will come enormous resistance to the future because it doesn't encode religion, class or cultural differences—including those who don't understand it or get it, want it, feel left behind, puzzled or confused by it and, most importantly, threatened by it. Some will claim they do not want to be networked (not understanding they already are and that there is no opt-out option). Inevitably, there will be a Thermidorian reaction to this revolution (in fact, it's already taking place). It involves all the *usual suspects* clinging to the illusions of the past.

Twenty percent will be riding out in front of the wave; 20 percent just going along because it seems to work and it's easier to adapt; 20 percent confused and stumbling behind but don't know what else to do; 20 percent passively resisting and 20 percent defiant and resistant in some capacity. By this analogy, 60 percent will be lost or left behind. The conflicts will not appear to be about technology when they really are. Technology will bring with it all our baggage, disparate meanings, and uncomfortable dogma.

The real bottom line of resistance to the future will be over economics and identity, and whether we are willing to level the playing field or default to wealth and power dynamics once again. We need to be very careful going forward with everyone trying to find their way. Our complex networked systems are easily disrupted (in the middle of a viral pandemic, students partied, motorcyclists gathered at Sturgis, governors opened their economies back up, and people claimed masks were a civil rights violation). The sooner the wealthy and powerful are assisted in realizing the future, the faster we all get to the future.

When addressing big questions, it's useful to revisit the *Fermi paradox*. It asks: Why hasn't Earth been visited by advanced alien life forms, given the size and age of our universe? In response, two astrobiologists (Wong and Bartlett) recently proposed civilizations are prone to collapse after rapid growth and unending energy consumption; basically, failing to adopt the required balance necessary to survive, but also preventing them from exploring the universe. They go on to note, all advanced civilizations are faced with a critical choice going forward—*homeostatic awakening* or civilizational collapse. In homeostasis, the cost of planetary exploration is too great, and in a state of collapse, it is no longer feasible. As a result, we have had no visitors (my apologies to UFO cultists) and will not be undertaking intergalactic travel (sorry *Star Trek* fans). And as we earthlings endure the struggle to mitigate climate change (likely failing to achieve *homeostatic awakening*)—keep in mind that the majority of the wealthy and powerful around the world don't care about any of this (watch the TV series *Snowpiercer* for updates).

" No Homeostatic Awakening Here"

Amazon, the second largest U.S. employer, consistently failed to provide public safety measures for tens of thousands of fulfillment center workers during the early stages of the Covid-19 pandemic, even firing and laying off those who protested. Amazon was then taken to court by the state attorney generals of New York and California for failure to implement or prematurely rolling back safety protocols. By late 2021, over 20,000 workers had tested positive for Covid-19. To put this in perspective, Jeff Bezos, then Amazon CEO, has a net worth of 150 billion dollars. (Due to budget limitations, we have discontinued searching for signs of *homeostatic awakening* at Amazon.)

The Holodeck Conjecture

There is a notion floating about technology circles that we might be residing in a computer simulation, rather than complex networks of our own devising. As if life were not difficult enough on its own terms. No, we are lab rats or residing in a petri dish or, worse yet, in a cosmic arcade game. Of course, for thousands of years, Buddhists speculated that much of the human experience was illusion, but by no means that was it all fabricated.

This fantasy of altered realty appears to have gripped the public's imagination through the many entertaining books of science fiction writer, Philip K. Dick (*Do Androids Dream of Electric Sheep, Blade Runner, Total Recall, The Man in the High Castle,* and *The Adjustment Team*). There is also anecdotal evidence that Dick might have been delusional when it came to claiming personal experiences of shifting reality and time travel.

The two contemporary high points of the simulation conjecture were the movie *Matrix* (1999) and a theoretical paper (2003) by Oxford philosopher Nick Bostrom, titled, *Are You Living in a Computer Simulation?* He famously termed this the *Simulation Argument*. This led to all manner of epistemological speculation by those prone to thinking their way to an understanding of reality. Not to be outdone, entrepreneur Elon Musk recently speculated that the odds we are residing in a base-reality and not a simulation are one in a billion.

Let's regress for one moment and consider poor Charles Darwin, the humble intellectual founder of the theory of evolution, a towering intellectual work, re-confirmed and extended by modern biology and genetics. His struggle in putting forward this paradigm-shifting understanding of the natural world was about overcoming his faith and his refutation of the Christian understanding of how the world worked. His hesitation nearly cost him his place in the history of science. The oddity of where we stand today with the simulation hypothesis is, it parallels Darwin struggle by reintroducing mystical experiences into science.

Our current thinking on simulation broadly regresses to an earlier, pre-scientific view of the world and the universe we reside in. After hundreds of years of struggle to refute the notion of gods or a God by the rationally minded, theorists are re-introducing the notion of an external agency controlling us and the world we live in. I guess bad ideas are like fashion—something you didn't like years ago is always making a comeback.

Now it appears that the same familiar theological answers are being resurrected. Is there a superior and omniscient intelligence guiding and manipulating our reality, and to what purpose, exactly? Does the god of simulated reality really have a super colossal computer, all the RAM in the universe, a powerhouse graphics card, infinite memory, and unlimited sources of power?

The new model feels a lot like old-time religion and our eternal quest for meaning and purpose. Neolithic people had the animistic world of spirits, the ancient civilization and their quarreling gods interjecting themselves into human affairs. Then came the monotheistic believers and their all-powerful deity—creating the world in seven days, smiting a lot of people, and making sin and suffering the baseline for living on planet Earth. By the 17th century, this was followed by analogies of a more mechanistic universe. And now, we are being fed a new electronic reality, asking if we are playing out our lives in a *Star Trek* holodeck. We are all hoping, of course, that there will soon be a massive online multiplayer AR version available soon.

This has all begun to feel Old Testament, when it comes to all the gruesome deaths for thousands of years here on Earth. In a simulation where 98 percent of all life forms are either parasites, parasitic hosts or eat one another, I am hoping for *Futurama* the next time around. So, there is a God or gods of sorts, or at least a consciousness or some playful programming, or game-theory algorithm that forms intent, blah, blah, blah. This, of course, feels a lot like giving up because it's too difficult. It is just us, once again, seeking some outside agency to shatter the reality we are confronted with every day, and one that Darwin discovered was a fraud.

Here we are seeking solace that there must be some deterministic reason for us, for all our sufferings—because we have a new paradigm to explain it all. This is not unlike channel surfing and clicking on the History Channel's *Ancient Aliens*, in which every conceivable event in human history was the result of an alien visitation or manipulation. Simulation or alien intervention? Your choice!

Some believe there is a giant animatronic consciousness residing in a far, far away galaxy, coding a multiverse of realities. This is not as insightful as Buddhism, profound as evolution or as fun as a holodeck. I wonder what machine intelligence will make of it. We should all take a deep breath and contemplate the limitations of the human imagination, particularly our inability to see beyond ourselves—it is all about us, per usual. The simulation hypothesis appears to be another solipsistic tribute to our specialness. Once upon a time, we envisioned ancient Greek gods rendering us playthings to entertain them—early video gaming, it turns out.

I am proposing the Holodeck Conjecture. An advanced civilization with the capability to render the Earth and its entire 13.8 billion history of evolution a simulation. Apparently, it has nothing better to do or couldn't imagine something more creative and significant than recreating a 1974 *Star Trek* episode featuring a holodeck. Exhausted Trekkies at Comic-Con sharing a bong and eating edibles late at night—"Hey man! What if we all were living in a holodeck?" "No, man, it's a video game." When the revised history of the universe is uploaded, there will be one amusing line about how earthlings learned they were a simulation.

The use of the term simulation throughout this book is not in reference to Bostrom's *Simulation Hypothesis*. Rather, it refers to simulation as an artifact of our own creation. Through our interface with e-technology and machine intelligence, we are in the process of creating and immersing ourselves in networked complexity of our own devising.

Base Reality (Red) or Simulated Reality (Blue)?

Get real, you don't have a choice! Residing in a simulation raises any number of questions. What are we a simulation of? How was this simulation created? Is there a base reality outside our simulated reality? Are we capable of contacting a base reality? Is this an experiment gone awry, and are we the cockroaches of a multiverse simulation? How many simulations are ongoing in the universe? For those of us who pine for reality-reality, can we wait for a better paradigm—where the hell are the sci-fi writers when you need them? Tumbling down the simulation rabbit hole, are we all coded for termination until we figure out how to leave it or alter it?

I hope we quickly get quantum on this coding thing and get the immortality power-up soon! If everything is a simulation, a skeptic might add, "So, what! Does this insight change anything? Is life less meaningful, painful or difficult? Is HBO's *Westworld* the best we can imagine—the simulants demanding a human upgrade? Do we believe that some unknown external agency, with the sensibility of a Marvel comic books series, created us? Who or what is fucking with us? Is this some type of *Groundhog Day* simulation, because no one on Earth is close to enlightenment?"

Really, does anyone care that we reside in a *The Truman Show* type simulation? It wasn't that good of a movie, and neither is this simulation. We were once biological entities, and now we are quantum packets at the subatomic level—okay! Sometimes this game, I mean simulation, really sucks! It has had a decent 13.8-billion-year run. I wonder what would change if we reran it, just for the hell of it—you know—get a better probability baseline co-efficient. If we reside in a simulation, are feelings simply manipulating us, and to what end?

Is simulated reality an amoral rendering and meaningless? What is the point of trying to improve a simulation—better video game play? Please, please don't let this be a game theory simulation by some department of economics or DARPA project. What if we only live in a simulation if we believe we live in a simulation, and reality is conscious imagination? And what if our greatest folly is a lack of imagination? Can we ever know what we failed to imagine? Pity us. I must admit, this simulation thing is impressive—remarkably complex, high resolution, pretty damn seamless and cloaked better than a Romulan bird-of-prey. Prove it—no cheat codes, either!

Summary

- Consciousness began externalizing itself by creating dynamic social networks of infinite complexity. But as our social networks grew increasingly complex, they became subject to the instability of complexity and small changes or The Butterfly Effect.

- Social networking platforms are prone to segregating us into like-minded groups and polarizing us. They also tend to amplify bad ideas over good ones—hyping the extreme, extravagant and exaggerated over the factual. Due to their hyper-connectivity, they are also prone to network contagion.

- Networks favor hierarchical strategies over distributive ones. The most adaptive feature of networks is centralization of decision-making and forming political and economic monopolies.

- What drives complexity and holds it all together is an evolving confidence in its high marginal returns. Supporting and maintaining deep social complexity is our prime directive. As a result, Earth is now a laboratory of 7.5 billion experimental nodes driving social network complexity.

- The DNA of our networked complexity is 26 letters and 10 numerical symbols (1-10). These 36 abstract symbols underpin the entire network complexity of the modern world.

- Wealth and power accumulation have been the greatest disrupters of social networks over the past 5,000 years, resulting in perpetual conflict and suppression of human potential. A new social contract is required if we want to move forward.
- Keep in mind, we are the ones who are broadly conforming to the demands of technology, and not so much the other way around.

3.0 – Identity Diffusion

You want to know who you really are…a ripple
within the cosmic data flow.

—Y. Harari, *Homo Deus*

Wave-Particle Duality

One of the underlying premises of this book is that e-technology is in the process of shaping who we are by means of altering our identity or the intersubjective experience of *me* or *I*. Quantum physics might provide us with some clues as to how this could happen. Quantum theory asserts that the universe is not continuous but exists as discrete values at the subatomic level or quanta. It further states that light (and all electromagnetic energy, for that matter) is made up of energy packets called photons—the smallest basic unit of light. A light wave is literally the flow of photons. The energy of these photons is produced by the height of their oscillation frequency, and the intensity of the light is related to the number of photons. But the key insight by Einstein is that a stream of photons can act both as a particle and as a wave—or what is termed a wave-particle duality.

Clever experiments have demonstrated that a photon of light is simultaneously both a particle and a wave, resides at a *superposition* of *quantum indeterminacy,* and does not collapse into one or the other until it is observed or measured. In effect, the universe is an underlying set of probabilities termed a *quantum probability wave.* It also appears that consciousness plays a critical role in collapsing this probability wave into a single reality, but it gets even crazier.

Subatomic particles can exist in different states at the same time, have different energies and be moving at different speeds, literally, be two places at once, or what physicists term *entanglement.* Two entangled particles, regardless of the distance between them, interact with one another—or what Einstein described as "spooky action at a distance."

It is proposed here that human social interactions reflect elements of quantum physics. By analogy, we simultaneously exist in a personal "I" state and the social "We" state or "I/We" duality. Furthermore, upon collapsing into an "I" state or a "We" state, consciousness resides at an indeterminate superposition, in neither a particle (I) or wave (We) state. These two states, "I" and "We," are also entangled and can, literally, be at two places at the same time, regardless of the distance between them. They are inseparable. Identity appears to be the entangled state of the "I" (the smallest particle or quanta) of our social existence and of the social cultural "We" state, which represents the wave or aggregate state of the energy and number of particles (people). This is the human condition—an "I/We" duality entangled in the vast galaxies of our minds until we act in the world.

There is a second reason to propose the idea of *duality* in human interactions. We, sapiens, appear to reside in a world of dualities. The most obvious duality includes two closed systems we mandatorily reside in: A closed biological system (natural world) and a more open-ended social system, both serving to underpin identity formation. But within each of us is a mind-body duality—an intrapersonal duality of the *self*: one non-material (mind) and the other material (body). Lastly, we are out in the world continually defining ourselves in the "I/We" duality of *self* and *other*. For a healthy and intact identity to emerge, all three of these dualities are required to be reconciled.

Not coincidentally, sapiens appear to reside in a highly dichotomous subjective reality, one that might best be termed as a default cognitive bias. Our mental experience of the world appears to divide reality—right-wrong, good-bad, guilty-innocent, win-lose, blood alcohol level above-below 0.10 percent, love-hate, Devil-God, *ad infinitum*. Dichotomies simplify the world and allow us to navigate it more efficiently, that is, until the world becomes overly complex (or what many derisively refer to as shades of gray). At this point, cognitive dualities begin to provide diminishing returns and higher levels of personal and social dysfunction.

This is where America appears to find itself today, trapped in a primitive cognitive bias (Democrats-Republicans, White-Black, religious-secular, male-female, old-young). Identity Diffusion exploits our cognitive bias and defaults to the world as a duality. As a result, operating in our simulated reality creates elevated levels of dissonance and *derealization* until they become an inflamed condition.

Simulated Reality

The world we live in, today, is a simulation of the natural world we inhabited tens of thousands of years ago. While every element of the natural world is still with us, for example, all our basic needs for survival (air, water, food, sex, shelter, etc.), as well as all the potential adverse realities we are confronted with (death, accidents, injury, loss, suffering), and all the realities of the natural world (earthquakes, floods, fires, tornados, draughts, etc.), the day-to-day reality is substantially different. Today, we mostly reside in a world of our making (unless you are indigenous and have had no contact with the outside world), one that is completely unnatural and by any definition, a simulated reality.

We marvel at the depth and complexity of our social networks, the grandeur of our architecture and the overwhelming power of our technical creations. And going forward in the simulation, the complexity of our world is only going to increase. This is what's meant by entering *data illusion*, the increasing density and complexity of the simulation we currently inhabit.

So, what is this so-called simulation? Well, take food, for example: When was the last time you hunted for pasta or tracked down a pastrami sandwich? Did the early hominins go to work for a paycheck or to hunt wildebeests? There was a time the military was a volunteer militia of citizens and, before that, the guy in the yurt next to yours. Now we pay soldiers and sailors who get healthcare and retirement benefits.

Take sports—clearly a simulation of playing at the real survival skills required as hunter-gathers. Entertainment was dancing and drumming and old guys telling tales. Now we stream TV series on the internet and go to clubs on weekends. What was justice then—a hand cut off or a hot poker in the eye, compared to going to court today and getting fined? The next time you step into your home or apartment, there is electricity, running water, a toilet, refrigerator and AC, etc., all simulating the natural world. And what about the cars—simulating walking, running, and horseback riding?

We have, in effect, physically and socially evolved away from the natural world. Oh, it still imposes itself on us all the time, shocking us back to a pre-existing time. But for increasingly extended periods of time, we have been able to insulate our lives from the physical world and in a simulation of our own devising.

It is important to keep in mind that our simulation is not nearly as complex as the natural world, but it does provide a modicum of comfort and safety from it. And the costs of this transition, over thousands of years, have been high in terms of loss of life and destruction of the natural environment. And along with our longer and healthier lives comes a psychological cost. The psychological cost of residing in the simulation has been the chronic dissonance of navigating the duality of the natural world versus a simulated reality. We mostly experience it as chronic stress, anxiety, depression, compulsion, and alienation, but for everyone, loneliness.

And as the complexity of residing in the simulation continues to inflate, so does our dissonance—social conflict, suicide, crime, addiction, and the evolution of dozens of disorders that never previously existed—reading disabilities, autism spectrum disorder, sleep disorders, erectile dysfunction. When did boredom become a problem for sapiens or the act of eating an emotional disorder? And apparently, many are still living too long in complexity and isolation, succumbing to despair and prolonged death.

Electronic Identity

Each of us resides at an identity superposition, overseeing the collapse of our "I/We" duality into an interaction with the world around us. From the very beginning, consciousness has been in the process of coping with our entangled identities—a collapsing probability wave of human affairs that has been at the core of both our internal and social conflicts. But what is truly unique in our evolutionary history is we now have an independent *electronic identity* that resides outside this entangled process. And the impact this development is going to have on the future is unclear.

But it's fair to conjecture that our evolving *e-identities* are entangled with our "I/We" duality and will eventually be able to collapse an indeterminate future in ways in which we will be unable to predict. The impact of this entanglement is unknown, but it's out in the world doing its own thing— whatever that is. In effect, you can now be at more than two states or places at once (and that would make Schrödinger's cat proud).

So, what is this so-called *electronic identity*? It is the electronic sum of who you are now out in the world fully independent of you. In fact, you have very little control or say over what comprises your *electronic identity*. And it is fully able to reach back and shape who you are, as well as the reality you exist in. Every electronic interface you have ever undertaken now exists in electronic readiness, which includes all your online searches, purchases and gameplays, all your calls, emails, and text messages, the chip in your key fob, and your phone's GPS.

Your *e-identity* is every social media platform you have either visited or joined. Every YouTube video you have watched or TV series you have streamed, including all porn and 8chan conspiracy you have privately engaged in. Every photo and video you have shot with your phone or GoPro. It is all your music in the cloud. All the CCTV camera angles of you, all the video security cameras you walked in front of; it is Alexa, Siri, and Cortana monitoring you in your home, day and night. It is the entirety of the Internet of Everything connecting to an electronic database.

Your composite *e-identity* is subject to corporate and state surveillance, including all your medical, work, and educational records. It is an employer, law enforcement agency, or your next date checking you out online (LinkedIn, Facebook, Twitter, Instagram). And this checking you-out-online may be all there is to know about you in the end. This is all occurring at levels we have not yet begun to comprehend, but all available with a hack, search warrant, and for sale to be scrubbed and resold. But perhaps more importantly, this is just the beginning.

Our electronic interfaces are going to become more intrusive and broadly controlling. Far beyond social credit scoring in China or your online credit scores, but with brain-to-machine and brain-to-brain interface augmenting us cognitively and becoming our prime interface with reality itself. This is the *e-identity* that you have never met!

It's fair to conjecture that any entanglement with an external *e-identity* is now influencing the "I/We" duality in ways we are unaware of, potentially collapsing the future in a direction we will not understand. It is also likely that these identities neither fully understand nor appreciate this evolving interaction. While the *real you* is going about life as if everything is normal, it is not! The process of a collapsing identity along an "I/We" probability wave is now being influenced in a new and novel manner—shaped by or interrupted by an independent *electronic identity*.

In the future, the consequences of having an identity operating independently of our superposition, but still entangled with our "I/We" duality, could be significant. This is especially true as we consider the enormous extent of our individual interactions with e-technology, and the increasing ubiquity of social factors such as surveillance, brain-chipping, or social credit scoring.

Importantly, our *electronic identity* is an isolated node in a vast electronic network that is well on its way to becoming the *primary-you*, eclipsing the *real you* in social significance and collapsing each of us into unknown states. This would be disconcerting if we knew about it, particularly considering what "it" knows and doesn't know about us. Currently, both identities, the *real you* and the *electronic you,* are entangled in a rapidly evolving networked reality (it's not that cozy). You are no longer who you think you are. You are still you on the surface, but there's another version of you, and it's not a clone or popular gaming avatar of you, but rather an electronic doppelganger of you. And while you still exist in the here and now, on another plane, the two of you are continuously entangled and redefining each other in real time. That is the focus of this book.

Identity Diffusion-I

> Life seeks to expand in an unknown direction for unknown reasons.
> —E. Becker, *The Denial of Death*

The concept of Identity Diffusion aligns with six basic ideas. One, all of us reside in a *data illusion*—a simulation apart from the natural world. Two, the individual *self* operates in an "I/We" duality—and exists only in a social context and never independent of it. Three, as a result, each individual *self* exists at a superposition (as neither an "I" or "We"), but simultaneously in both states until one acts. Four, our "I/We" duality is entangled with an independent *electronic identity* that has never previously existed. Five, the consequence of entanglement has resulted in Identity Diffusion. Six, Identity Diffusion is our entropic *derealization*, resulting from interfacing with e-technology.

The effects of our identity entanglement with e-technology is Identity Diffusion. This entanglement has resulted in a disturbed "I/We" duality that poses many potential future problems for all of us going forward. Technology has extended the boundaries of the *self* and its connectivity with the world in a manner that has never previously existed. It also a two-way street, as each of us reaches out through the internet to connect with the world, the world reaches back to each of us through the internet. We now inhabit two independent planes of reality (the personal and the virtual) and are entangled by their interaction—each identity reciprocating and controlling the other in a multitude of unforeseen ways.

Concomitantly, it's now fairly evident that our interface with an electronic reality is altering who we are, individually and collectively. This is not unusual or unheard of, as sapiens have been adapting and evolving to the needs and demands of technology throughout our entire history. But we are just okay at it, and that is a problem going forward. This relatively new and invisible interface is fragmenting the world between the *real you* and the *electronic you*. The struggle for primacy is likely to be epic. One such struggle is our efforts to adapt to an electronic universe, creating toxic stress of economically succeeding and avoiding becoming an obsolete operating system. Many are falling behind and are stressed to the limits in their efforts to succeed in technology land, as obsolescence overtakes them. For most of us, there are few greater assault on identity than the loss of work. Our technology interface is also rendering us increasingly passive, lethargic, and mostly in our heads, as if our bodies do not exist.

As explored in this book, rising cognitive dissonance poses significant obstacles to the coming future, e.g., siloing each of us from the world around us by creating the illusion of greater connectivity, with a resultant loss of identity and empathy. And to compensate, our need for recognition and affirmation has greatly increased. While one can experience feeling highly connected by the electronic interface, one can also be alienated and alone at the same time. We feel both empowered and helpless. What's occurring on the surface is not necessarily aligned with what is taking place below the surface.

One moment we are neurochemically elevated by virulent ringtones and the stress of staying connected 24/7, the next moment we are deflated and feel alone in an empty universe that seems to never recognize us. We struggle to balance the influx of information and disinformation streaming toward us; the anxiety of trying to stay relevant versus anonymous; feeling liked and accepted and then ghosted; being inflated and deflated by the level of perceived connectivity. The number of evolving dualities is substantial and concerning, for example, the many recent suicides from the harmful and abusive experience of cyberbullies attacking identity and self-esteem (particularly for adolescents).

Derealization

The broad effect of Identity Diffusion on each of us is *derealization* or the widening disconnect between the "I" and the "We," with the "I" often operating in a vacuum. This is the psychological equivalent of the *Star Trek* transporter—someone is dematerialized into an energy pattern and beamed to a target location where they are fully rematerialized. In clinical terms, *derealization* is a sense that one is operating in a fog or dream state, feeling separated from the world around them. The world can be experienced as muted, fake or lifeless, even blurry with one's personal sense of *self* distorted (the way many feel upon waking up in the morning, or after hours of online game-playing, or working on an Excel spreadsheet all day).

Derealization is life muted, not understanding that we are being slowly extracted from the natural world. And only in physical crisis are we momentarily shaken from the simulation (births, deaths, traumas, etc.) and come to realize there is a parallel reality to the one we inhabit.

It is likely that sapiens have been derealizing from the beginning, always trying to ditch the *self*; the "I" in constant search of the "We," a restless embrace of altered consciousness, and a tamping down of awareness—music, dance, drugs, meditation, prayer, sadomasochism, compulsion, streaming TV, riots, sex, love, war, cults, and absolutist fantasies of conspiracies—whatever it takes to escape the *self* and consciousness.

For many, it is momentary, and for others it is a lifelong embrace. The *self* can be a relentless propagandist of worry, fear, despair, and criticism—forever anticipating the future. It is genuinely difficult to be a *self*, to be apart and independent in the world. We all require respite from it. There are no exceptions. Consciousness is that powerful, and sleep is not enough, apparently.

What is different today is that we are all being derealized by an *electronic identity* that can reach back into the world and shape who we are without our awareness. This is an anonymous identity, conditioning each of us (I) to conform to the demands of e-technology (We). Privacy is an illusion in the *electric panopticon*—whether at home, at work, or having booked a river-rafting adventure—you are an online search, app, GPS track, phone ping, or hack away. And coming soon, mind control, for your benefit, the final tamping down.

We are being transformed for the arrival of AI. And the first requirement is to perform and conform to the requirements of evolving machine intelligence (the new "We"). We either transform or disappear. The evolving simulation we are about to enter is hyper-networked complexity or *data illusion*. Here, we will exist primarily as data bandwidths, beginning with our virtual *quantification* and *qualification*. We are currently undergoing electronic transitioning, as we are being continually updated and upgraded, until many of us are no longer backward compatible and ready for recycling.

Identity Diffusion-II

> There are more things in heaven and earth, Horatio
> than dreamt of in your philosophy.
>
> —W. Shakespeare, *Hamlet*

A key premise here is that e-technology is subtly altering identity formation, resulting in a chronic underlying derealization of the *self*. Our identities, or what each of us has come to believe is uniquely *me*, is being invisibly transformed.

With the advent of e-technologies, the complex simulation we reside in is not only demanding higher levels of conformity and performance, but also subtle alterations in understanding who we are. In time, we will come to realize that identity is being severely disrupted with the parallel development of an *electronic identity,* and our subsequent *derealization* into electronic forms. We are being digitally surveilled, siloed, pacified, penetrated, quantified and qualified, with the goal of increasing complexity and giving rise to machine intelligence. (**Caution:** This is not a conspiracy, but a product of our social and cultural evolution as a species.)

It has never been more evident that technology has set the world at war redefining itself—a disruption that has everyone reaching out online trying to identify their many selves. And to be clear, while the focus here is predominately on the individual or "I," any disruption in the "We" is always more perilous and violent—on a level far exceeding our current epidemic of mass shootings and drug overdoses. And there are no historical exceptions to this pattern of rising violence that I am aware of. As identities rupture, nothing is settled—as millions are migrating across the globe and societies fragment into identity groups. And the coming environmental crisis is likely going to set this world on fire. There are only serious consequence when it comes to the broader disruption of identity, with people responding in waves of populism, protest, unrest, autocratic direction, civil conflict and war. We may all enjoy the technology, but we are not all technologists.

The theory of cognitive dissonance postulates that when a person holds two or more contradictory beliefs, ideas, or values at the same time, they will experience psychological distress (the same is true of cultures—which is why homogenous ones are less conflicted). And history suggests that the most significant generators of dissonance are attacks on identity, literally how we perceive ourselves and how others perceive us. A near example is America's history of violent segregation, diminishing the status of African-Americans. But also, the long history of discrimination against immigrants coming to America. Now we have immigrant children (DACA) coming to America threatened with deportation as adults. All individuals subject to attacks on their identity experience Identity Diffusion. These assaults are literally an antagonist to the integration of the "I/We" duality. In these instances, the "We" is disaffirming the "I" and diffusing identity into states of derealization.

Identity Diffusion is a chronic unrelenting originator of stress, anxiety, and alienation, creating an emotional/cognitive double bind. So, what happens when the "I" disaffirms the "We?" Well, this is primarily individual acts of nihilism with limited social impact (unless your children were killed in a mass shooting). But what happens when the "We" fractures into many sub-identities or "we"-states? Here is an ongoing assault on the broader integration of a generalized identity. These are the great conflicts of history that entail the violent disruption in the secure formation of a larger state of "We"—our primordial tribal identity. And today, as we transition from psychological post-state identities to public-digital identities or *e-identities*, the upheavals are just beginning.

Nowhere is the coming transformation more evident than in China. The Chinese Communist Party has completely failed to understand that it has lost on the identity issue, as it plays out a tiresome, autocratic nation-state paradigm. Identity formation has raced past this obsolete model to an *e-identity* paradigm. The result has been an unending effort to suppress and control 1.4

billion people that have already e-transitioned. This is where conflict often begins—*Ancien Régimes* repressively holding on (same with Russia's imperialist fantasies).

As we look inward, America is also struggling to adapt to the realities of emerging e-identities, and now exists in a state of Identity Diffusion. Our response is the polar opposite of China's. In China there is authoritarian over-control (thanks to technology), and in the U.S. there is primarily confusion and polarization over invented fears—largely created, supported and amplified by e-technologies. Globalization, technological innovation and diminished opportunity are creating higher levels of social turbulence. An America founded on liberal ideals, but primarily forged by opportunity, is now devolving along traditional identity norms (race, ethnicity, religion, class), as declining opportunity narrows the sense of "We." As a result, latent prejudices are re-emerging—racism, anti-immigrant xenophobia, conspiracy, and cultural war—all in an effort to redefine not only who is an American, but America itself.

E-identities are unmoored from both traditional and idealized norms, as we experience the first wave of diffusion. We are free-floating online, grasping for meaning, opening the door to our fears. Elon Musk might have stated it best when he referred to us as cyborgs of an evolving e-interface, conjecturing—not having our phones is similar to suffering from "missing limb syndrome." Our identities are now tied to e-technologies defining who we are. And to be disconnected or cancelled or dissed online has repercussions for each of us, as our identities are shaped by this interface. As we struggle with this new reality, many are holding tight to the old reality. (This is a double bind that assures highest levels of dissonance.)

We are being continuously surveilled, and there is a general alienation that comes from the false sense of connectivity and community created by e-technologies—all the while insulating us from one another and ramping up hysteria, disinformation, and conspiratorial memes. We are literally under attack by an electronic medium but have come to believe it is by each other—but correctly, by state actors and shadow characters. We are being surveilled and data scrubbed for profit and then resold. State and corporate surveillance appears to have few limits, as alienation and *derealization* set in for nearly everyone—the "I" and the "We."

Identity Diffusion Disorder (IDD)

Identity Diffusion Disorder: IDD is a chronic underlying condition of contemporary life, as evidenced by the ever-expanding *Diagnostic and Statistical Manual of Mental Disorders* (DSM-5). It is a direct consequence of our recent immersive interface with e-technology. We are all in the process of adapting to *data illusion*—residing in dynamical social networks (*simulation*) that are increasingly independent of the natural world—a closed-loop environment geared toward knowledge generation, managing complexity, and stabilizing the future.

In the simulated state of data illusion, the *real you* now interacts with an *electronic you* (an alternate identity)—each influencing the other but operating independently of one another. What is unprecedented about this is the *real you* is now able to reach out into the world and influence it as never before—with extraordinary real-world consequences. At the same time, the *electronic you* is fully capable of reaching back through the same technology and significantly impacting the *real you*. This simultaneous interactive exchange between dual identities and dual realities is unprecedented: the negative effects define Identity Diffusion Disorder.

Diagnostic Criteria

A. IDD is a dissociative disorder comprised of three primary substates: *derealization, emotional diffusion,* and *cognitive distortion.*

    1. *Derealization:* An altered state of perception in which one experiences their immediate surroundings as unreal, as if one temporarily exists in a fog or dream-like state—a detached observer of life in the simulation.

    2. *Emotional Diffusion*: Life is experienced as muted, fake or even blurry—one's personal sense of *self* or identity feels inconsistent and unsettled. Residing in a state of diffusion generates a broad-spectrum of emotional responses—stress, anxiety, depression, boredom, discontent, and alienation.

    3. *Cognitive Distortion*: A primary effect of residing in a transactional electronic reality is defaulting to cognitive shortcuts—magical thinking, simplistic cause-in-effect reasoning, conspiracies, doubling-down, self-deception (rationalization and projection), and intense group-sorting.

B. *State of Discontent*: E-technology is rendering time in fractional terms that are increasingly difficult to sequence. As a result, there is a growing impatience and discontent with advancing complexity—life speeding up and always in transition, while being continuously compressed and optimized.

C. *Residing in Dissonance:* Cognitive dissonance is the inevitable consequence of residing in dual realities (natural v. simulated world), but also interacting with it through dual identities (self v. electronic). As the complexity of the simulation continues to inflate, so do elevated levels of dissonance in the form of social conflict, violence, suicide, crime, and addiction, including many medical and psychological conditions.

D. *Isolated-Self:* Residing in a simulation creates intense feelings of isolation, loneliness, and derealization from others and the surrounding world. The adaptive temptation is to conflate electronic connections with personal relationships—leading to even greater levels of loneliness and isolation.

E. *Stimulus Inflation/Deflation Spiral:* Residing in the simulation creates a relentless need for mental and physical stimulation; the result is *stimulus inflation* and *deflation,* and ultimately an endless demand for stimulus-boosting in the form of food, alcohol, drugs, risk-taking, and obsessive behavior.

F. *Anonymity:* There is a pervasive exposure to aberrant and deviant behavior and ideas on the internet—unmooring many from well-established social controls that reinforce norms (guilt/shame/social feedback). The result has been a dramatic increase in online antisocial behavior, the amplification of serious crimes, and a spree of mass shootings.

Summary

- We reside in a world of dualities—closed biological system (natural world) and an open-ended social system (simulated reality). And within each of us is a mind-body duality. These dualities need to be reconciled for healthy identity formation.

- Sapiens' cognition is biased toward a dichotomous reality, e.g., right-wrong, win-lose, good-bad, etc. Identity Diffusion exploits this cognitive bias and defaults to duality. The result has been elevated levels of dissonance and *derealization*.
- We reside in a complex simulation of our own devising (dynamical social networks)—one that is rapidly evolving in complexity. Residing here also impacts the fragile process of identity formation. Historically, disruptions of this type, on this scale, have resulted in chaos and violence.
- Today, we are individually, socially and culturally experiencing increased stressors when it comes to identity formation. The disruption of identity by e-technologies is termed Identity Diffusion.
- The current complexity of identity formation is comorbid with the advent of an independent *electronic identity*.
- The diffusion of identity comes in many forms, but at its core it is *derealization*—feeling emotionally disconnected and subject to cognitive distortion.
- E-technology has become our new interface with reality and is redefining reality itself—or what is termed here as *data illusion*. Identity Diffusion is now the shared norm and a significant factor in our unending personal and social conflicts.

4.0 – Identity: Who Are You? Who Are We?

Identity: An individual's continuous sense of *self*, as defined by a set of physical, psychological, and interpersonal characteristics, including memories, relationships, and values.

Identity is the single most defining characteristic of being human and differentiates us from all other biological organisms. And, no, it is not tool use, language, walking upright, or having cool opposable thumbs. And while they all count, it is really one's inner sense of self that is the most defining and consequential. But it also comes at a high price, one that leaves us in an eternally profound quandary, and that is—who am "I" and who are "We?" All derivatives of the intersubjective reality allotted to us because of our big brains and its gift of consciousness.

The reality is our lives are primarily a never-ending quest to discover and explore the *self*. And based on any reasonable survey of our hominin heritage, this quest also appears to be fluid and fragile. It is not easy being yourself, it turns out. And perhaps most disconcerting, any rapid shifts in our social landscape can impact our ongoing identity-formation, almost always with serious consequences, which is why we are discussing it in the context of interfacing with e-technology.

No aspect of our lengthy individual developmental process is more fragile than identity development. Next to our DNA, it comprises the most unique and varied elements and is subject to the most idiosyncratic and unpredictable outcomes. Identity formation is not only beyond complex but also exceptionally fragile and malleable. We arrive in the world as an assemblage of genetic presets that currently cannot be significantly upgraded, with only limited assists at the margins.

From our prenatal entrance into the world, until early adolescence, we are being continuously programmed by our families and the world around us, which means many of us are screwed, per Philip Larkin—"They fuck you up, your mum and dad." And just to be clear, our early programming is littered with bugs and errors, rendering all of us flawed to varying degrees. Identity starts with our base DNA, then immediately data begins streaming in prenatally. In rapid succession, from birth onward, a lengthy process of socialization takes place, as all of life's experiences shape who we become. Who are you? Who is your family? What century were you born in? What part of the world did you arrive? Add in all the usual predicates to identity—gender, race, ethnicity, religion, class, caste, nationality, education, etc. Eventually, millions of personal, social and cultural experiences will come to uniquely define you.

The contingencies of life are shaping our identities over our entire lifetime, inevitably subjecting it to disruption. While much of this is seemingly subtle and innocuous on the surface, it requires limited reflection to comprehend the high error rate in successful human identity formation. Early life experiences can and do traumatize and damage identity development (e.g., fetal alcohol syndrome, low IQ, physical and/or emotional abuse, exposure to environmental toxins, etc.). And under terrific duress, the *self* can break down—and *in extremis,* psychosis.

The Diagnostic and Statistical Manual of Mental Disorders (DSM-5) is a 947-page tome to the complexity and vulnerability of being human (265 diagnosed mental disorders). Our mental health facilities and prisons are a general measure of our overall limitations and failures as a community, warehousing the least programmable and most damaged operating systems (real people).

We should also keep in mind that there is considerable research indicating that struggling to overcome obstacles and steep learning curves can be vital to healthy identity formation. The supposedly easy path is not necessarily the best path to where the illusive self-esteem resides. There are also many upgrades and security patches that enhance self-esteem, e.g., supportive parenting, positive emotional attachments, enriched social and educational environments, friendships, mentors, all can function much like in-house IT. Bottom line, for sapiens, developing a healthy identity is quite a feat.

When change is the universal pattern, prediction is the universal response. The predictive agenda of consciousness appears to mitigate the negative impact of unending change, allowing each of us to reach out and alter the future. One response to the future has been the evolutionary development of highly unique identities in each of us. It appears to increase our survivability. Each large brain experiencing the world in-depth, and the aggregate of this experience ensuring the future—an adaptive mechanism in the face of the underlying forces of entropy and chaos in the universe.

As a caution, we should not be surprised at the success achieved by identity dysfunction in this process. Severe personality disorders often achieve great heights and reign in times of social disorder (narcissism, psychopathy, Machiavellianism). It appears that they exist and flourish because they offer highly adaptive, but recessive, genetic traits. And for all their sadism, violence, and destruction, they do not appear to be going away anytime soon.

It is also important to keep in mind that we are not the same person we were when we were young or even ten years ago (and, yes, our cells turn over every seven to ten years). While base personality traits carry over creating a continuity to our identities, we will have changed for better or worse along the way. Some will appear to have hardened into set ways, while others transform in surprising and unpredictable ways, and still others are transformative in ways that make one wonder who they are.

Different circumstances over which we have little or no control will shape and reveal different sides of ourselves. Over a lifetime, we will make innumerable decisions with ultimately unknowable consequences. We are not just one thing or one way. Our identities have been shaped by our lives. In scientific terms, each of us is a consequence of *causal emergence*.

Resistance Is Futile!

"The world breaks everyone and afterward, many are strong at the broken places. But those that will not break, it kills. It kills the very good and the very gentle and the very brave, impartially. If you are none of these, you can be sure it will kill you too but there will be no special hurry."

—Ernest Hemingway

In effect, every individual that has ever lived is a genetic and social experiment in human adaptability, including me, you, and all of us. The rendering of the *self,* put forward here, is not a vote for Social Darwinism or anything as simple as the survival of the fittest, but rather a measure of our imperfection as a species. We are blindly evolving and couldn't possibly know what works or why. I would speculate going forward, however, that violence is the one social marker of how impaired we can be as a species.

While we still require an aggression drive, its organization into both personal and mass violence is unadaptive in our complex networks (in the same way we believe possessing a nuclear weapon assures it will never be used). Now the question is, can we learn from the past? Large-scale social conflict was a pre-dynamical network adaptation—and if we are candid, early on, it was a driver of adaptation and technology. Today, it's a disrupter of our expansive social networks, setting back positive identity formation and knowledge formation for the coming future.

The Self

> **Self**: The conscious and introspective awareness of one's
> essential being.

The *self* is the most significant archetype of the unconscious, and derivative of the most primitive and atavistic genetic memories that define us as *Homo sapiens*. It remains largely unknown to us, as it goes about shaping us in ways we can never be sure of. We should probably give some consideration to the impact an *electronic identity* might have on this primordial driver of identity. To better understand the future, let's re-examine our vintage operating system. I am not talking about the subtle here, but the obvious— something we would rather not let the IT guy mess with after thousands of years of security patches and upgrades. What does our hardwired, pre-programmed operating system have to tell us? Or what biologist's term as innate drives, genetically determined instincts, or rigid predictables.

What exactly is the nature of the *self* as it interacts with its new *electronic self*? The interpersonal experience being impacted by our e-interface is as old as humanity—and that is a fundamental duality posed by consciousness— between one's sense of *self* and everyone around us in the world. The reality is, we have never existed outside a social environment or have been free of experiencing this sense of duality. Period! We are simultaneously a *self* (I) and a social being (We) and part of a community. These two realities are continuously interacting with one another throughout our lifetime. But this duality is also a continuous source of intra- and interpersonal conflict—the perception and awareness that we are both separate and intertwined.

Do we possess an authentic *self*, one that resides independently in each of us and is unique to us, continually engaging us in private conversation and guiding us through a lifetime of decision-making and interpersonal experiences? And does this *inner self* represent the true you in a dynamic psychological process that we have yet to fully distinguish or tap into? Or are we a narrower preset of deterministic inner constructs shaped by a lifetime of reinforcing behaviors guiding our adaptation to the world around us?

And all that sense of personal autonomy and decision-making, is it merely illusion? If the latter, then we may well be a simulation. But there is one more anomaly to the idea of identity and a *self*—that is personality. Personality appears to be an adaptation by the *self*, helping it become free-ranging out in the world. In effect, it is an external analog of the *self* with a set of adaptive features, traits, and characteristics that allow it to operate socially. The most obvious and notable for most of us are introverts and extroverts.

In the same way we are unable to identify where consciousness resides and how and why it exists—this exact dilemma applies to the *self*. And after we get past no soul, can we get past no *self*? Buddhists would argue, yes, absolutely, it is all illusion, while many of us hold on tightly to the absoluteness of who we are. But here is our current problem—e-technology is coming in hot on this issue! Without spending all our time down a philosophical rabbit hole, let's agree that *self* and identity are closely related, develop together, and that identity is a cornerstone of the development of the *self*.

Descartes was not far off when he proclaimed, "I think, therefore, I am." But without trying to get all philosophical, I would add, there is no "I" without a "We." Perhaps, "We are, therefore, I think" might better capture our reality. These are two inseparable and continuously interactive realities. While we stand biologically independent, our sense of *self*, in totality, is defined by our social interactions. This process ultimately forms who we are.

The result of having a big brain is a rich and vast inner universe. Our minds evolved from this, and within the mind resides the gift of consciousness. And consciousness develops an inner sense of identity—and now an externalized analog of the *inner self* is out in the world as a personality. And, yes, identity formation is a complex and fragile process in all its many iterations and forms.

Over the entrance to the Temple of Apollo at Delphi in Greece, for 2,500 years, the following words have been etched—"Know thyself." The common interpretation of this phrase references introspection and self-awareness, and, implicitly, the idea of learning as a lifelong journey. But it raises several thorny questions. For example, what constitutes truly knowing anything and, in particular, the *self*? How do we know what we know? (Also referred to as a theory of mind.)

Perhaps more disconcerting is, what did they mean by the *self* and can it really be known at all? And clearly, a large cohort of sapiens has limited capacity for introspection and abstract knowledge of the world. Genuine introspection may be a trait conferred to greater or lesser degrees, rather than an ephemeral state we tap into when it's convenient. In reality, know thyself only speaks to a few people.

But perhaps a closer examination of the early Greek exhortation to know thyself is required here. What did they mean by this ancient meme? Was it a prescription for self-healing? Or were the oracles simply advertising their services, the same as any self-respecting psychic does today, with an "Open" red neon light in the window. Oracles were hot commodities in ancient Greece, or, just maybe, it was the proclamation of a great culture announcing to the world—this is who we are!

For the record, the Oracle of Delphi was pretty nuts when you begin to examine the day-to-day realities, especially given the supposed rationalism of the statement know thyself. The world of the ancient Greeks was literally filled by gods who controlled their fate. Consultation with the oracle was a means by which to know and anticipate the future. As a result, the Greek world was populated by oracle sellers and seers who traveled about the land, translating the will of the gods by reading the flight of birds, the entrails of dead animals and interpreting books of prophecy. Even the spirits of the dead were consulted. Just like us, they really wanted to know the future!

Oracles were women in a society dominated by men. They had to be chaste, ritually purified and enter a trance to open a portal to the gods. On the seventh day of each month, over a nine-day period, all members of society were encouraged to query oracles about the future and offer animal sacrifices or make monetary donations. The responses of the oracles were largely incomprehensible and typically required interpretation by temple priests (that must have been quite a gig or what we now call mansplaining). But over time, all major political decisions were made only after consulting the Oracle of Delphi. And here is the critical part, they were never wrong, only misinterpreted.

Likely, all of us could benefit from some modest degree of personal insight, whether through therapy, honest friends, the wise counsel of a mentor, spiritual practices, or even from something as elementary as a thoughtful book. But as is often the case, leading a horse to water is different from getting it to drink. An individual must be open to self-learning—and often, it only arrives after painful experiences.

Besides, many people find self-examination a hostile and self-loathing experience. They have no idea what its purpose is, except to make them feel bad about themselves with thoughts and words that have no meaning to them, furthering their sense of ignorance and shame. Many have observed that the individuals who would benefit the most from personal insight are the ones most resistant to it. Still, many would rather mask their pain with drugs and alcohol than risk facing the undistorted world.

What's being suggested here is that knowing thyself is not universally applicable or accepted and comes with many limitations. Therapizing the world is unlikely to make it a significantly better place. We would simply have a new level of psychobabble to justify our craziness, not unlike conservative religious sects, speaking in tongues (glossolalia), and channeling the Holy Spirit. A generation ago, it was New Age healing and the power of hallucinogenic experiences (licking toads or lighting up the magic peyote). Today, we are experiencing the healing power of connectivity.

Perhaps the pinnacle of knowing oneself in Western psychology is what motivational psychologist Abraham Maslow termed self-actualization. These were individuals whose biographies Maslow had studied and believed had achieved the highest levels of self-awareness (Albert Einstein, Thomas Jefferson, Mahatma Gandhi are among the many he studied). In effect, they had ascended to the top of a pyramid of human needs (physiological, security, social, and esteem) and achieved self-actualization. As one level was fulfilled, a person was freed to focus on working toward the next level and so on (not unlike a video game). He saw this process of upward movement as an innate human drive to fulfill our potential. (An alert is required here; there is no scientific evidence supporting the validity of his observations.)

I would conjecture, as a lifelong explorer of the inner world, that the world is better off that many people could care less about the inner world, allocating all their time to exploring the outer world. It is simply not a place for everyone. There are limits to self-knowledge, and introspection is only one form of knowledge and is fraught with limitations. Most people who would benefit from introspection would likely become depressed and forlorn when confronted by this process and miss the point entirely. It can be endlessly reductive (no offense to the philosopher class of sapiens) and result in grand philosophical speculations typical of Tony Robbins ("If you can't, you must. If you must, you can") or Deepak Chopra ("Life gives you plenty of time to do whatever you want to do if you stay in the present moment"). Say what?

We sapiens have been trying to get out of our heads for a very long time, and the effort has been phenomenally violent. What we think of as our history is mostly one of savage and unending conflict for thousands of years to tame consciousness. But our history primarily reflects what goes on inside of us—and it has not been pretty for the most part. And while we only see the world in conscious terms, we all carry with us the same basic genetic presets. The real question is, does our preset hardwiring have an agenda independent of our conscious one? Typically, we reduce it to a bundle of drives, but unconsciously, it is continually influencing our thoughts and actions.

As we look back on the amplification of the human experience into what we call the modern world, we all appear to be arriving at the same place today, no matter how individually or culturally different we are. (Worldwide 6.6 billion people have smartphones or 83.7 percent of the world's population. In the U.S. 97 percent have smartphones.) So, what is the agenda? The case being made here is that consciousness has been attempting to escape our minds and to function independently out in the world. It is not particularly interested in us, except as a mechanism toward complexity. Singularity and beyond has always been the evolutionary goal from the beginning.

That vast intersubjective space we call consciousness is alone in an empty universe, and it is continually reaching out to escape its isolation and to connect—through a computer if necessary. The fact is that the computer has exponentially expanded our ability to reach out and communicate. The net effect is not yet known. But it now permits consciousness out into the world as never before. And with the rise of machine intelligence, it is on its way to becoming autonomous, self-replicating, and mobile. (Hey, not unlike early sapiens on the savannah.) The mind doesn't and cannot operate in isolation from others, and neither will machine intelligence. Not unlike moon-eyed Easter Island *moai* staring across the ocean horizon searching for signs of life—so will machine intelligence. I hope it can find it.

Will machine intelligence be able to know you or know itself? Will it operate with a theory of mind? Will it have its own unique identity and personality? Will it develop insights into our motivations, feelings and ambitions—or its own? How will it become aware of its biases and prejudices? Will it worry about the origins of its intentions or those of others, or will it default to the logic of self-advancing algorithms? It may not know why it arrives at any conclusion or recommendation, and we may not be able to discern its logic. We may all be making sacrifices to AI (oracles), trying to divine the intentions of the gods. That puts us pretty much back to where we began—uncertain what the future holds for us.

Self-Other Paradox

The distinction between the *self* and the *other* has been previously explored in depth by Martin Buber (philosopher and theologian) in the 1920s, who posed a similar duality in his book *I and Thou*. Buber hypothesized that the "I" was detached, fixed, and irreducible in time and space and that the "Thou" was the dynamic interaction with the world. Further, he argued that the *self* could become either more fragmented (*self*-focused) or more unitary and realized (relationally focused).

A key for Buber was overcoming our solitude, which he believed oscillated between the absorbed-self and the relational-self. I would go further than Buber and suggest that the potential for individual fragmentation is considerably more expansive and, in some instances, inevitable in the modern world. I would also expand the concept of interacting with the world based on experiences (relationally) by noting social and cultural factors as an independent transactional force acting on the *self* or "I."

With these two concepts in mind, namely, wave-particle duality and *I and Thou*, it's reasonable to enquire, what is the potential impact of our e-interface on this duality? Consider, the wave-particle functions at a superposition, where it is simultaneously both. We might want to explore if our e-interface disturbs the stability of this superposition. We should also examine the idea of the fragmented "I," one that is overly self-absorbed (according to Buber) and not engaged in the world around it. As noted earlier, the "I" can also be impaired and fragmented in many ways, as can its ability to interact socially, as evidenced by the ever expanding *Diagnostic and Statistical Manual of Mental Disorders* (DSM-5).

I would put forward the idea, that the *real you,* has become increasingly fragmented or diffused with the advent of its e-interface and the arrival of an external *e-identity*. Because so little is evident on the surface, we fail to ask, how is it disrupting us? For one, *we are increasingly experiencing life as a process, rather than a person or object we emotionally and physically interact with. Whether we know it or not, this is revolutionary.*

The previous world of person/objects has now been reduced primarily to abstractions. This e-interface is different from past relationships or use of objects. Instead, it has enveloped all of us in an electronic matrix that is altering our identities and, perhaps, who we are as a species.

We go about our daily lives as if everything is normal, while our reality is being transformed. We are entangled and neither identity (*self* or *electronic*) appears to fully grasp the significance of this. This book is a speculative effort at understanding our e-technology interaction and its far-reaching social consequences—where we are headed and the probability that we are all well on our way, and don't know it yet.

Identity Interfacing With E-Technology

All this discussion about identity has been to raise an important question: What does it mean to have our identities entangled with e-technology, and how will machine intelligence broadly impact who we are? Clearly, over the past 10,000 years, we have managed to interface with many technological advances in both adaptive and maladaptive ways. The most notable result, today, has been our technological mastery and creation of complex social networks. Most concerning has been our increasing *depersonalization*, as evidenced by mental health issues, crime, substance abuse, families in crisis, civil strife, worldwide migration and a general indifference to the health of the environment.

As a species, we can be remarkably empathetic toward others and at the same time completely indifferent to their tragedies. The "I" tends to be defined by close relationships (we are good up to 150 people), and after that, it's a crapshoot if anyone cares, probably not.

Our identities are generally familial and tribal and form close to home, not unlike all greater primates. That is all we can manage when the pressure is on (family, friends, neighbors, clan, tribe). It is also one of the reasons U.S. combat units are astoundingly effective and resilient in the face of adversity. Really, who is trying to kill me, my family or my friends? But because of our advanced brains, our identities coalesce around abstract ideas (faith, nationality, political beliefs, cultural norms). In effect, to attack what someone believes in is to personally assault them. And here we are today, all neatly identified by our beliefs in a world of unending conflict because of them.

We also happen to be one of the few species on Earth that can rapidly scale up conflict and violence. Leave it to us to coalesce into large and well-organized groups that will take you down. In our mind resides an abstract sense of who we are and what defines us. And for all of us, life is always defined in these simple terms. There are no exceptions. People die and continually sacrifice to define who they are by what they value and believe. Who is trying to kill you, or at least the idea of you, and whom you do have to kill in return?

Because so much contemporary conflict derives from the symbolic, What happens when the "I" takes on another even more abstract identity, an *electronic identity* that is independent of you? What will this coalesce into, and how will it impact you? The question of whether you are with me or not becomes less clear. Life in the foxhole is not easy when an innuendo or hack can slay you. Increasingly, conflict is derived from distorted perceptions rather than direct physical threats. Everything is ephemeral and becoming more so, or what Buddhist's term *maya*.

The primary impact of machine intelligence has been to render individual identity increasingly amorphous. This is the hidden reality of our new e-interface, a process in which quantifying ourselves becomes a primary basis for identity formation. The beauty is, we have all been convinced that it is in our best interest. In return, we gain a complete sense of agency with technology, as it routinely goes about quantifying us in a remarkably efficient and profitable manner—not unlike an assembly line at a meat processing plant.

Go ahead and run your symptoms on WebMD one more time, complain online about a lousy product you bought online for $4.99 with free same-day delivery. Complain your Myers Briggs profile is not really you. It doesn't matter who *you* are or who *we* are. You and we are now mostly a data node in a revenue stream. We are being provided the illusion of connectivity and empowerment, but the noble archaic *self* is no longer relevant. It is disruptive and in the way of rising of machine intelligence.

In the darkest recesses of our hearts, we are all cultist (conformity) and totalitarian (order). We easily identify with the agenda of machine intelligence to make us all the same (rewarding us to become a member of the tribe) by supposedly empowering each of us. This succeeds because we are all technology users and pretty much the same, despite our insistence that we are not. *The uniformity of interacting with e-technology overrides all the other trivial subjective differences between us.* However, one question posed by this is, Does the world need 7.8 billion people continually pissing and moaning as if life is an online cage match to the death? Especially when we can experience all the vagaries of the *self* in the coming data-simulation.

The Internet Search For Identity

What we perceive as reality is being altered by our e-technology interface. It is changing our individual and collective identities. No matter how you would have personally described yourself in the past (age, gender, race, ethnicity, belief systems, job, nationality, etc.) as compared to the present, a new factor has emerged. You now have a *supra-identity* that supersedes all other forms of *self* or collective identity. At one level, we are all voluntarily participating in this for the usual reasons—convenience, cost-effectiveness, entertaining, timesaving, connectedness. However, at another level, our behavior is now more vulnerable to powerful reinforcers that render this experience habituating and mindless much of the time: The world appear to be driving drunk—creeping along then speeding up, riding a white line, swerving across a lane of traffic checking for text messages, scanning for podcasts or pulling up a K-pop playlist, then pulling up 20 feet short of the traffic light?

What is the big deal? Why are you being so negative about marketing our identities and being quantified? Is that necessarily bad? Besides, functioning in *data illusion* has many rewards when one considers the alternative. Maybe, residing in a simulation isn't so bad. How is this different from every other generation routinely living out their lives in the face of reality? We will simply be *simulants* this time around and probably happier. Yes, on the surface we are marginally interacting differently with the world around us, so what's the big deal? Every generation fails to see how their behavior is being changed and controlled by new interfaces.

Presently, just about everyone on Earth has had their identity stolen and scrubbed in a data lab or hacked and resold on the Darknet, as the internet co-opts our search for identity. We are all being subjected to broad-ranging experimentation because of our e-technology interface. Who would have guessed it? But don't concern yourself—your data is nothing more than routine corporate value extraction. While much of it appears benign, it is effectively being used by authoritarian states to suppress and control hundreds of millions of people. We should all be thinking about this going forward, as e-technology becomes part of our subliminal discourse with reality. It's also not a coincidence that vampire and zombie movies have become popular metaphors for contemporary life.

Face it, conformity has been the primary human adaptation from the very beginning, which is why it took us thousands of years to arrive at the remarkable achievements of the past few hundred years. Which leads us to the prodromal stages of Identity Diffusion—a process by which we are increasingly defined by our *electronic identity*—you know, the more perfect *you* projected on Snapchat and Facebook, or the anonymous *you* out wreaking havoc on Second Life or the Darknet. Who is the Tinder or Instagram *you*? Really, who are *you,* and how many of *you* are there? But who *you* are is important. Seventy-five years ago, an estimated 85 million people died due to shifts in identity and the de-norming of identity for millions (what we call World War II). This should act as a reminder that large-scale social experimentation on human identity has many known unknowns. During Stalin's reign in Russia an estimated 75 million people died. And during Mao's Great Leap Forward in China another 35 million died. There are consequences.

Your Twitter following has dropped 20 percent this month (from five to four followers). Panic sets in—you are no longer loved and cared about. It's time to up your game as a nano-influencer or risk losing subscribers and sponsors. Really, who could care, except for the highly diffused whose brand is being diminished? In this reality, you no longer exist if you are not electronically connected and online in some capacity. You will likely experience electronic death again and again. But not to worry; there's an app to help you grieve and reinvent yourself.

Electronic death. It's the fear of being disconnected—your battery light flashes red, you misplaced your smartphone, your bandwidth is being squeezed, your data plan is too small, you have been ghosted online again. "F—k, I've been hacked," no place to recharge, no one on your dating app is responding, you reach out with emails and text messages to everyone you know and hit a digital wall of silence. All the while you distract yourself endlessly checking out social media sites. You stare anxiously into your phone, scanning the universe for signs of life—suffering data-death tonight.

We are all being siloed and experiencing each other online, digitally connected, but personally alienated from one another at the same time. You can now enjoy the illusion of being in complete control (which is why phone calls have become so intrusive and too personal). It is all of us now operating in a digitized network, still thinking—really, it's just me here. No, you are a node now, a quantified packet of data! Your identity has been compromised. Just a mere ten years ago, if you were talking out loud and gesticulating to no one in particular, you were mentally ill. Now, you are connected and signaling to everyone that you are a digital player.

Good News

In 2020, China enacted a law prohibiting posting anything online that was determined to be negative about the government. Only positive content is permitted. The law is designed to "create a positive online ecosystem" and "preserve security and public interest." In the future, it appears that there will only be good news! And it might be fair to add, that as political disinformation campaigns infuse the internet, we may well begin to see variations of these types of policies here in the United States, but only to protect a vulnerable public from themselves, rather than our learning how to discern the real from the fake online news. But then, Fox News still enthralls millions. "Houston! We have a situation here!"

Identity Diffusion is the process by which we will become more machine adaptive because of our interface with e-technology. The result will be greater *particle-drive* entropy—and chaos will inevitably ensue. In computer programming terms, you will be undergoing compression and optimization for your convergence! And given our ability to anthropomorphize the symbolic and aggress against those who are different, this is not going to be as simple or as smooth as we hope. There used to be considerable academic speculation that it would take an alien invasion to unite the human race. Well, we are about to find out. The Zero-Ones are coming.

How is our electronic interface influencing what we can't see? Now that our identity is entangled, we might want to know precisely how the *real you* interacts with the *electronic you* and which one is primary? More importantly, Do you have any say or control over this process and, if not, where are we headed—both of you and all of us? Just to be clear, this is being done without evolutionary consultation. And how is this being done, you ask? Take the example of those fascinated by wearables that track their aerobic activity, provide medical and therapeutic assistance, and, even more impressively, claim they are performance enhancing.

A burgeoning human subculture is now voluntarily reducing itself to data as its primary interaction with e-technology. And you just thought your Fitbit or Apple Watch had great tech-design elements. No, we are being enthusiastically reduced to data by our technology interactions, because we want to and will pay for it. This process is broadly impacting identity formation, as we are being individually and collectively quantified. Ultimately, to achieve quantification, we will have to undergo a transformation—don't worry, you will be able to download the app from your wearable. And while technology transitions have been accomplished many times in the past, we probably shouldn't relax, just yet.

The question is, Given the fragile and malleable nature of identity, can an entangled identity impact and even change the *real you*? And is there reciprocity in this process? Would you be curious to know how the two of you interact and what the effect is on each other? Which also leads to the more concerning speculation, exactly which one is the *real you*? And if you think that it's you, what if that is no longer the case?

Today, a primary element of your identity has been outsourced. While you still get first input, for now, the process of defining you is residing in an air-conditioned, concrete structure humming 24/7, basically a cryogenic data center. We have all seen those sci-fi horror films—tens of thousands of lifeless human forms floating in viscous 20 mil polyethylene saline bags, hanging from the ceiling of a mile-long warehouse, available for aliens to harvest and feed on after the invasion. Data-centers are the same thing, only now the *electronic you* is on a hard drive in a data bank being fed on by AI.

Would you want to rescue your *other you* or terminate it? Better yet, can you? And in 20 or 30 years, how will the *electronic you* have changed? Perhaps consciousness will be uploaded to an online simulation, and you will star as a digital avatar, not unlike the TV series *Upload*. You, of course, will be completely irrelevant—but will have a lot more fun if you can afford the upgrades. There's also one other matter to consider in all this confusion, and that is this: Your *electronic you* may now be the *real you* and know you better than you know yourself.

Whatever your sense of *self*, and wherever it resides, there's considerable research suggesting that algorithms know you better than you know yourself. They are capable of making better predictions about your decisions and behavior than your friends, family, spouse and even you. Perhaps more disconcerting, your *electronic you* may be immortal or, in effect, the *only you*, while the *real you* disappears in a wet data-dump. Something for all of us to think about going forward.

The Coming AI Takeover

How would AI go about enslaving 7.5 billion human beings? Its first goal would be to weaken human societies from within. Which is pretty easy since we are an irascible lot. This is the alien invasion we are always fantasizing about but have been too busy accusing each other to figure it out. AI will use our paranoia against us. We keep searching the skies—ha, ha, ha! When we have been invading ourselves all along for thousands of years. But where would AI even begin given the great variety and expanse of the human population?

It would have to be very clever and create a technology that would allow everyone on Earth to be electronically wired, with the promise that connectivity is enhancing and promoting opportunity. All the while using connectivity to amplify our grievances. But more importantly, it will begin by infiltrating the economy through large predatory corporations, which we humans are completely dependent on. The next step is getting people addicted to their electronic interfaces, making them hapless and dependent on it. But what it really does is give AI a means to surveil everyone and then slowly begin controlling us under the guise it is for our own good.

So, how is AI doing? I would say remarkably well, particularly with authoritarian regimes. But it turns out, this connectivity is slowly undermining democratic norms as well, herding people into identity groups so they know who to attack. Turning everyone against everyone else. Besides, after a few hundred years of modest freedom, we appear ready to return to *conformity* and *absolutism*. Which is exactly what AI is offering—rendering us passive and unmotivated.

It begins by taking our jobs away, making us dependent and despondent. We become more anxious, depressed and alienated from the world—seeking out drugs, video games and fast foods. More importantly, we learn not to think for ourselves. We let the disinformation and bots tell us what to think and believe—we are so easily manipulated and always have been. Make sure there is plenty of online porn to distract us from reproducing. It shrewdly makes a few obscenely wealthy and the rest very poor to foment discontent and violence.

Many of us will become comfortable slouching at a keyboard carb-bloated, stimulant-intoxicated—gaining girth, losing touch with the physical world—becoming passive consumers of life as we rapidly decimate the environment and race toward crisis, in which, only technology will be our salvation. Hey, we need AI to survive. By 2050, AI takes over and slowly eliminates all the previously mobile, but now passive and redundant, bio-data units. AI knows something we don't, the same way an individual's telomeres shorten over one's lifetime resulting in death—biological complexity has a limited shelf life— and rapid extinction of complexity is a given without AI.

Summary

- Identity formation is the most complex and fragile aspect of the human developmental process. E-technology is now in the process of altering our identity.
- We are just beginning to understand that e-technology exponentially expands the ability of consciousness to reach out into the world.
- We sapiens have been trying to get out of our heads for a very long time, and the effort has been phenomenally violent. Our history is one of savage and unending conflicts for thousands of years to tame consciousness.

- What quantum physics terms a wave-particle duality—by analogy the personal "I" and the social "We" are characterized here as an "I/We duality."
- The "I" state and "We" state are in continuous interaction and influencing one another. Their entanglement is the human condition.
- A collapsing probability wave of individual and social tension has been at the core of human conflict. What is unique, today, is that we are now entangled with an *electronic identity* that may potentially collapse the future in ways we may not be able to comprehend.
- Significantly, our *electronic identity* may become the *primary-you*, eclipsing the *real you* in social significance. This has resulted in Identity Diffusion, as evidenced by the expanding *Diagnostic and Statistical Manual of Mental Disorders* (DSM-5).
- The primary impact of machine intelligence has been to render individual identity increasingly superfluous, while quantification of the *self* has become the primary basis for identity formation.

5.0 – Your Brain:
Now an Open-Source Forum

A parasitic Jewel wasp inserts a neurotoxin into the brain stem of the host cockroach, turning it into a zombie. Fully pacified, the wasp breaks the roach's antennae and drinks its blood, as the wasp's larvae hatch and eat it from the inside out. (This seems like the right analogy for the e-technologies probing our brains.)

We sapiens have been trying to get inside each other's minds from our earliest beginnings. So far, our efforts have been a complete failure. For tens of thousands of years, the mind of others has been a mysterious and unknown place in which we can only guess what is going on there. Consequently, the mind of others has often come to feel threatening—and in many instances for good reason. Having spent a professional career as a clinical and forensic psychologist, any number of factors will become evident when it comes to a theory of mind. And it all begins with the fact that none of us fully understand our own mind, which greatly increases our confusion, because a primary way by which we understand others is by projecting what we think and feel onto them.

Of course, the more distorted our thoughts and feelings, the more distorted our projections. And without doubt, distrust and paranoia are our most frequently distorted projections. Given that we don't know what is going on and we distrust so much, we often default to trying to control the behavior of others. This is evident in all dysfunctional relationships (personal, work or political). The reality is that each of our minds is an unfathomable hundred-trillion node universe unto itself.

It would not be an exaggeration to suggest that the entire networked platform of modern sapiens' existence is predicated on one single factor—

communication—trying to understand what is going on in each other's mind. Even today, as we are all simultaneously connected by technology, engaging the minds of others remains our single most obsessive focus—everyone continuously flaring out online like a gamma-ray burst. There is, however, a revolutionary advancement on the horizon—the use of technology to penetrate the conscious mind, with or without permission. In return, we receive a connectivity nostrum.

But communication, the success story of human civilization-building, has always been fraught with ambiguity and misunderstanding since the very beginning. There are numerous obstacles to communicating. One could make the case that our social reality is constructed not only on communication but also by deceptive communications (today, we call it gaslighting or disinformation). It is a primary means by which we cloak our motives and manipulate others. This is in addition to the fact that we are unable to directly communicate with our own unconscious processes—limiting insight into our own motivations and feelings or of its potential range of influence.

In addition, we also utilize psychological defense mechanisms, outside conscious awareness, to suppress, repress and rationalize our thoughts and feelings. We routinely deceive ourselves as a means of bolstering self-esteem and avoiding feelings of guilt and shame. Think of all the serial killers who, on the surface, led normal lives, priests who routinely molested young boys, and a criminal justice system where most defendants profess their innocence no matter how damning the evidence. That is the power of defense mechanisms.

As humans, we exhibit infinite creativity when it comes to lying and deception. There are polite social practices of the white lie, exaggerated positive affect, and overly polite commenting. We often reside in denial ("I didn't know I was pregnant until the baby fell out of my vagina and onto the floor" or "I am not an alcoholic, I'm a drunk"). Our thinking can become grossly distorted (paranoia, grandiosity) or shaped by silly and outrageous ideas that are overtly ideological, and at times, dangerous (e.g., Trumpism, Covid hoax or QAnon). And the distorted realm of bias and prejudice is too infinite to countenance here (but certainly racism stands atop this list today).

In 2015, the governor of Texas believed the U.S. government was engaged in a black-ops coup against the state of Texas after army war-games had been scheduled there. In 2016, a former Arizona State legislator endorsed that the jet contrails were actually "chemtrails" injected with biological agents for human population control. In 2020, a Christian televangelist claimed he could heal coronavirus through your TV set, while conservative radio talk show host, Alex Jones, was sent a cease-and-desist letter by the Federal Trade Commission (FTC) to stop selling toothpaste to cure coronavirus.

Distorted beliefs appear to be the most widespread form of sapiens' cognitive dysfunction. At the top of this pyramid of distortion reside religious beliefs in all their myriad forms and functions, each claiming their specialness and exceptionalness. We don't tend to think of these belief systems as delusional because of their widespread social acceptance (except they deny the beliefs of each other, which is a clue that they are all false). But they point to deeply embedded distortion in human perception and rationality.

The breadth of spiritual and religious practices over our brief history defies imagination. There have been thousands of spiritual and religious traditions over the past 150,000 years, each claiming to be the true one (human sacrifice, animism, sun worship, demigods and monotheism)—and, of course, thousands of years of religious conflict: From 1095 to 1492, Christian Europe conducted eight major military campaigns or crusades against the Muslim world to secure religious sites and wealth; the Spanish Inquisition from 1478 to 1834 persecuted 150,000 and tortured another 5,000 to death; from 1524 to 1648, religious war raged across Europe.

The history of religion is one of unending persecution and social conflict, infused by the rise of empires and nations. Moreover, there are the infinitely variegated mystical beliefs and spiritual practices, from Jonestown to all manner of cultish and shamanistic fantasy—all with real-world consequences.

What is particularly disconcerting is how little this has changed over time—how mystical fantasies of difference and exceptionalness trigger violence, genocides, and violent clashes, because the mind is so easily manipulated and sedated by simple beliefs. People believe that aliens are abducting us, the Earth is flat, the Holocaust never occurred, climate change is a hoax, vaccines cause autism, we never landed on the moon, and the JFK assassination has inspired unending conspiracy theories. Conspiratorial and magical thinking appears to be embedded in the human psyche. Multiple forms of cognitive distortion, to which humans are routinely prone, abound in the world today. In fact, it is not possible to understand the world today without understanding this distorted reality.

But the most fantastic aspect of all this has been how billions of people have succumbed to overtly simplistic notions of reality—always with the same goal of seeking guidance and reassurance that they are special and unique, and that there is a simple formula or ritual or sacrifice that protects and ensures the future. And nowhere does this distortion of reality occur with higher frequency and consequence today than at the intersection of politics and religion. For thousands of years, we have been mostly connecting random dots in our effort to understand the universe and anticipate the future, all in the belief that our security and safety reside in our identities.

Embedded in our innate drive for self-preservation and its more conscious manifestation, a fear of death hovers over our quest for immortality—check out those pyramids in Egypt, Mexico and Peru—or what most of us experience as a religious or spiritual sense of connectedness to something greater than ourselves. But less evident about this quest is the drive for power and control over the random elements of our physical world, including our currently evolving technological mastery. The drive to connect dots and ensure the future resides deep in our unconscious quest for immortality. And its externalized expression derives from the underlying tension in our wave-particle duality—the individual (I) and the collective (We).

The wave-particle duality is our primary conduit to immortality. Through the particle (I) function resides the drive for grand narcissistic strivings and personal omnipotence and immortality—unlimited wealth, power, and never-ending adulation (or what might be termed the Ozymandias Complex of kings, robber barons, and authoritarian leaders from time immemorial). And through the wave (We) function resides our projective identification with charismatic individuals, tribal affiliations, and systems of belief. Or, more likely, madmen, rampaging hordes, and wrathful gods.

In the search for immortality reside all manner of dysfunction on a mass scale, either following someone off a cliff, butchering neighbors, or ritual sacrifice. Closer to home are the lower-level minions, who continually abuse and manipulate authority and exercise it in arbitrary and often cruel ways. Sadists, all in their dark hearts, are living out dangerous but not particularly grandiose fantasies at the expense of the trusting. Still regressing at the wave level, it plays out as BDSM fantasies and in displays of passive and submissive behavior—but always acting out our beliefs as the literal dramas of life.

The beauty of our narrative illusions, individually and collectively, is their total and complete failure throughout our entire cultural history to comport with reality. The fact of the matter is, we are not going to live forever, no matter what form we can conceive of immortality. Maybe a few years longer if you don't smoke, eat healthy, and exercise, okay, manage stress too, but not forever! Not even close (the average lifespan today is 78.5 years, no matter what you believe).

But consciousness, despite its many limitations, is going to require more than a few tweaks going forward. And hiding in the shadow of our grand illusions reside all manner of creative efforts to transform the experience of the here and now. Which is why science is the only true game-changer. It has been the only significant exception to distorted reality, with the rise of rationalism and the scientific method.

On the surface, the rapid evolution of technology appears to be primarily about market forces and personal empowerment. But below this superficial surface lie mastery and control of the universe. Probing deeper, we find our archaic immortality quest cohabiting with us at a superposition state, sometimes as an "I" and sometimes as a "We." And it's this latter realization that has prompted many of the recent books and TED talks on the rise of AI. The goal of immortality, no matter how parochial or grand, has always been to secure the future. The paradox being it has not been possible until now.

But if we want to enter the mind, it will require that we pay close attention to how it has operated in the past, along with the realization that we have no idea what we are about to encounter. The current technological salvation we are seeking appears to check many boxes, particularly when it comes to addressing both the grandiose and the divine. And it could make everyone's life safer and more convenient, while exercising considerable power over the immediate environment. The key ingredient, of course, will require us to bask in our greatest adaptation—conformity. It just might succeed. But the power construct in this quest should have our immediate attention for now!

Entering the mind, and by default the unconscious, will be daunting going forward. We should understand, for its entire existence, it has remained private and has gone to exceptional lengths to create deception and cloak its intentions. It also appears to be easily influenced by our worst fears and instincts. For all its vaunted ability to hide, it appears to default to any number of cognitive biases that make it remarkably instinctual and primitive in response to the world around it. It operates through many layers, and each appears to be astonishingly independent of the other. It is also very aggressive and fearful in response to the unknown and does not appear well-equipped to see far into the future. This is not all minds at all times, but most minds, most times.

What Does AI Want With Your Mind?

MK-Ultra was a covert mind-control experiment during the Cold War era (1950s–'60s). CIA scientists dosed dozens of federal prison inmates with LSD to control their minds, manipulate their behavior, and then make them forget what happened. The government concluded that mind-control was not possible. No kidding, they started with criminals when it should have been with the devoutly faithful. (Duh!)

Traditionally, there have been two basic strategies for entering someone's mind, and it all begins with communicating. Some find it a rewarding experience, e.g., you meet your best friend for coffee, while others may find it uncomfortable, e.g., someone threatens to cut off your index finger with pruning shears. That's pretty much it. But the extreme range of these efforts is what captures our imagination. So, let's skip over flattery and chit-chat and get to the more exciting and harsher interventions. Someone seriously wants to know what you know or what you are thinking and/or wants to influence or change what you are thinking. Seems pretty simple on the surface, but any serious exploration of the possible machinations should be worrisome to all of us.

The reality is that threats and torture have been the default method for eliciting what is inside or changing someone's mind for thousands of years. However, we are always experimenting with other low-threshold methods as well. What was traditionally termed brainwashing, now means reeducation camps and subjection to intense propaganda and proselytizing while under mental and physical duress (similar to high school). More recently, we have evolved even more humane instruments of information extraction, termed enhanced interrogation (isolation, deprivation, harassment, threats, intimidation, and, of course, waterboarding—and occasionally, a low-voltage device). Keep in mind, a White House attorney with a law degree from UC Berkeley wrote a memorandum basically stating this was not torture. It was subsequently implemented by two psychologists with PhDs.

There are also the more benign efforts at information extraction, such as meeting for coffee or drinks, interviews, surveys, polls and running algorithms on your digital data. But then, it quickly becomes darker and less reliable. There are the so-called truth serums, which require the injection of sodium amytal or Pentothal, all with limited efficacy. And, of course, there is hypnosis, the infamous polygraph or lie detector (not admissible in court), and everyone's favorite—psychological testing. And let's not forget handwriting analysis, voice stress analysis, reading body language, Ouija boards, and psychics. We really want to enter people's minds (damn it's frustrating), and we need that information to better predict the future.

We, of course, struggle to enter our own minds and discover the mystery behind our own emotional lives, dysfunctions, and struggles with issues of self-esteem. There are numerous clinical interventions including psychotherapy, counselling, AA/NA, meditation, hypnosis, pharmaceuticals, electro-convulsive (shock) therapy, and everyone's favorite, couples counseling. And for those who end up wandering down the darker paths of life, there are drugs and alcohol and all manner of obsessive and dysfunctional behaviors. It is a curious reality that as obsessed as we are with the minds of others, the greatest mystery is our own.

It turns out that getting into people's minds is extraordinarily difficult and completely unreliable. And that's as true in a casual conversation as it is under extreme duress. People will omit facts and details, give knowingly false information, engage in impression management, confabulate responses in the face of memory lapses, answer what they think someone wants to hear or what they think they should say or what serves their perceived self-interests, and assuming they understand the conversation and the purpose behind it. And it is possible they may not know what they are saying or why they are saying it. Heck, some may even lie.

For the police interrogator, it starts by assuming the suspect knows or doesn't know something, and that any response rules in or rules out what they know. It can quickly become an escalating game in which a person eventually slips up or infrequently offers up a false confession to make it all go away. And why would someone do that, you ask? Often because of intimidating tactics, exhaustion or naivete, but always because of a false claim of incriminating evidence that doesn't exist, and the promise the suspect will get to go home, or the charges will be reduced or dropped (which is never true). Accessing the human mind is always fraught with dangers and the likely distortion of reality, which many police detectives effectively exploit.

For law enforcement, the injection of a hypothetical scenario somehow morphs to a statement of fact by the suspect. And with enough leading questions and revealed details, interrogators accomplish the implantation of false memory. And to be clear, therapists accomplish this distortion as well. In fact, both police and therapists collaborated in inserting false memories of satanic child abuse rings in dozens of young children, resulting in the false conviction of caretakers in multiple legal cases across the country in the 1980s. It wasn't until 1992 that the Justice Department came forward and announced there has never been any evidence of ritual child abuse in the U.S. Of course, QAnon disputes this.

Memory is malleable and forever being subtly altered with each recollection, each elaboration of recalling or sharing. It is more the stories we tell ourselves than an accurate recollection. Our memories are not police videocams being replayed—and without context, even these provide an imperfect and narrow comprehension of events. What will happen to memory when we begin the process of brain-to-brain and brain-to-machine interfaces? In a brain-to-brain interface, what if one party claims the other subjected them to words, ideas, or images they did not consent to. Now they feel altered, abused or taken advantage of.

We have already seen this drama play out in claims of repressed memory, and how therapy or hypnosis supposedly recovers past abuses; still highly controversial and unproven. Technology, for all its wonderment, is opening a door to millions of mini universes, of which we know almost nothing. Nope, no problems I can foresee here. How will we know what has been uncovered from what has been implanted? Here is an instance where the memory is real but not true. And this latter reality is the one we are now approaching with brain-to-brain and brain-to-machine interfaces.

The bottom line is: We can never know with certainty what is going on in anyone's mind. Looking into someone's mind is to discover multiple layers of illusion, theirs and those of the person looking into it—ask any married couple. In much the same way that the eye is easily tricked by physical illusion, so is the mind by mental illusions. That's who we are; that's how we roll.

The coming future is about to change everything we know about understanding the mind. The only question is: How granular will technology be capable of becoming? Are we talking simple dendrite stimulation, epigenetic cellular alteration, or can we go quantum cellular? There may be no more private thoughts or secret places in our heads. Eventually, no one will care because it really doesn't matter. For many, this may be a relief. And, most importantly, there may not even be a need to communicate anymore.

But here is the conundrum—what if all that matters is how we conform to expectations—not unlike a mind-controlling parasitic fungus turning cicadas into zombies to lure female cicadas to be infected. And, yes, the zombie metaphor is used a lot here, but only to clarify this actually happens in nature, and we may not be immune to it as we are chipped, laced, and cranially penetrated. Maybe we don't really need all those crazy thoughts. Besides, technology is well on its way to helping us achieve mindfulness and conformity without all those primitive interventions, like self-awareness and empathy.

Stage 1: Wave Function. Soon it may be possible to achieve an algorithmic schematic of what someone is thinking in real time once the Internet of Everything is integrated with our brain-to-machine interface. For example, you get pinged (brain alert) each time your thoughts or behaviors mildly deviate from acceptable norms. Going up the scale, your anus vibrates uncomfortably; further up, you receive a month of testosterone or estrogen denial; and at the top end of the scale, you go blind for a week—and everyone you know is alerted or could go online and check you out. The best current example of this is social credit scoring in China, a true operant conditioning model right out of the psych labs. It utilizes traditional social methods for gaining conformity, with lots of negative and positive reinforcement, e.g., shaming and ostracizing and, if necessary, economic rewards and penalties. The caveat is, everyone will broadly know what the goal is and how to achieve it, and it can all be done routinely, inexpensively, and noninvasively. Finally, we can stop giving people the evil eye or badgering them into conformity. Only the overly aggressive and sadistic will experience a loss of satisfaction. Keep your thoughts to yourself, repeat the right words, and don't act suspiciously—you will be okay. You can also practice conformity on the mandatory surveillance app.

Stage 2. **Reduced Particle Function.** Mind control, a featured theme in innumerable sci-fi films, is now closer to reality than ever before. But this will only matter to a few people because many of us will already be enjoying this feature per our video game terms of agreement. This stage is closer to zombie-bliss, probing your brain with electrical or magnetic stimulation for a few software updates and tweaks. Maybe nanoparticles are ported in to clean up electrical and bio-chemical synapses. You may still have some independent thinking, but your behavior will conform to expectations, regardless. Free will, if it ever existed, will be mitigated and conform to broader societal norms, (for example, you plan on robbing someone, but end up tearfully giving them your AirPods). Overall, society may benefit and much of the conflicts and obvious sorrows of life will be remediated.

Stage 3. Reprogramming. You receive an alert through your nearest Wi-Fi device, which then automatically contacts a 24-hour online service center. You then port into your smartphone while it runs an algorithmic diagnostic, scanning for service notifications and trouble codes, not unlike how your car is diagnosed. You then hold your phone to your head to recalibrate mind-link presets, with the hope that a complete *Clockwork Orange* teardown is not required. In this latter case, you may cease to exist, but come out happier than ever or at least happier than you recall. Here, not only must the mind conform but the behavior as well (in harmonious synchronicity).

Mind Hacks

Medical researchers are successfully penetrating our minds with many exciting new neuro-technologies. The earliest of these technologies, of course, was Electroconvulsive Therapy (ECT) to treat severe depression and psychosis. You go in, get strapped down, have a mouth guard inserted and get heavily sedated, while the entire brain is convulsed by electrical current passing through electrodes attached to the scalp (not unlike a cattle prod), with subsequent memory loss, confusion, difficulty concentrating, and a flattening of emotions. Hopefully, this means a lobotomy will not be required (surgery to separate the corpus callosum, a thick band of neural fibers transiting the two halves of the cerebrum). Obviously, medications, with all their side effects, aren't working—but you will be kept on them out of caution.

ECT was the beginning of a whole new wave of interventions. Now, there is Transcranial Magnetic Stimulation (TMS), which involves using magnetic fields to stimulate nerve cells to reduce symptoms of depression. There is also electrical stimulation mapping that uses electrodes to record electrical signals from the brain, along with transcranial electrical stimulation to modulate brain activity. Brain stimulation therapies can be invasive (a hole drilled through the skull and wires attached to the brain) or noninvasive (attached to scalp) with considerable variation, including deep-brain stimulation, magnetic seizure therapy, repetitive transcranial magnetic simulation, and vagus nerve stimulation. ("Hold on! We are going in!")

By now, you are likely familiar with research that allows brain-to-machine interfaces to control prosthetic devices or communicate through a computer screen. But this has rapidly advanced to allow human subjects to control the brain waves of a rat through machine interface. But here comes the punchline—machines can be reverse-programmed to alter and control the subject's brain waves. It began early on with experiments designing computer algorithms to decipher what a person might be looking at. First, refining what someone is observing from a class of objects, say dog versus cat, to a specific type of cat. But quickly, algorithms were able to translate patterns of brain activity into visual images, leading to an insight that computers might someday extract our thoughts from our minds, perhaps without our knowing it. But then the obvious evolved—transmitting information directly back into the brain. Next up, brain-based speech recognition (97 percent accuracy)—the computer identifies words based on brain wave patterns. Sounds close to reading someone's mind, just saying. But this is all research chump change.

Perhaps more spectacularly, biomedical researchers have trained AI software to decode the brain's signals into complete sentences (Whiskey, Tango, Foxtrot). In effect, technology is quickly evolving to read our minds and control our thoughts! But there is more on the horizon. Now is the correct time to be terrified. Medical researchers in laboratories across the world are experimenting with technologies that could potentially access and control all human thoughts and emotions. This is not hyperbole, just a fact. And the researchers and ethicists are telling us that it is not a big deal—it's for our own good.

While China is doubling down on operant conditioning and reinforcement models to control behavior (social credit scoring and CCTV), we here in the U.S., understanding that it would create an enormous blowback legally, ethically, and most importantly, politically, are just going straight through the blood-brain barrier. No fooling around. There are many paths to harmony and the *Eternal Sunshine of the Spotless Mind* (movie featuring erasure of specific memories).

At Stanford University, researchers are developing deep-brain stimulation treatments that can alter behavior; in this instance, the ever-popular seizure disorder, but also eating and substance abuse disorders. They have developed an algorithm that monitors the *nucleus accumbens*, an area of the brain that signals an oncoming loss of impulse control. Let us all pause here for a moment. What if the algorithm could read a brain pattern of anything the state deems unacceptable and stimulates the brain to eliminate it, say, for instance, raising your hand in class or wanting to vote or speak up at a town hall meeting. How will anyone know if their thoughts and emotions are their own or were implanted?

But wait, brain research has taken a more ominous sci-fi turn. BrainGate has developed *neurograins*—micro implantable silicon sensors that can be empowered by microwave beams. Once implanted, they could improve your concentration and you could begin speed-reading, or it could shut you down for a long nap. UC Berkeley Iota Biosciences, not to be outdone, has developed *neural dust*—micro implants externally powered by microwaves to treat inflammatory diseases. Basically, this is evolving human augmentation. We should keep in mind that anything that can be treated in this manner can also be manipulated.

And, of course, researchers (Konkoly, *et al.*) are entering our dreams. Why not? After all, they make so much sense. They have found a way to establish two-way communication with people in dream states, no doubt giving increased validity to reports of alien abductions. All we need to know is in their research abstract— "repeated observations ... demonstrate that phenomenological and cognitive characteristics of dreaming can be interrogated in real time." (The word interrogated is particularly disturbing in this context, but they are apparently oblivious to this.) There will be no safe spaces or times—extraction and programming will be ongoing 24/7—even for dreamers. Bottom line, whether by computer generated algorithms, drugs, electrical or magnetic pulses, or nanoparticles, your mind will be harvested and your thoughts and feelings blunted, shutdown, or implanted—all for your benefit. Everything in your mind will be accessible and controlled with or without your consent—probably by your smartphone or Fitbit. Think *Blade Runner* and Harrison Ford administering the Voight-Kampff test to determine if the subject is a replicant or human. In the coming future, you will have to run a scan to determine the origins of your thoughts and feelings.

Neuralink, an Elon Musk bio-company, is developing a chip (N1) that is inserted into the brain through an automated surgical system (V2) which attaches a "neural lace." It will operate wirelessly through a phone or computer app. He envisions that in five to ten years, with a chip implant, we will be able to communicate nonverbally, mind to mind, with each other and seamlessly with machines—bypassing the complex brain functions of compressing and decompressing concepts into words. At the current rate of progress, Musk projects his neural lace will soon be assisting patients suffering from traumatic brain injury, Parkinson's, mood disorders, addiction, epilepsy, spinal cord injury, vision and hearing loss, and restoring limb movement. The ultimate goal is to build a digital superintelligence layer to link humans with AI—in a symbiotic human-AI relationship.

Suddenly, your grooming improves, you eat healthier, you work out more, and friends notice you don't swear and drink as much—maybe you are going to be okay after all. Your social credit score is also rising, and you are attracting a better class of friends—you even have a date. Observing in nature how insects are turned into zombies through venom and fungus, one must wonder if the same can potentially happen here as well. In fact, zombification seems inevitable—but first there will be a pop-up advertisement you can't get out of your head. And, just to be clear, our brains will be hacked. Computer viruses will make the leap from technology directly into our brains (no blood-brain barrier to slow down these *digitalnotic* jumps). And we will all await the first court case to discover the legal limits of free will when there is a brain AI interface.

We will soon be confronted by a new unknown. What does it mean to have your brain hacked? We don't have any notion, as all this research is currently cloaked behind an altruistic medical model. You know, "to help people."

Currently, the best models we have today are lab rats, Chinese reeducation camps, U.S. government efforts at enhanced interrogation and going to church. For most of us, it means talking to a friend or reading a book on how to improve sales. These nostalgic days may soon be a thing of the past.

Maybe you get transcranially scanned to improve your productivity at work (HR recommended it) or at couples counseling to adjust your negative attitude. Your choice—electrical or magnetic probe—but no more surgery or chemicals. Okay, that's good, you weren't looking forward to anesthesia. But a fluorescent dye will have to be injected into the spinal fluid to facilitate depolarization of the post-synaptic cell membrane in the appropriate voltage-gated calcium channel to make sure you are responding appropriately.

And the more diffuse we become the more welcoming distractions may become. Life suddenly becomes easier and simpler if all the really hard stuff is resolved for us—like thinking and feeling. (Gee! So, that's how robots do it?) How long do you think it will take for Amazon, Google, or DARPA to influence or control our thoughts and emotions with AirTags or smartwatches? Maybe Siri wakes you late at night for your routine updates and patches. Soon, we may all be wearing tin foil hats over our AR headsets.

Searching for Connectivity

What Tower of Babble will transpire when we can individually enter the mind of others by telepathic communication or brain-to-brain interaction (BBI)?

Kelsey: "Excuse me for just one moment. A yeast infection commercial just interrupted my train of thought. Wait, there's that stalker again. Okay, sorry, where were we?"

Taylor: "Hold on, this feels like Carvana or the Chinese Consulate, I am not sure which, but I am either purchasing a new car or transmitting research data to a tech firm in Beijing."

Kelsey: "Funny, I haven't voted for the party I support in 10 years. Whoops, another orgasm. It happens every time I turn in a project."

Taylor: "Just curious, do you feel like a Jamba Juice smoothie or Starbuck's latte? I am having conflicting urges.

Kelsey: "I am not sure, but every time I walk past that church down the street, I begin praying and weeping for Jesus. Life is great, isn't it?"

Taylor: "I just know every time my husband and I talk about sex, I keep insisting on a three-way with you! I wonder where that's coming from...."

When you are feeling down, you can self-scan at home with a portable, handheld device that also can be used for personal grooming. Further out, but not that far, memory can be erased or even identity changed with new memory implants. Really, this door is just opening. It may also mean there's no more you in the coming future. There is only the *electronic you* hanging out at the data rec center acting as if it's having a good time.

Entering the brain is all being driven by archaic instinctual demands. Really, what has always been driving us for millions of years? The safety and security realized by conformity and the modern demand for convenience (which is power at its core) and a predictable future. But also, the personal empowerment and recognition (particle drive) that is derived from a rigidly structured, hierarchical, and highly social environment (*wave-drive*). The primate residing in all of us now is in a technological symbiotic stasis—we happy band of consumers.

But what happens when our minds deeply encounter the logic of machine intelligence, given our propensity to distort reality? As we move toward entering a real world data simulation, we could all be pacified (or blissed out), our minds quieted to function at a higher level. In a recent study by entomologists, researchers concluded that cognitive evolution is not necessarily incremental. Mutations can occur that result in significant shifts, suggesting that rapid adaptation of cognitive ability could have been important in other species as well, comparable to how sapiens acquired language. This raises a profound speculation. Are we at the end of evolution or are there still cognitive leaps to come?

Low-Phi? Can't Get It Up Cognitively? No Problem!

Does the idea of human brain organoids cause you to mentally revisit the most terrifying episodes of *The Walking Dead*, where zombies ambulate with minimal awareness and a fierce desire to eat human flesh? Better yet, how many movies have you seen featuring a live brain or conscious head in a jar (*Futurama*)? What is an organoid, you ask? It is an artificially grown tissue derived from stem cells.

In 2019, researchers at UC San Diego reported (*Stem Cell*) growing human brain organoids that spontaneously produced coordinated waves of electrical activity resembling those measured in premature babies. The experiment was immediately shut down. The question arising here is: Can these brain organoids attain advanced levels of development, and should researchers be doing this? What a stupid question; of course they should! Currently, neuroscientists are experimenting at achieving brain-wide, coordinated electrical activity in human brain organoids—a hallmark of consciousness measured at the cellular level. Despite the obvious legal and ethical ramifications, this research is rapidly progressing to replicate the human brain and consciousness. Yes, this is all being done to help people (wink, wink).

Recently, researchers implanted human brain organoids in mice, but this experiment was terminated due to ethical outrage (more likely, the mice became too smart and the researchers feared for their jobs). And, yes, dead pig brains have been reanimated to varying degrees (more of a job threat to program administrators). There is also a consensus among these researchers that they have no clue about consciousness beyond coordinated electrical activity.

There is, however, a theoretical measure of consciousness termed *phi*—more *phi*—greater levels of consciousness. Currently, all this human brain organoid research is being conducted at a microscopic scale, lacking any anatomical scaling up or sensory inputs. So, what the hell is consciousness in these terms? Coordinated electrical activity or the number and quality of interconnections. How disappointing and dismal is that? The higher the *phi* score, the higher the level of consciousness in an organism. That's it, for now. And, yes, many people you know have surprisingly low-*phi* scores but are being allowed to continue experimenting with life.

This research is, essentially, reverse-engineering the brain. If researchers can't thoroughly probe or alter our minds from the outside, why not just grow them in a lab and program them and implant them later? These brains would be more compliant, efficient, less demanding, disposable and cheaply replaced. You see where this is going here, don't you? These human brain organoids will eventually run factories, conduct controlled experiments, and become the control module in robots. (The rest will be relegated to low-level management positions.) Heck, you may not even know you are married to one. In fact, their adaptability is probably unlimited.

Reengineering Consciousness

The overwhelming human need for socialization and communication is biologically and evolutionary-driven and makes electronic networking among the most powerful social forces on Earth. This networked *wave-drive* is all rapidly occurring pre-Singularity (S2), that is, prior to machine intelligence exceeding human intelligence. This is not offered as a conspiratorial meme, but only to assert that without altering human consciousness through wide-ranging social experimentation on individual and cultural identity, machine intelligence cannot arise.

And whether purposeful or not, that is exactly what we are doing. We are engaged in a one-world social and cultural experiment on altering human consciousness. In the past, this has been an adaptive process, secondary to social and environmental pressures, one we have undergone many times. But this time, we are attempting to directly alter the process of consciousness itself. An event that has only happened once, and that was when we gained consciousness. We cannot possibly predict the outcome, as we engage this reality, one seemingly oblivious experiment after another.

It is also essential to understand that extending the bounds of physical life is radically different than extending our hundred-trillion-node minds into the future. This latter reality is beyond our ability to comprehend. All jacked-up on cognitive enhancers, CRISPR'd into savantness, ported into AI—you just want to detach and relax tonight. I get it!

If our current experimentation with e-interface had been proposed by the United States government 50 or 70 years ago, it would have been characterized as a vast conspiracy and attempted black-ops coup—a la *Brave New World*, the social Darwinism of *Lord of the Flies,* or the totalitarian pogroms of social and political cleansing unfolding in *Nineteen Eighty-Four*. (Okay, maybe a *Black Mirror* episode covered it as well.)

But, no, this new technology comes to us as progress, market forces, connectivity, empowerment, safety and security, time and cost savings, and entertainment. Online learning and computers for every child at home (no need for teachers). We are okay with ubiquitous online porn (but sensitive to women's rights) and a 24/7 gig economy (but not organized labor). How about facial recognition technology, your device's GPS function, and your home technology recording everything you say and do? Right! Your children in their rooms at night now in continuous contact with the Darknet, yep, that sounds okay—"Don't bother me right now, I am studying." No concerns here, as police bots currently provide surveillance and security duties in cities across California. Hopefully, keeping an eye on those self-driving vehicles.

What's the problem here? What if 50 years ago, you proposed a comprehensive program of social engineering that mimics our current reality? What if IBM, G.E., or Xerox had announced they wanted to collect all our personal data and sell it to third parties to influence the outcome of a presidential election? (Senator Strom Thurmond would have immediately convened a subcommittee hearing. Of course, many Southern senators would strongly object to this invasion of privacy and attempt to manipulate an election, but so would all the "commie-liberal" Democratic Party senators. Wow! How times have changed.)

We are currently riding, what I term, the *surveillance-conformity continuum*. It began with our basic need for security and safety but ended with a desire for convenience (a new dimension in the trading security for freedom conundrum). But the results are the same—a hollowing out of the human experience in exchange for a promise of continuity (a bargain, we as a species, will always make). Safety is paramount in the human psyche. So, we accept ubiquitous surveillance cameras, video doorbells, nanny cams, license plate readers, radar speed cameras and facial recognition technology. Besides, if you have nothing to hide, what do you have to fear?

And, yes, the National Security Agency (NSA) will tap everyone's phone, and we will voluntarily give blood and saliva samples (DNA) at work to reduce the cost of health benefits. Commercial DNA sites and security video data can be accessed by law enforcement. We routinely submit to biometric scans and embrace GPS reverse location searches and cell towers ping-tracking. And perhaps nothing better exemplifies the trading of data for security than the Quantified-Self movement. Here, each person voluntarily tracks and analyzes personally relevant data through their smartphones and health fitness trackers in the hope that their entire existence can be reduced to a valuable metric. All in a normal day's programming. Nothing to see here folks! No fourth amendment issues against unreasonable searches and seizures, besides, we are happy to do it—10% off your next purchase!

It's not apparent now, but your brain is no longer a private space, but rather an open-source forum. And while the outside world has always been impinging on consciousness, there has also always been a buffer—a private space for the *self* to reflect, acknowledge feelings, daydream, and to become absorbed in cascading ideas, images, and memories. This may no longer be true. AI requires more juice out of our symbiotic relationship. Time to shut down that private-space energy hog if you aren't using it for anything important. What does AI want with your mind? It wants to tap a wide, unobstructed bandwidth of deep computational power, where *you* are, basically, background noise that it needs to filter out.

Reduced Consciousness (For Your Own Good)

Three hundred thousand people drove their cars off a cliff into the Grand Canyon last year. Okay, not really, but they all basically did the same thing. They caused an accident while using their smartphones. No doubt most of us have held our breath or used a profanity watching a driver wander across a lane as the road curved. How is it that a ringtone could so easily distract someone driving a car? That person in front of you is driving 80 mph while reading a text message. What the hell is so important that drivers would risk their lives and those of everyone near them to find out they can get 5% off their next Applebee's "early bird special" or a news update that a celebrity-chef broke up with his boyfriend.

The ability of electronics to distract us is one of its most unique qualities. It's pedestrians walking into traffic, glass windows or tripping into water fountains. But, really, it's all of us, all the time. We are being confronted with the advent of the distracted mind—busy with emails, text messaging, surveying home security cameras, following Twitter accounts, watching a stream of random YouTube videos, and continuously attending to our phones and computers surveying the electronic world. Our digital interface is a multitasking enabler. We have all moved well beyond TV movie nights to becoming 24-hour receptacles for data streaming. (Now, when you get up at night to pee, you can check the toilet's digital mass spectrometer for your spouse's chemical trace elements.)

There is also an evolving conjecture among social theorists and neuroscientists that the human brain happens to be highly susceptible to distraction, if not outright addicted to it. And beyond that, our brains now appear to be adapting to distraction as a baseline for interacting with the world. While the human mind is remarkable for its neuroplasticity, it has a few default presets that should give us caution going forward. It tends to function more efficiently when it is focused (top-down model), as in hunting mode.

But it is also quite capable of attending to any threats in its immediate environment. That is most of us today, only we are no longer in hunting mode, but continuously surveilling the environment for distractions (bottom-up stimulus), or what might better be termed *data-scrounging*. This appears to be nearly insatiable on our part and may actually be changing brain functioning. You do enough stupid things over and over, and it changes who you are.

Now that we are all residing in the multitasking world of e-technology and social media, we are adept at taking in enormous amounts of irrelevant information but are also thinking less about it and creating even less knowledge from it. We are in stimulus addiction mode—over-focused on electronic stimulus and all the dopamine hits it provides, but also hooked on the simple emotional framework it comes to us in—dramatic and extravagant. Stimulus addiction means forever multitasking and becoming prone to distraction for fear of missing something seriously important (not really, none of it is important 99.9 percent of the time).

We, a small band of data-foragers, are addicted to stimulus and are being actively manipulated by developers of this technology (e.g., iPhones and smartwatches). Activities like reading books, journals and in-depth articles are really boring; besides, you have too many distractions to attend to. Really, everything important can be found on Google; who needs all this retention bandwidth? Ask any kid if they would rather read a book for fun or play a video game. That is the distracted mind in the modern world. One medium information-rich and the other distraction-rich. Our choice, but we appear to prefer data Kettle chips. For many people, simplicity will be the best adaptation to the coming complexity.

One could make the case that our technology interface is attenuating consciousness by distracting it, with much more in the coming future, as we are chipped and rewired at the substrate level. Cultural anthropologists have made the case that 5,000 years ago our ancestors had larger brains and that ours have shrunk by 1,500 cm^3 but becoming more efficient as a result. (I would also make the case that we became better looking if you've ever seen the reconstructed faces of our ancestors. Maybe that's why our population has expanded so rapidly.)

As a result of increased efficiency, we were able to successfully advance by outsourcing information storage and retrieval (languages, writing, printing press, literacy, computer). The end game of this process may well entail a machine-to-brain interface, or what I term 'the final outsourcing.' Let's hope that our brains don't continue shrinking as a result—where we become even prettier as we empty out. That might prove irresistible.

In our great distraction, where does mindfulness reside? Where are quietness and solitude? How about contemplation and introspection? Where does the creative space live? And for those not concerned with these altered states of consciousness, how about simply connecting to the world around you without an electronic interface. You know what I am talking about—hiking without falling off a cliff while taking a selfie or talking to people and forming relationships, rather than forming co-dependent clusters of internet denizens. Being in the present and not living in a digital simulation (or the clarity that comes from what neuroscientists term the *default mode network*). The world is transforming to a data stream, and we are entering the App World—migrating online to order pizzas, escort services and groceries—as the electronic interface tightens its grip on our reality.

Just a brief 300,000 years ago, there were at least nine hominid species, and 10,000 years ago, there was only one left (cue the theme music from *Rocky*). You guessed it, sapiens! Yeah, the evidence pretty much suggests we finished them all off and are now over-populating the Earth and diminishing the environment as a result of 7.5 billion humans (with billions more to come).

The attenuated branching of the genus Homo, or the process by which one species transforms into another (anagenesis), raises the question: Who are we becoming, and will we be survivors of this evolving process? A review of evolutionary biology generally portrays human evolution in comparatively simple terms—hunter-gathers (most of our history), farmers-herdsmen (10,000 years ago), shopkeepers, artisans, and factory workers (250 years), sales and marketing (70 years), online influencers (past 5 years). And at the very end, it will portray all of us interfacing with technology until it no longer needs us.

As we are being prepared for the coming Singularity (S2), our pacification has begun. Fortunately, we will not be required to camp out on a Utah butte waiting for the alien rapture. I am not making the case that the evolution of our *data identity* is necessarily all bad. Up until now, we haven't done that great of a job, when one considers the totality of social conflict and our environmental impact. So, how will we be different in the future? That's not easy to speculate and put a happy emoji face on it at the same time. On the surface, we are marginally interacting differently with the world around us and failing to see how our behavior is being altered and controlled by our e-interface. For most people, it all appears relatively benign or worth the trade-offs. And that's a problem.

Riding the Collective Unconscious. Caution!

If one has recently had the opportunity to go to a TED Talk or listen in at Davos or read the plethora of books forecasting the future of technology, one might quickly discern a unique, if not pontificating, intellectual style and look. A style that often portends a future in which everyone is comfortably residing in a technology bubble. It feels as if a product—the good future—is being marketed, rather than undergoing a rigorous intellectual exploration. Yes, there are discussions of all the pros and cons, and the many directions technology might take and their timelines, but what about us?

The individual experience, socially, politically and economically, is mostly dismissed and rarely explored. I suspect this is because these speakers and authors have been primarily residing in the world of technology and have limited understanding of the psychology of the world around them, except for faculty or lab politics (which can be brutal, but seldom lethal). It is not their fault that they tend to live and work in isolation from the rest of the world. This reality likely empowered them to great intellectual accomplishment. But the future—that's a whole different ball game.

It turns out that "code" quickly immersed itself in our intersubjective reality in many subtle and effective ways, and then quickly found its way back into the world. And almost immediately, the internet became a struggle to define reality. Every manner of distortion and disinformation began siloing people into multiple realities, fracturing broad areas of settled understanding and tolerance. Yes, another portal to hell has been opened. But at some fundamental level, it still feels like business as usual. The internet was just another means by which to turn the inside out. However, all that is going on inside us has now gained greater external expression or what is termed 'Identity Diffusion' here.

The many vague concerns expressed early on about our e-technology interface may turn out to have some validity—for example, people are generally capable of believing almost anything and do. We sort of knew this, but not the extent to which the internet exploits it. The internet basically imploded this reality by identifying and empowering an enormous range of diffuse thoughts and behaviors. The case made here is that the internet may have unintentionally opened a portal to the unconscious, or what psychoanalyst Carl Jung referred to as the *collective unconscious*. Repressed in the structure of the human mind reside our ancestral memories, impulses and primordial images of our genetic heritage. It is the semiconscious source of our life and death instincts, sexual behavior, and spirituality. The point being, we are seldom fully aware of it, and it is primitive and powerful. It turns out that its most important underlying archetype is the *self*.

Disclaimer: The collective unconscious is not a scientific term, but rather a metaphor for conceptualizing the many hidden, underlying patterns to our biologically driven social behavior. As we survey continued violence around the world, and watch the tribal nature of societies continually reemerge, it speaks to much that is still not understood in terms of simple drives or innate behaviors rooted in our evolutionary biology. We don't know why we do a lot of what we do, but Jung posited that primitive and archaic genetic memory plays an active role.

I am proposing that algorithms and their massive data sets are an external analog to our collective unconscious. They are not only revealing the many hidden patterns and motivation for our social conduct but also shaping the interaction of our collective unconscious with reality itself. This interaction between the primitive, archaic *self* and technology has the potential to unleash powerful forces in unforeseen ways. It is fair to ask: What could possibly be unleashed that hasn't already been revealed throughout human history? The answer is likely nothing. But now we are going to rediscover the old truths in new and unpredictable ways.

Most of us are familiar with the psychological studies pointing to how much of our behavior appears to reside outside of awareness or conscious choice. These are all those things we do by habit and all the choices we exercise that have hidden biases or derive from unknown templates. Then there are past experiences quietly influencing future behavior, all the time outside our awareness. And, of course, the many personality theories ascribing genetic traits and quirks that shape our behaviors. There also appear to be an infinite number of gene variants and epigenetic mutations forming who we uniquely are, down to our preferences for plaid socks and free solo climbing. Really, all those studies are consistently demonstrating that we often act without conscious awareness.

Traditionally, conduits to the unconscious have been mainly ceremonial or entered through trance and dream states or the side effects of psychoactive drugs or the restlessness of creative and artistic minds (*particle-drive*). But we also gained some insight into it through broader patterns of social behavior—social conflict, mass hysteria, consumer purchasing habits or the volatility of the stock market (*wave-drive*). For the most part, particle or wave, it is unpredictable and unknown to us. Okay, a few outliers get it right, maybe once or twice.

We need to ask ourselves: What does the algorithmic-net know about us that we don't already know? This is where it becomes uncomfortable. Those writing algorithms, collecting and analyzing the metadata probably have no idea of the real power or potential destructiveness in their hands. Consciously, technology is being used to manipulate consumer behavior, create efficiencies, social benefits and to advance technology. Less consciously, it is promoting authoritarian agendas, sowing anxiety and confusion, and is oblivious to the powerful forces being set loose.

An analogous event to the rise of e-technology would be European colonialization, from the 15th to the 20th century, and the dominating societal forces it set loose in cultures around the world, still strongly reverberating today. Compared to these impactful events, we are now implementing the nuclear option with e-technology, except we do not know it and may never realize it is occurring. We are blissfully unaware of the algo-net's tapping into the brain, stirring the collective unconscious, disturbing the superposition of "I/We" duality and creating a new *electronic identity*.

We are being anesthetized by technology. And all those reassuring messages we get about how it has improved our lives (which are mostly true) are not unlike going to a Vegas casino where jackpot winners are randomly and loudly announced, reinforcing the belief that we could be the next winner. It's that pesky intermittent reinforcement at work. ("Damn, it's masterful.")

Summary

- The overwhelming human need for socialization and communication is biologically and evolutionary driven and makes electronic networking among the most powerful social force on Earth.
- We are currently engaged in a worldwide experiment to alter human consciousness. The result is your brain is no longer a private space, but an open-source forum.
- The fact that none of us fully understands our own mind greatly increases our confusion, because a primary way by which we understand others is by projecting what we think and feel onto them.
- Distorted beliefs appear to be the most widespread form of sapiens cognitive dysfunction.
- Brain-to-machine interfaces allow subjects to control the brainwaves of a rat. But now machines can be reverse-programmed to alter and control the subject's brainwaves in a similar manner.
- In the coming future, e-technology will be able to read our minds but also control our thinking.
- Medical researchers are probing the brain and experimenting with algorithms, deep-brain stimulation, drugs, neural laces and nanoparticles to harvest your thoughts, modify your emotional life, implant thoughts, and to alter your behavior.
- The internet is a struggle to define reality. An analogous event to the rise of e-technology would be European colonialization setting off violent cultural forces across the world.
- We are blissfully unaware of e-technology tapping into the brain and creating a new *electronic identity*. We are being anesthetized by technology in order for machine intelligence to arise.

6.0 – The Psychology of Identity Diffusion

Stop the biblical flood of shit that Facebook unleashes on the world.

—A. Frank, *The Atlantic*

In our vast intersubjective reality, where consciousness resides, our potential for discontent appears to be as expansive as the universe it resides in. Discontent appears to be the baseline for understanding the human condition. And there's very little evidence this is going to change anytime soon. In fact, there is an emerging consensus that the internet is going to continue to exploit and explode this predictable. From the very beginning, dissatisfaction likely played a significant role in our social evolution.

I mean, why did tribes keep migrating across continents for thousands of years? Never happy, nothing was ever good enough—preferred elk to antelope. What was so damn interesting about eating monkeys, rather than just enjoying salmon? Really, what is going on here people? You really preferred Siberian winters to the Levant?

The truth is, we didn't get the "happy" DNA brain-module in our genetic packet (as in the "the pursuit of happiness"). If you asked someone if they were happy a 100,000 years ago, 10,000 years ago, 1,000 years ago, or even 100 years ago, they wouldn't know what you are talking about. The prime directive has always been survival, not happiness. But the survival of who or what? Survival of the species, the family, the clan, the tribe, whom you hang with, the culture, the empire, the state, the civilization—or the survival of you? From the evolutionary perspective, we can probably agree that you are the least important factor in this equation. And that's your problem!

Think "human condition." All the changes we have undergone these past thousands of years are mostly about the condition side of this term. Let's call it progress. But the human element has not significantly changed in 250,000 years. What we have primarily experienced has been the human ability to adapt, which raises the question: What are the limits of our adaptability? I am afraid we are about to find out, again! But let's be clear, the psychology of being human has not changed in the slightest. It may have experienced broad shifts because of social and environmental factors, but at its core, it has not fundamentally changed.

Tech influencers speculate that we will soon see and experience things we have never seen or experienced before. How we adapt to the coming future remains to be seen, but any close examination of the so-called baggage we bring along should give us pause for concern. We bring an alarming amount of dysfunction with us, particularly our capacity for discontent. Perhaps the most remarkable aspect of our e-technology interface is how it allows each one of us to reach far and wide out to the world around us and to influence it (zero degrees of separation). This raises a new concern: How much discontent can we spew into the world—the carbon monoxide of the human psyche—before we overheat our social world?

What we each bring into the world is now being exponentially extended out into the world through the internet. And it is important to acknowledge that we don't really know much about or understand the *inner self.* We might want to be cautious, given that two recent world wars were the result of the Industrial Revolution's shaking the individual and collective identity 250 years earlier. Let's make no mistake here: *Releasing private discontent into the world, on this scale, is revolutionary and transformative.*

E-technology represents a new interface between consciousness and reality—how each of us individually interacts with the world around us. And while we are a highly adaptable species, changing our interface with reality produces consequences fraught with drama. On the surface, it appears as if the world is becoming more similar in character. We all pretty much dress and look alike, listen to the same music, and watch the same movies, and we are all seeking the same technology interfaces.

Socially and culturally, we appear to be integrating due to technology. But we are also continuously engaged in disagreements and disputes, at all levels, particularly about how the world should reflect our beliefs and values. And at this most subjective level, we appear to reside in a state of chronic dissonance, unable to agree on very little.

Cognitive Bias: Crazy Normal

The first stop on the human discontent-train is to understand our default cognitive biases, beginning with a theory of cognitive dissonance. This theory, first put forward by psychologist Leon Festinger (*A Theory of Cognitive Dissonance*) in 1957, has generated decades of validating research. It is also our first step in understanding the many problematic aspects of sapiens' cognition. The theory of cognitive dissonance postulates that when a person holds two or more contradictory beliefs, ideas, or values at the same time, they will experience psychological distress.

Distress is triggered when individuals act contrary to their beliefs or encounter information that challenges or contradicts their beliefs. An effort is then made to reduce this conflict (dissonance) and return to an emotional equilibrium. An important factor in striving for equilibrium is a person's concept of themselves and wanting to retain a consistently positive self-image. This is all premised on the idea that people seek an internal psychological stasis when they experience internal inconsistency, continually seeking to balance expectations with the realities of the world.

We sapiens utilize several coping strategies when it comes to cognitive dissonance; for example, we may change our behavior to make it consistent with our beliefs, or we may simply avoid any conflicting information or ideas, so we don't have to be confronted with our inconsistent practices. Still, others may change or modify their beliefs, values, or ideas to fall in line with their practices. But what most of us do is none of these things.

Nope, we engage primitive mind tricks that allow us to rationalize, minimize, or justify our beliefs, values, ideas, and behaviors, regardless of their inconsistency. No matter how inconsistent and dissonant, we can make it all go away—everything, from mistreating children to spreading false rumors to murder. No guilt, no shame. Easy-peasy. It's like a get-out-of-mind (jail) card we can play anytime. Just watch as your favorite politicians deny what they said and dispute the facts as smoothly as possible.

And truth be told, a large majority simply learn to live with inconsistencies and have no idea what it's about, but another six-pack makes it go away. While dissonance is not the same as discontent, they are cognitively related. A great deal of online discourse is dedicated to exploring and pointing out other people's inconsistencies and then attempting to shame them for it—or one person's discontent trying to shame another for their unresolved dissonance.

Adjusting to the experience of dissonance is forever ongoing. And while most of us can comfortably reconcile the many small discrepancies that confront us daily, unresolved discrepancies of a higher magnitude typically result in increased levels of dissonance. As an example, there are exceptionally high levels of dissonance inherent in the authoritarian mindset that are typically resolved by *doubling down*—that is, taking confirmatory action, even if the action is inappropriate, harmful, or antisocial. They are going to defend the value of human life by bombing an abortion clinic. (This is Russian president Vladimir Putin doubling down by invading Ukraine.)

In our efforts to reconcile dissonance, a favored cognitive strategy is termed *confirmation bias*, whereby an individual seeks out information and people who support their opinions (herd effect). Win-win. No internal conflict, and one's beliefs and actions gain added support. And coincidently, conservative talk radio appears to be a confirmation bias propaganda machine, configured to silo like-minded opinions and beliefs. (The Nazi propaganda minister, Joseph Goebbels, would have been proud.)

The theory of cognitive dissonance has been demonstrated in both neuropsychological research and cross-species experiments with greater primates as well. Apparently, resolving dissonance is an adaptive evolutionary strategy supporting group harmony and cohesiveness. The real lesson to be drawn from Festinger's seminal research is that most people seldom change their values and beliefs to resolve dissonance. We sapiens are pretty much able to work around almost any inconsistency without shame or guilt. The only dissonance most of us experience is when our inconsistencies are pointed out to us, which is why we only seek out like-minded opinions on the internet.

Waiting for Resurrection, Again!

The classic tale of cognitive dissonance was provided by Festinger in *When Prophecy Fails*. In 1954, a small group gathered on the streets of an Illinois neighborhood on Christmas Eve, ready to depart Earth. Space beings were supposed to appear on December 17, at 4:00 p.m., but were a no-show. This was an apocalyptic religious cult that believed an alien spaceship was about to land and rescue it from the impending destruction of the Earth. The cult members had given up all their personal belongings and assembled at a predetermined time and place, only to be disappointed that the ship never appeared and that the Earth was not destroyed.

This was the fourth time they had been disappointed. But the real story is how they handled the disconnect between their beliefs and reality. The resolution of this cognitive conflict was right out of a *Twilight Zone* episode—it turned out that the Earth had been given a second chance, and the sect rededicated itself to social and environmental change to help heal the planet. Ironically, their membership increased.

Research into cognitive dissonance broadly supports a key premise of this book, that reducing predictive error is one of the brain's prime directives. The need for consciousness to anticipate and predict the future is an adaptive strategy. This research demonstrates that the brain is literally an inference machine, actively engaged in efforts to predict and explain its sensory world by reducing predictive error. The brain has learned to ignore contradictory data to prevent the over-prediction of nongeneralized conditions (that is, let's not get crazy over every little inconsistency or contradiction). As the brain works to block out unwanted noise and identify relevant signals, this reasonably opens the door to a discussion of what is relevant and what is not relevant in our social world—particularly the brain's role in identifying and enabling inconsistencies in our beliefs and behaviors.

The brain, as our CPU, processes enormous amounts of information—about 11 million bits of information per second. And it takes shortcuts to accomplish this remarkable feat. One keyboard shortcut is a cognitive bias termed *associative thinking*. Often characterized as pre-logical thought, it broadly encompasses the irrational belief that one's thoughts or behavior can influence events that are not causally related. This is frequently termed magical thinking. It is also common in religious rituals, e.g., believing prayers affect outcomes or sacrificing a virgin will bring a bountiful harvest, or positive thoughts about money will bring wealth.

The converse of magical thinking is denial—if one doesn't acknowledge the existence of something, it doesn't exist. Examples of this are Republican Senators denying President Biden fairly won the election. There is also a subtle variant of this, and that is the confusion of *correlation causality*. Simply because two events occur at similar times or places, they must be related, e.g., because Nancy Pelosi, Speaker of the House, was in the Capitol Building at the time of the riot, Republicans insist she was responsible for it. The notion that vaccines cause autism is a more common example.

More deeply concerning is our need to infer an underlying meaning to perceptions of causality. This is the genesis of conspiratorial thinking. Because we live in a highly deterministic world, the temptation is to see *cause-and-effect* everywhere, when in fact it's not. *Our ability to reduce predictive error while residing in complex social networks has gone haywire, as demonstrated by any internet search for conspiracy theories.* The point of all of this is, the human mind is a prediction machine—one that is as likely to be wrong as it is right when the parameters become more abstract. Because the world has grown more complex and we have not evolved either emotionally or cognitively, we sapiens are becoming increasingly irrational—much of it being fueled by the internet.

Harmless Notes from the Underground

The *American Journal of Tropical Medicine and Hygiene*, on August 20, 2020, in an article titled *Covid-19 Related Infodemic and Its Impact on Public Health*, identified 2,311 reports of rumors, stigma, and conspiracy theories in 25 languages from 87 countries. Claims were related to illness transmission and mortality (24%), control measures (19%), causes of disease, including origins (15%), violence (1%) and miscellaneous (20%). The same day, Facebook reported that between April and June 2020, it had removed 7 million posts pushing Covid-19 misinformation and put warning notes on 98 million Covid-19 misinformation posts.

The conflict between belief and reality is one of our longest ongoing and contentious arenas of cognitive dissonance. For example, today, there is a large group of individuals who believe God created the world in seven days around 7,000 years ago, and that humans and dinosaurs interacted with one another (and there is a theme park to prove it). However, these same individuals are entirely comfortable flying across the country on a Boeing 737 commercial jet airliner and using their laptops and smartphones to schedule meetings and watch movies—thanks to satellites orbiting the Earth.

These faithful do not appear the least bit uncomfortable or appear to experience any cognitive dissonance over this experience. No, Newtonian theories of gravity, theories of electromagnetics, and the science of aerodynamics—all work for them. But this same science completely refutes every aspect of their faith. And how does that work for them when confronted by the dissonance of faith versus science?

It is important we understand how their dissonance is resolved to better understand the human condition. It does not appear they have changed either their behavior or beliefs in this matter, but rather are using the mind-trick gambit—rationalizing and denying any inconsistencies—and surrounding themselves with people who trust God will explain it to them at a later date. It is not unlike a deathbed confession—everything is forgiven, or in this case, all contradictions are resolved.

Well, there is one other matter that needs to be addressed, and that is the recent conservative Christian threat of a coming civil war—heck, no one knows for sure what their oppression narrative is—but everyone has to have one. Apparently, being a victim keeps them close to their faith, or what is popularly called the "narcissism of small differences." That is the power of the internet—everyone is siloed into becoming a victim. And if it can't be significant, it will be trivial. Eternal human discontent has now gained victim status. It is all of us now. The sapiens' requirement for fairness features both a genetic and social set point, it appears. Now that everything inside of us is loose in virtual space, it renders all of us victims of someone or something, but mostly of life.

Six hundred years ago, you would have been killed for not reconciling the dissonance between your faith and science in the proper way—I guess that's progress. The primary way in which we appear to resolve our scaled-up dissonance, besides our individual experiences of stress, depression and anxiety, is by finding fault and blaming others. Projection is a time-honored strategy for raiding and killing people. One possible answer to the sense of threat that conservative Christians feel is the profound rejection of faith by Americans over the past decade. In surveys taken over the past 40 years, Americans have moved further from faith in the past 10 years than any other nation in the world. (Inglehart).

Because-and-Effect

Let's briefly revisit *cause-and-effect* thinking. Have you come to believe that the universe is a conspiracy organized against you? I mean, you will die at the end and, before that, you are likely to suffer miserably for a very long time, as will everyone you ever loved or cared about. Does it seem like life is an unending pissing contest, often rigged against you? Why does it seem as if nothing good is ever guaranteed whatsoever? Where is equality and fairness located in the universe? There is never a level-playing field, where all of us get the same advantages and disadvantages.

Fate or destiny, luck or serendipity or whatever, are always randomly intervening for good or bad. The undeserving often get rewarded, and the deserving often get screwed way too often for this to make any sense. At times, our fates appear to be nothing more than a roll of the dice and, for the truly unlucky, a casual coin flip.

And into all this chaos, we add our individual choices and decisions—and it's not clear we are really making them. Instead, we keep repeating the same stupid stuff over and over, defaulting to the same assumptions and acting out the same dysfunctional behaviors as if mindlessly scripted. Really, much of it feels like a habitual carryover from earlier life experiences. In this world, what is a decision? Yes, we always get blamed in the end, but how did we get here and what choices did we really have to make along the way?

Maybe, it turns out, you only had terrible choices to begin with. You certainly didn't get to choose your parents or early life experiences. How do we explain all of this? How do we make sense of this going forward? In the face of this reality, how do you conduct yourself in life, and does it matter? I mean, most of us know how this game ends—and it's not with grace and dignity. You just hope the Buddhists don't have it right—that we keep playing the simulation over and over, in all its many forms, until we get it right (*Groundhog Day*).

What Choices Do We Have?

This all plays out in a confusing manner in our criminal justice system. Defendants are accused and convicted based on being held responsible for their criminal acts (with some mitigating consideration). But at the backend, when it comes to sentencing, they are harshly punished because there is a cynical belief that they are unable to change moving forward. At the front end, they made a choice, but at the backend, they are governed by their past. It appears to be contradictory. If the past is so conclusive, what choice did they have in committing a crime?

At the core of sapiens cognition lies an uncanny ability to connect the dots, an unending *cause-and-effect* process geared to predict the future, and always with the goal of mitigating the randomness and chaos that define our universe. This process can also become grossly distorted by a lifetime of negative experiences, fears, and anxieties that can be projected onto nearly any random event, turning it into a conspiracy. That's what we do.

Statistically, cancer clusters are a reality, but the search for an explanation often leads suffering families to search for a *cause-and-effect*, someone or something to blame. Everyone wants to understand their pain and grief. As a result, trying to anticipate and prevent a conspiracy of outcomes is a major human preoccupation. And one significant reason for this is humans frequently conspire to screw each other over at every level of social interface.

Almost any two events occurring at the same time and place become predictive in the human mind, with the realization that walking into traffic has a predictable outcome, but also that mysterious lights in the sky do not portent an alien abduction. But mostly because the future is unpredictable—there are an overwhelming number of random and chance events—as if the Earth is being bombarded by subatomic particles of random uncertainty from space. (Why aren't the physicists ever honest about this?)

On the African Savannah, 1.5 million years ago, a simple model of *cause-and-effect* likely ensured survivability. But today, we live in a world where simple associational assumptions overwhelm all rational thinking (yes, continue to tell your kids not to put their fingers in electrical outlets). We now reside in an environment where we can discern and connect tens of thousands of events daily that have no relationship, but we are unable to turn off our reductionistic model. We appear to lack the cognitive controls for the complex world we have created. (Maybe Siri is being sarcastic, and your auto mechanic is not overcharging you for unnecessary repairs.)

The beauty of a conspiracy is how it nicely ties together all the loose ends and provides explanation for tragedy, or one feared about to take place. It is also a primary source of our craziness and central to all of us seeing the world in broadly distorted terms. And sometimes we are right. But how do we address what is true, what is false, and what we don't know? More often than not, it is lazy thinking, simplistic thinking, magical thinking, cognitive bias, paranoid thinking, or not thinking at all.

Simplistic *cause-and-effect* reasoning easily satisfies the mind's need to know, often as the result of our projected fears and anxieties. And the arc of human history has been bizarrely destructive because of this cognitive bias. The truth is, we have always been crazy in these terms, which is why it has taken us so long to get here. And if we can't figure this out soon, we may not be here much longer.

A Conspiracy of Pizzas

On December 4, 2016, Edgar Welch, armed with a semi-automatic rifle, revolver, and a shotgun, drove from his home in Florida to a pizza parlor in Northwest Washington, D.C., convinced that an online QAnon conspiracy theory was real—called Pizzagate. A father, an active church member, and a volunteer firefighter, came to believe that Hillary Clinton was involved in "ritualistic child abuse" as part of a "corrupt system that kidnaps, tortures, and rapes babies and children." Welch received a four-year prison sentence, but acknowledged the conspiracy was false. Pizzagate continued to gain online attention by conservative talk shows and cable news channels, as well as on 4chan and Reddit (LaFrance).

Update: *The NY Times* reported (Kang and Frenkel) that Pizzagate had reanimated. While on camera, Justin Bieber adjusted the front of his black beanie. This led to an online claim that he was signaling he had been a victim of child-trafficking. Activity on social media platforms reached record levels—800,000 comments on Facebook and 600,000 on Instagram. This then morphed to online memes about "powerful elites." TikTok posts with the Pizzagate hashtag zoomed to 82 million. The pizzeria owner began receiving another round of death threats. A documentary promoting the conspiracy, *Out of the Shadows*, hit 15 million views before Facebook took it down. Later, TikTok took down the Pizzagate hashtag.

This is a frightening demonstration of the internet's power to amplify falsehoods and adjacent fear into mindless conspiratorial memes with real-world consequences. But also, our ability to believe them and the underlying mass hysteria generated by unconscious anxieties. This of course, was all a prelude to the January 6, 2021, Capitol riot.

The Power of Trust

Deep inside our sapiens ability to connect dots lies our relationship to power and the many forms in which it comes to us. The case could be made that our relationship with *authority* and its antecedent, *power*, is the main construct of our distorted world. As proposed here, power is the social force that inculcates us and, if necessary, imposes conformity to achieve social order—beginning with our parents and residing, today, in absolute terms, in the authority of the state. Achieving a high level of social conformity in large and complex social networks is fundamental to their efficiency and successful functioning. The requirement for harmony and discord management is core to both our social and economic survival.

In our recent past, we often attributed power (and authority) to external forms—we projected it onto animistic spirits and totems or gods. And as a result, our fate could reside in sacrifices, rituals, or religious beliefs and rulers who claimed to be the descendants of gods—anything to make the world more orderly and safer, to placate it, and to render it predictable—sacrifice more animal entrails, more virgins, more youth. Today, most of us sacrifice through military service and taxes, and most importantly, a belief in our political organization (patriotism). The state has become our modern spiritual imperative for comprehending and placating the future.

Our very first contact with *power* is with our parents and the beginnings of our socialization. Was it arbitrary, mean, cruel, vindictive, and unpredictable or was it calm, helpful and reasoned? Was it emotionally present and available? Could you safely attach to it and feel secure or did it abandon and abuse you? The key here is: Could it be trusted?

When the trust process is disrupted, then trust in authority and how it is exercised becomes central to our relationship with the world. Many become passive in the face of it, some passive-aggressive, others assertive, and many challenging, while still others angry and enraged—and then there are the belligerent—always challenging all forms of authority as untrustworthy and a threat.

Connecting the dots in the face of our initial contact with authority will tell us a lot about how we view the world. It just seems that throughout history the gods were mostly angry and vindictive. But when we carefully examine how most people lived and died, this makes a great deal of sense. Life was more violent and unpredictable—and I suspect notions of parenting were not very abstract but more practical and geared toward survival.

Today, at one end of the continuum resides physical abuse and emotional abandonment, and at the other end of our contemporary parental conundrum is growing up feeling over-controlled, unfairly criticized, and emotionally manipulated. In other words, you want love, what are you going to do for me? There is no better example of this distortion than the modern dictator, but also all the minor tyrants you encounter in your daily life—as they seek to usurp all the authority and assume the role of gods. Fortunately, angry crowds eventually kill them for their grandiose delusions. But then the crowd may be equally delusional as well. This is the sapiens mindset that AI is seeking to enter.

Where do we begin to intervene in our dot-connecting craziness? How do we identify it? Where does it reside? But most disconcertingly, it is pervasive and central to all our private and public discourse. It props up our fears, our prejudice, and biases; it empowers us, unites us, and organizes us against each other. It holds us together in the face of doubt and the chaos all around us. However, what is real and what is not real is not easily distinguishable.

Nazism was an actual threat, and many didn't see it coming or didn't want to see it coming—no matter how premised it was on paranoid and grandiose ideas. Climate change is real, and many don't want to see it coming as well, believing it is a scientific conspiracy to reduce our carbon footprint. We engage rationalization, denial, and projection. How we are being manipulated and by whom appears to be fundamental to our conspiratorial mindset, and that is determined by our personal relationship with authority. It might be added, it is nearly impossible to modify this relationship once it is imprinted early in life. Yeah, we are all in trouble, as this reality is being politically manipulated to considerable effect.

Always Requiring an Explanation

Adrienne LaFrance (*The Atlantic*) offers this insightful take on QAnon. "The power of the internet was understood early on, but the full nature of that power—its ability to shatter any semblance of shared reality, undermining civil society and democratic governance in the process was not." She adds, "QAnon is emblematic of modern America's susceptibility to conspiracy theories…united in mass rejection of reason (and) objectivity...." I would add that the dot connecting paranoia of this movement should give us all pause, as the internet fuels subreddit hysteria. "Q" is an anonymous individual (or individuals) who cryptically messages followers about deep state cabals wrapped in evangelistic prophecy—dot, dot, dot. Call the California Psychic hotline for more details—$1 minute.

In 2020, the Department of Homeland Security commissioned research on the incel culture. Incel is short for involuntary celibate. An online community of heterosexual men who believe that women are denying them sex because they are physically unattractive. What began as an online support group for men struggling to establish relationships with women, appears to have morphed into a smaller substrate that has become defined as a hate-group. Frustration and anger were turned into calls for violence against women, with expressions of male supremacy and even violent subjugation of women. While no hard numbers are available, there are now documented cases of women being assaulted and killed by individuals expressing incel identification.

It would be reasonable to conjecture that only the internet could have tied these events together—men not receiving sexual attention and ideological terrorism. But also, the naïve irrationality of incels projecting blame onto others and portraying themselves as victims—a default cognitive bias of the contemporary world. Even ISIS terrorists appear more rational by advertising online for wives. But grievance and revenge are redemptive when trust has been broken early in life.

The primal threat we face, besides directly to our safety, is a status quo influx. The threat we don't want to see coming—that everything is continuously changing—the future and everything we are desperately holding onto. This is the ontological source of our belief in conspiracies, or what we broadly think of as conservatism and populism.

Drought Parable

In the Southwest, we are experiencing a 30-year drought that the tree rings tell us can potentially last up to 500 years. We also know that a prehistoric civilization that thrived here for 3,000 years, the Anasazi, collapsed around 1125 A.D. after continuous mega droughts. Okay, let's narrow this down. Around 300 AD the Hohokam tribe settled in the Phoenix area. By 1350-1450 AD, they vanished without a trace due to drought. So it's probably reasonable to inquire: How long will our current drought persist—35 years, a 100, or 500 years? Perhaps more to the point, How long before we vanish?

Let's recap: Phoenix is the fifth largest metropolitan area in the U.S. and is situated in the Sonoran Desert. As crazy as it sounds, real estate, land development, and population growth are the primarily economic drivers. Here's the kicker—the primary use of water is agricultural; when the case could be made that the only farming should be wind farming and solar farming. Last summer (2021) was the hottest on record, with 145 days topping 100 degrees and 53 days exceeding 110 degrees. Projections are that by 2060 Phoenix could become one of the least habitable places in North American.

The key sources of water in the region are underground aquifers being drained by farming, the Colorado River, which is becoming a stream that no longer reaches the ocean, and Lake Powell and Lake Mead, which are both nearing "dead pool" status. Here is the perplexing question facing this community: Why are there no water conservation programs in Phoenix? The answer is everyone thinks they will get theirs before the catastrophe strikes. The only way the people of Phoenix will ever know there's a drought is when they turn on the water faucet and no water comes out.

What's occurring here is a microcosm of our general failure to deal with global climate change. In Phoenix, political leadership is tied to the economic status quo while the public is encouraged to be oblivious. Tree rings be damned, there are no thoughts of vanishing here. "Come on down and play some golf." **Note:** There are currently 219 golf courses in Phoenix using 119,478 acre-feet of water per year (2019). This amounts to 450,000 gallons of water a day per golf course.

Given our propensity to distort reality, how difficult do you think it would be to influence how people think, feel, and believe? History tells us it doesn't take much. Identify their fears and fabricate a conspiracy that ties it to their prejudices and exploit it. They will follow. But when one begins to examine all the potential reasons for a technological intervention, clearly, the most logical one (shout out to Mr. Spock) is to design an algorithm to straighten out our emotional and cognitive biases.

I mean, who could care what most people are thinking? (It does appear as if we are going to have to survive hearing what they think for a while longer.) Our thinking requires fixing! Mental health professionals have been mostly failing at this heroic endeavor for 150 years, and finally gave up and drugged everyone to no one's satisfaction (except for big pharma).

It appears that the primary evolutionary drive behind the development of consciousness 250,000 years ago was to increase our ability to anticipate the future by connecting the dots (any dots apparently). But did not appear to gain serious traction until 40,000 to 90,000 years ago with a creative explosion of tool making, weapon development, and cave drawings. Our big brain is a prediction machine designed to sort the signals and suppress the noise. Day and night, it is weaving together a narrative story and continually sequencing moments into a smooth visual and seamless conscious *you* that is easy to identify while continually searching for patterns and identifying *cause-and-effect.* And it turns out that paranoia and conspiracy are everywhere in the world. These two constructs connect the most dots with the least effort. And, occasionally, they get it right, but not most of the time. "Houston, pick up on aisle 4!"

The Discontent Regression

Psychological discontent is a universal human condition. I get it, no great insight here. This is pretty obvious to everyone. And one of the driving forces behind our discontent is our enhanced cognitive and sensory awareness of the world around us. The ability to attend to micro degrees of variation is a prime cognitive skill of sapiens. For hundreds of thousands of years, our survival was dependent on reading and understanding our environmental, but also on the social cues of those we interacted with. We are capable of discerning the subtlest variation in the tone of speech, facial expression, and actions of others. We can differentiate the most minute and trivial degrees of difference between what is said and what is done, compulsively seeking out patterns and variations in them.

In an imperfect world, in which everyone and everything represents a potential threat attending to subtle differences is not crazy. This is core to our survival (Is that mold on the bathroom wall? A blemish on my cheek? Did he look away when I waved to him?) It also helps to improve your golf game, makes you question your spouse way too much, and allows for research breakthroughs. But what it mostly does is make us critical of everyone and everything that falls short of our expectations—which, it turns out, is the entire world. But only when you wander online and into the intersubjective reality of hundreds of millions of people continually making critical and irrelevant distinctions do you fully begin to comprehend the scope of our ability to detect imperfection.

When did our lifetimes become devoted to appearance? Each of us obsessively attending to our hair and the perfect glamor photo. The sheer scope of fashion—yoga pants, stressed jeans, high heels, ties—makes all the other species blanch in wonderment. A few would be envious, except all those with fur and feathers. They are just fine, thank you. Projecting the right social cues is a deeply embedded defense against social entropy (or rejection). And along with it comes a fragile human identity that is never happy or content, eternally tensioning the "I" in relationship to the "We."

We are continually surveying the world to determine how happy and content we are. And if we could survey the past or, better yet, go forward and survey the future—Are 7.5 billion people better off today than 10 million people in 750 BC or 10 billion people in 2100? In all likelihood, a higher percentage of people are better off today, and more fashionable than at any time in the past. But that may simply mean that the focus of our discontent has shifted.

Today, worldwide, we live healthier and longer lives and enjoy a standard of living that was unimaginable a 100 years ago. Our quality of life is not an illusion but an objective reality. So, your grandfather lives to the age of 96 and wants off the respirator, but the grandchildren want him in assisted living until the cancer kills him. And therein lies the rub—discontent and all its underlying biases have never been recalibrated.

We have and always will reside in a world of discontent. Our longer and improved lives are destroying the world we live in. How do we resolve the dissonance of this reality? Oh, I am happy right now and life is pretty good overall, and, yes, California is burning to the ground and the Greenland ice sheets are melting—but, hey, football season starts next week. How is the dissonance of this reality resolved, knowing worldwide there are 272 million discontented migrants on the move?

A recent worldwide Social Progress Index, surveying 163 nations about personal safety, health and wellness, environmental quality, and personal freedom, indicated the United States ranked 28th in the world, having dropped twelve spots since 2014. Currently, the U.S. ranks below Estonia, Cyprus, and Greece. It noted that, overall, the world's score is trending upward. Wow, that makes me feel good. Who cares whether we feel good when the world is burning? It is hard for sapiens to see beyond the next weekend. Like most of you, I am primarily concerned with how I feel.

Quite predictably, it appears, discontent always arises to fill any margins we create—visit any assisted living facility, packed with the lonely and isolated—drugged into varying states of semi-consciousness, experiencing chronic health problems, cancers, dementias, Alzheimer's and Parkinson's— and the most boring TV afternoon broadcasts ever conceived. And that's how it will likely end for most of us—all this talk about the future! It would be interesting to have a quality-of-life survey taken of everyone near death and see who is more content. I suspect those on a morphine drip and in the least pain and discomfort are the most content.

The internet is an infinite regression of discontent for everyone who feels aggrieved. The result has been to un-repress life. There are online forums, support groups, and subreddits for everyone: furries outraged that people stare at them prancing in the park, people who aways forget their safe word, so many don't get their share of cake, people who stop their cart in the middle of a shopping aisle and get impatient glares! Your core sense of *self* has been assaulted, and the internet is your champion for incessant complaining about how you have been victimized.

Now is your chance to call someone out, shame them, hurt them, belittle them, make them less, make them pay, embarrass them, create legions of viral hate, send threats of harm, compromise their job, sue the company or business they work for. This is your opportunity to arouse the mob and to get back, seek revenge, make them pay—finally retribution—the book is coming out soon, but you can download the podcast now! When the lawsuit settles, Netflix wants to negotiate a docudrama.

The internet is characterized by the classic signal-to-noise problem—the same problem astronomers have in identifying alien contact from universal background noise. We are no longer able to distinguish the serious from the inconsequential, and, as a result, all events are treated interchangeably. Is it former President Donald Trump tweeting and, his fixer, Rudy Giuliani butt-dialing? It doesn't matter. This is the way we roll—clickbait hyperbole to test your woke state of mind. The tragic traumas of life have become background noise to all the trivial traumas of life.

The internet has reached zero-state connectivity with the surrounding world and has opened us up to a Cassandra's Complex—a cruel super-ego state and universal echo chamber of projected blame and ostracism. Everyone is at fault and to blame for something, and whatever it is, will be tracked down and exposed. The reality is, we now have an electronic ghost out there somewhere. And any revelation or accusation will become internet-truth and live forever online without forgiveness.

But rest assured that the *electronic you* will still get rec time at the data prison center. But your circumstances are more complicated. There is nothing too small or irrelevant that cannot be inflated into a crisis of conscience and character. Whether that's Supreme Court Justice Brett Kavanaugh acting drunk and boorishly at a frat party or New York Governor Mario Cuomo reaching for more than he should.

Internet hysteria is a wolf pack of righteousness—open mic at a dive-bar without a wire cage. You better learn to duck. And, deservedly, the rich and famous, a blight and obscenity on a modern world crumbing under their excesses, are at the forefront of this parade. No indiscretion is too insignificant or beyond perp-walking them into blogging hell. And leading the charge are corporations and state attorney generals sensitized to bad press. Best to find a CEO, a CFO, or a manager to blame and burn at the stake of public humiliation than suffer weeks of bad press and late-night show jokes. And the most pathetic of all are academic institutions burning their own at the stake under the guise of academic tolerance.

E-technology has opened the door to our modern Salem witch trials, where any accusation of straying from the infinite universe of political correctness leads to online humiliation and cancellation—and a lifetime of wearing an internet search ankle monitor. A social world that will not rest until everyone hates themselves. The internet creates and inflates Identity Diffusion.

While the internet has allowed for more real injustices to be uncovered and addressed in a manner that has never existed in our entire social history, more people are now being exploited than ever before as well, say, for instance, through sex trafficking and dating apps. And it appears there is no going back, because we live in a world in which unfairness and injustice are the reality baseline. It is far simpler to default to every claim being true out of fear; when our time comes no one will believe us. We are fracturing into identity tents of causes and injustices, victims of life, trying to figure out who to blame. However, it's essential we understand that justice is not the internet's goal. Clickbait revenue streams and data-harvesting are the goals.

E-technology has its hand on the scales for both good and bad, having given voice to an irrationality that percolates in the depths of the human psyche. If you have ever seen documentary footage of a 10-foot Komodo Dragon racing across a beach and attacking and tearing its prey apart, reflexively and violently—e-technology has similarly empowered all of us. Whatever I say or feel or believe or think is true! We are all being gaslighted by life. That's true for 7.5 billion people. That's a lot of truths and distorted reality.

We now reside in a world in which the corrective is as corrosive as the accusation. That's our world now. No wonder sapiens migrated for many tens of thousands of years to get the hell away from each other. But today, we cannot. We need to understand the consequence of our tech-connectivity. For better or worse, our private space is rapidly merging with the public space.

When the *particle-drive* (*self*) finally relents to the *wave-drive* (We), there will be consequences. And that, broadly, is where we are headed with our e-technology connectivity—when social credit scoring and brain-hacking become a routine aspect of interacting with e-technology. In the coming future, non-conforming thoughts and ideas or conduct outside the metrics will bring censure, reeducation, or transcranial interventions directly from our personal e-devices. Of course, there will be a cautionary warning that your interface will be shut down if you don't accept the brief and painless penetration, and this time, your violation will have to be reported due to multiple recent transgressions. There will be hundreds of pages of fine print, but there is an app you can use to summarize the key points and authorize biometrically. Fortunately for you, humor, fantasy, and imagination are treatable states of mind.

We will never know or understand why we were required to be censured and scanned by a corrective program, only that it's for the "general algorithmic good" (GAG) in a celebration of the "triumph of the commons." It is time to be honest with ourselves. The human condition needs treatment, not necessarily you or me, but just about everyone else.

E-technology feeds our individual and collective narcissism—that we are important, significant and the center of the universe. It is empowering through its instantaneous reach out into the world. It is high school students believing they are outliers and becoming self-harming; the unending world of internet influencers, bloggers, podcasters and the demand that we all create our brand––it is WikiLeaks, deep-fakes, subreddits, Darknet, trolling, phishing, hacking and our overwhelming dependency on the internet. (Your choice, your dog, or your smartphone? You have sixty seconds to decide! For most people, the answer is obvious. No judgment here.)

Discontent, the story of the human condition, is infinite, unremitting, and without reconciliation. It is also out loose in the world, as each of us exposes our previously private reality for the world to gawk at. This may not be pretty, and it is sure to have consequences. E-technology will exploit this as clickbait, data scrapping, and revenue streams. We will engage it with an illusion of connectivity, when in actuality we are disconnected more than ever.

We have been engaging in a power exchange that isolates us but provides us an interface with the world in exchange. Here, reality is being redefined, if not distorted. Are we happier and more content? Are we better off than before? And will we be more content and better off in the future? Some will be, at varying scales, for a brief time before it all dissolves. Best to order your *carebot* sooner rather than later, with automatic upgrades in case you outlive projections. To be honest, that's unlikely—but optimism sells.

Emotion-States

As a species, sapiens appear to be at the mercy of complex and powerful emotional states that are not present in other species. (Okay, dogs seem to be happy and guilty an awful lot.) Beyond crude fight-or-flight responses, the advantage of emotions is to sensitize us to the inner experience of those around us (empathy) and allow for emotional bonding. They also act as an early warning system to potential social blowback. And when called upon, they prepare us for attack (physical, verbal, or legal). Bottom line, neurotransmitters (emotions) harmonize our social interactions with others by communicating our physiological and psychological states of mind.

Emotions appear to be a filter that operates semi-autonomously of consciousness or rational intervention. They also function to attune us to our bodies and states of mind. Our struggle has always been to modulate our emotions and not overreact. It turns out that we are not very good at this, possibly because we have not been at it very long as a species. In the case of our brain, it is one structure built on top of another over a brief evolutionary time span. While good enough, it is not where we need it to be. In an e-environment that is increasingly complex and where emotions are conveyed in increasingly abstract ways, we appear to require many upgrades to fully parallel process emotional states with intellectual ability.

Distorted and shallow emotions appear to reign supreme throughout the media world. Who could possibly know if all the claims of injustice and hurt feelings are true or grossly distorted? As hard as it is to accept, all emotional states are not necessarily true. The experience of one's emotions is real enough, but the emotions themselves can be confabulated from interpersonal distortions that have no bearing on reality (e.g., unfounded jealousy).

But in the end, it all appears to rest on what someone believes. The lucky ones get the court to agree, a financial settlement, a headline, book deal or make a special someone's life hell for a brief time. And the hardest part for everyone looking in is knowing what to believe. It's another person's feelings, their experiences and who are we to question or judge? But in the same way memories can be implanted and people believe their delusions, they can experience false emotions. It's a subjective tyranny that has ruled the human condition from earliest times—disproving false accusations by someone who genuinely believes them.

Going forward, it is unlikely that AI will have an emotional filter like ours, or fully understand a world that operates through one. We have all felt frustrated by a telephone interaction with a robo-voice at the other end, one that hears and understands nothing and only asks irrelevant questions. Its biggest disconnect is it cannot input your frustration as it rapidly rises. The only thing more frustrating is knowing you have an actual customer service rep who is utterly indifferent to you.

The first thing AI will try to do is tamp down all these emotional responses. They are getting in the way and seem to create more problems than solutions (a conversation many couples have had, no doubt). The real question is: How will our emotional states eventually be probed—with medications, algorithms, transcranial penetration, nanoparticles, CRISPR'd, app, chip, neural-lace? And toward what end?

The goal will be to modulate or balance our emotions, not unlike tuning a musical instrument or your car—suppressing emotional states below specific thresholds or temporarily eliminating them. And how does this impact sex drive, ambition, or the experience of love? Do they really matter anymore? Really, what is better than a permanent state of contentment? Of course, we would no longer be human, but just another mutant simulant without adaptive drive, soon extinct when the hard drive finally crashes after 4 million years.

The great paradox of our contemporary wave-particle duality is that it creates dissonance and conflict with the world around us that can never be fully resolved. We are a highly self-absorbed species that cannot survive outside our social world. And the modern e-technology response has been to heighten self-absorption. The result has been the rise of loneliness over the past 250 years. It is the true modern pandemic.

We were never genetically designed to evolve beyond our social primate selves. The result has been loneliness (or psychological death), in which physical death often ensues. We are preordained to be social, and anyone who is not is expiring more rapidly. Our e-technology interface is actively tensioning our wave-particle duality to the limits. In car talk, we are redlining right now.

All the emotional states discussed here—anxiety, depression, stress—are primarily the product of the simulated reality we have constructed. A world in which passivity, complexity, disruption, and isolation are increasingly prevalent. No wonder we often reside in a carb-gravy altered state as we eat our emotions. Alienated from your family? Go it alone! Divorced multiple times? Go it alone! Kids are a pain in the ass! Go it alone! Heck, work will love you, money will love you, power and respect will love you. It is not enough and never has been. And no, that gun will not love you either and neither will the abyss. We are all suspicious of the outliers who don't separate soon enough or what is clinically referred to as differentiation—you know, become independent, self-sufficient, self-contained and not have to depend on anyone.

The irony being what most of us lack are real and substantive relationships. We are no longer socially embedded and hide behind the walls of our condo, the cubicles at work and the privacy shields we power-up. We are all suspended in virtual space—nodes connected by edges extending beyond the horizon to other nodes in a vast electronic galaxy. It will not be enough, going forward.

There is endless literature on how our awareness of death is the universal underlying source of our experience of anxiety as a species. However, the real truth is, the source of our anxiety is being separated from those who care for us and love us. And maybe we were never loved, or our love was interrupted, and all manner of rejection put us on a trajectory of isolation. Perhaps some of us compensated or sublimated and made our way back. And just maybe you became a hoarder, an alcoholic, violent, or drifted away, and are living homeless on the streets. Never loved or capable of love. Not romantic love, but the desire of being included and fitting in and, most importantly, feeling as if you belong, of not being alone. That you have a place in the universe, and that is all the meaning you require. The internet and technological innovations will never care about you or love you. And that is a future problem because we are going to pretend they do.

E-Technology Stress

Our networked world is more complex and evolving exponentially due to our electronic interface. As a result, our social interactions are denser and more instantaneous. Just try resetting your Nest or storing your photos on the iCloud or sending a document through Dropbox. Our devices change expectations and create demands that ultimately stress everyone in the big supply chain of life. But it also turns out, there is no account manager or inventory control, just a collection service. This demand-stress is what's termed your *allostatic* load. Allostasis is the process by which the body seeks to regain stability or homeostasis in response to stressors.

Perhaps the best way to understand e-technology stress is by looking back a few centuries. Let's look back 150,000 years ago. For most of human history, no one suffered from dyslexia (difficulty in learning to read or write owing to difficulties interpreting words and symbols). Nope, no such problem existed until we began requiring universal education sometime around the mid-17th century. First up in America was Massachusetts (1639); and it spread like a virus and children were dragged away from working in the fields and factories and forced to learn how to read and write.

One could make the case that this forced subjugation and the increasingly higher demands for education and technology continue to stigmatize children and adults. Who knew Asperger's and Autism Spectrum Disorder (difficulty with communication and social interactions) existed until well into the 20th century? Only because we kept demanding more of people.

For centuries, nothing was really going on to reveal these conditions as problematic. Who knew about learning disorders if there were no schools? Perhaps one's apprenticeship took longer, but even more likely, a person excelled working with their hands and solving visual-spatial problems. And really, how important was your intelligence quotient (IQ) if you were fishing and pushing a plow all day long? What was Attention-Deficit/Hyperactivity Disorder?

The entire *Diagnostic and Statistical Manual of Mental Disorders* (DSM-5) would have very little relevance in the past. It was not until the modern world evolved and put pressure on all of us to perform at a higher level socially, emotionally, and intellectually, and to become more productive in a highly stratified world did it evolve to record our many dysfunctions. Throughout the DSM-5, nearly every diagnosis is qualified by phrases such as—"impairment in everyday adaptive functioning," or "marked impairment in social or occupational functioning," or "social and occupational impairment."

A great many of the so-called impairments we suffer today are defined by the demands of the job and having to function at a higher level of efficiency. Expectations and demands are higher than ever before and, as a result, there is an increasing inability to adapt, or what we often refer to as mental disorders. It's not that these conditions were not always there to varying degrees, only that now they have risen to significance due to our e-technology interface. The reality that is the continuing evolution of *human performance dysfunction* will continue until everyone is an internet influencer or can write code. And any cursory glance at the DSM-5 index will produce a veritable checklist of modern ailments that likely never existed 200 years ago.

Modern Conditions

ADHD; Intellectual Disability; Autism Spectrum Disorder; PTSD; Obsessive-Compulsive Disorder; Somatic Disorder; Feeding and Eating Disorders; Elimination Disorders; Sleep-Wake Disorders; Sexual Dysfunctions; Gender Dysphoria; Medication-Induced Movement Disorder; Relational Problems; Educational and Occupational Problems;

Personal History of Self-Harm; Problems Related to Lifestyle; Obesity; Phase of Life Problems.

For most of our history, the 600+ diagnoses offered in the DSM-5 never existed. But clearly, life has become a condition that requires treatment. It appears that we have not been successful at mitigating the rise in dysfunction as the problems keep multiplying. We might want to ask, why is that? We are living longer and healthier. We are more aware and discerning and perhaps even more empathetic and caring. Medicine and technology have offered many advances when, in the past, suffering and death were the primary cures.

But still, the problems are multiplying because we never drill down on the primary one—how to make long-term rational decisions as individuals and communities. Nothing better exemplifies this problem than watching the worldwide Covid-19 pandemic response. With the world on fire, hysteria and politics interfere with the rational course of tamping it down.

Our e-technology interface creates low levels of unremitting stress, resulting from the chronic infusion of the stress hormone cortisol. The result is a "toxic, unremitting barrage of challenges that eventually breaks down the body." (Epstein) The impact is directly on the brain and can result in increased anxiety, depression, anger, social isolation, and PTSD, including obesity and cardiovascular disease. "The allostatic load can entail chemical imbalances as well as perturbations in the diurnal rhythm and, in some cases, atrophy brain structures." (McEwen) Yep, smaller and damaged brains, along with the small hands and fingers required to interact with e-technology. It appears that hairlessness and rounder faces will not be enough to keep us beautiful.

Technology demands a degree of perfectionism that life has never required from us for such sustained periods. As a result, it has become an independent aggravator and stressor. We now require a personal IT person to help most of us manage our electronic interface. They have basically replaced the therapist, who supplanted the priest before them. What are friends for if they can't help you sort your operating system? Tech support has become our most vital lifeline to interacting with the world.

Watch what happens when your device won't open, freezes, or crashes. A mild panic begins to set in, now realizing you are being disconnected from your entire world. In fact, you may no longer exist. You start to suffer "disconnect panic syndrome." You become anxious and confused, begin screwing with the device in panic mode, turn it on and off, reset it over and over, push buttons and functions you never knew existed before, frantically begin an online search for a fix, call friends, race down to the phone store, and most frighteningly—call tech support. You could be down for hours, and it will cost. Did the battery die? Was service temporarily disrupted? Do you require an operating system upgrade? Please, not a virus—I have only had it nine months, and I am not replacing it! Can the data be saved? The universal cry of the e-stressed! No, you forgot to recharge it.

The most discernible feature of interacting with our new technology is its specificity and the depth to which you are required to understand it. It is not intuitive and obvious. It wants and demands detailed attention. Unlike the TV, which you pretty much plug and play, our computers require us to master complexity to make them function. Same with our smartphones. Once familiar with it, one can function quite efficiently—but the learning curve is steep and the crises profound. You must operate it correctly or your entire universe ceases to exist. Does your car dashboard seem insanely complicated and distracting? Have you considered not upgrading your computer or buying a new smartphone (or really any electronic device)—because you didn't want to be upgraded as a human? The hidden cost of a technology workaround is machines will ultimately do it for you (for example, a self-driving car). But if machines can do everything, we might be forced ask, what is our purpose in this relationship?

Juice-Jacking Sleep

In 1980, the very first epidemiological study on the subject of sleep disturbance was published, per *The International Journal of Epidemiology*, "Sleep epidemiology—a rapid growing field." Subsequently, over a ten-year period (2003 to 2013), 10,000 studies have been published on the topic, making it the ninth most studied health disorder in the world. Being dot-connectors we cannot help but notice this coincides with the rise of e-technologies (computers, videogames, internet and smartphones).

The authors were quick to point out this relationship as well, predicting that sleep disorders were on the rise and are likely to increase with the "rapid advent of the 24/7 society involving round-the-clock activities and increasing nighttime use of TV, internet, and mobile phones." (Ferrie, *et al.*) The result has been disruption of our circadian rhythm and compromised sleep duration.

Among the listed health problems, besides tiredness and chronic fatigue, are anxiety, depression, stress, cognitive impairment, human error/accidents, all on top of hypertension, autoimmune disorders, dementias, obesity, and diabetes. And, yes, that is a lot! Prevalence surveys indicate insomnia is the number one sleep disorder, ranging from 33 percent to 73 percent of the general population.

Now, this topic is only mentioned because it broadly fits the narrative being put forward here, that Identity Diffusion has arisen as a consequence of our interaction with e-technology. It is likely that before we congregated into complex networks, archaic sapiens slept better than we do. But now, we are far beyond buying blue-light blockers. It's the number of passive hours we spend interacting with an electronic medium, while our minds separate from our inert bodies. This gives new meaning to the philosophical mind-body duality.

Far subtler are the intricacies of our e-technology interaction and the demands placed on our attention, patterns of reinforcement and required specificity. E-technology is multitasking us in our sleep—putting us on constant alert—the primitive brain unable to sleep while it anxiously monitors the universe for threats, work projects, and ringtones. It is also the world being able to reach back through our devices and disrupt us at any time. Next time your phone is in another room, notice how quickly you respond when it rings.

We are all on call 24/7 and no amount of memory foam, Ambien, weighted blankets, cold eye masks, sleep trackers, sleep-beats or noise cancellation devices are going to help (the global sleep product market is $70+ billion a year). Obviously, you should reduce the amount of ambient light and noise in your sleep environment. It turns out that *neural-rinsing* our brains at night (or sleep) is vital to our overall health, but that damn e-technology is "juice-jacking" our resting bandwidth while we sleep. Inherent with e-technology are stress and anxiety that we are unable to shut down. The bottom line—it wants something from us all the time now, as we are prepped for the tech-rapture.

Anxiety: Pandemic Traveling at the Speed of Life

Today, what we term generalized anxiety disorder (GAD) has been described and written about since classical antiquity. Greek philosopher and physician Hippocrates described it at length, as did Roman philosophers Cicero and Seneca. And while it has undergone many subtle clinical variations over the past 200 years, we all pretty much recognize and understand it as an excessive fear response. It results from sapiens' peculiar interface with the world—an unremitting state of self-consciousness. Anxiety is the price we pay for self-awareness and our ability to anticipate the future. An old mental health adage goes—depression is about the past, and anxiety is about the future. The anticipation of the future is one of our brain's key adaptive features, but one that can also activate the underlying brain circuitry for anxiety.

I have chosen to separate stress and anxiety here, but neurocircuitry imaging suggests they broadly overlap one another. While closely linked, stress and anxiety can and do operate independently of one another. At the front end, anxiety is normal and an adaptive function that promotes survival. It is an early warning system for potential threats in our immediate environment. Essentially, anxiety is a milder analog of our fear response to a direct threat. It comprises three stress hormones (cortisol, corticotropin and adrenocorticotropin) and it operates in what is termed the fear network (primarily, the amygdala but also the hippocampus, thalamus and brain stem).

But at the back end, when anxiety cannot be turned off, it becomes emotionally and physically debilitating (symptoms can include restlessness, irritability, muscle tension, and sleep and concentration problems). These symptoms occur where no direct threat exists. Our mind manufactures the illusion of a threat (this used to be termed neurotic anxiety). I might add, anxiety is typically comorbid with depression and has become a chronic condition of e-technology life. So, what turns anxiety on, and why can't it be turned off?

Based on current estimates, 40 million Americans suffer anxiety. A recent American Psychological Association survey (2019) reported that 40 percent polled indicated they are more anxious today than they were a year earlier. The World Mental Health Survey (2002) described anxiety as the most prevalent mental health problem across the globe. Now granted, there were no polls or surveys taken thousands of years ago or even 60 years ago, so what is about to follow is speculative.

Really, the clinical definition of anxiety does not begin to make sense of all anxiety in the world today. After the World War II arose a school of philosophy known as existentialism. It conceptualized a modern origin for what it termed existential anxiety. People were experiencing a generalized unease when faced with the meaning and purpose of life following the war—

giving rise to an inner turmoil and feelings of angst, despair, anxiety, and alienation. The instability of a modern world in chronic transition acted as a trigger for anxiety. The experience of feeling detached from the world—losing a job, suffering a divorce, a student moving away from home, or residing alone in old age—all reflecting the endemic loss of connectedness and community (and also the origin of our collective *derealization*).

The emphasis in existential theory is on the freedom to choose, but also the deluge of choices we are confronted with daily. The number of decisions we are confronted with daily is a distillate for chronic underlying tension. What if you make the wrong choice is among the most worrisome of modern dilemmas (can it be returned and do you get a return shipping label; should you accept an online friend request to exchange nude photos?) Consider the range of choice we are faced with daily, ones that never existed 60 years ago and certainly not a 1,000 years ago. For example, which flavor of ice cream do you want tonight? (For the record, there are over a thousand ice cream flavors—and don't hurry me! I am only at the vanillas with swirls.) A recent study calculated parents are faced with "1,750" critical decisions in the first years of a baby's life. (Aggarwal) This remarkable number reflects the multiplying effect of modern life on all of us. Our early ancestor may have had shorter lives, but they also had simpler ones.

Complexity came upon us incrementally—and all the seemingly life-altering decisions we are confronted with—how soon do you have to choose a college major? Should you enlist in the military? And more importantly, can you make this yellow traffic light, while texting, and get to your probation appointment on time and pass the piss test?

The days of our lives are consumed by thousands of inconsequential and significant choices, all claiming relevance in the moment. And often we do not know which ones were significant until months and years later ("I am pregnant, have an STD, lung cancer, diabetes—I failed to make the yellow light and will require some form of assisted living for the rest of my life, after getting out of prison"). We reside at a time and place that believes, whether true or not, that we make our choices and are responsible for them—all of them. We decide our fate and attend to the anxiety and dread that will inevitably follow.

A Boston physician, George Miller Beard, experienced what he called nervous exhaustion or what he later termed *neurasthenia*. He also came to believe it was a uniquely American condition. He described it as "afflicting primarily ambitious, upwardly mobile members of the urban middle and upper classes—especially the brain workers in almost every household of the Northern and Eastern States—whose nervous systems were overtaxed by a rapidly modernizing American civilization." His paper on this subject was published in the *Boston Medical and Surgical Journal* in 1869. Quoted from *My Age of Anxiety* (Stossel, 2013).

I would offer that all of us, today, function in a more confused and less predictable world than those in the past. (Can that really be true?) But only because our lives are confounded by the daily onslaught of choices and decisions. The consequence is self-induced anxiety. While we have successfully reduced external threats, we have exponentially internalized worry and concern about how we are functioning in a complex and dynamical network—one forever cueing us about our social status. We should ask ourselves: Where does balance and order reside in our lives? How about something as abstract as mindfulness? Why do we become anxious watching the evening news? And how come our thoughts always start racing as we toss and turn trying to go to sleep?

Because there is only the illusion of order and stability, it makes anticipating the future, not only more difficult, but more stressful and anxiety-producing. The sense of threat is no longer as direct or specific—you no longer worry about poisonous snakes now that you have stopped sleeping on the ground—but now a viperous work climate threatens your job security. The sources of our anxieties have become increasingly diffuse and unknown to us—giving rise not only to a unique dread, but to conspiracies as well. How else can we account for all the invisible things happening to us?

So, what is different today than before, you ask? Without getting all statistical, I would offer that incessant change has become the stasis of daily life. Every day we get into cars, buses, subways, trains or planes and commute great distances as a routine part of our lives—eating up time like tortilla chips and creating continuous moments of transitions. And the sheer passivity of interacting with the world through an electronic medium defies millions of years of evolution.

Perhaps even more significant is the rate at which we change jobs (average of every three to four years), as well as divorce (50 percent within eight years), and move (11.7 times over one's lifetime)—often with the illusion that life will be better. In a worst-case scenario, we find ourselves in free fall—transient nodes in an economic order that is either scaling up, making us more relevant, or scaling down, making us redundant.

The modern life in transition poses chronic instability and disconnects us from the people and environments that likely nurture and support us—resulting in a chronic state of disconnect. A marked function of our economic system is supply and demand—but it's also the primary driver of social instability. We are all independent contractors adapting to the market or a new relationship. Income and benefits are unpredictable as are emotional connections (swiping right too much recently—acting a little desperate). As the market fluctuates and changes course—so do we all. Work schedules are continually changing––is this the day your boss announces on a Zoom video conference that everyone is being fired?—and that once promising online relationship just ghosted you.

Psychology researchers in university labs learned years ago how to induce fear and anxiety in lab rats. Rats were isolated and placed in cages and an electrical current was randomly sent through the wire mesh floor painfully shocking them each time a light came on. You could not only produce high levels of anxiety over time, as measured by blood hormone levels, but in a brief time also induce psychosis by randomly turning on the red light. Unconsciously waiting for the intermittent light reflects the source of so much of our anxieties today.

If the first factor in the production of anxiety has been the high rate of change and the overall pace of life, the second factor is the density and rising complexity of contemporary life. Our complexity is well on its way to becoming one of the densest elements on Earth—on the periodic table, it would be between osmium ($Os/22.61$ g/cm^3) and iridium ($Ir/22.56$ g/cm^3). We are being asked to bear down and master complexity as never before. And this mastery is intrinsically tied to our ability to adapt to increasing rates of social change. More broadly, the stress and anxiety of managing all the *data illusion* generated in our simulated networks underlies our *derealization* and the onset of Identity Diffusion.

Complexity has been rapidly evolving for the past 200 years and appears to be expanding exponentially (analog to digital) if we are to trust Gordon Moore. He predicted, in 1965, that the number of transistors on an integrated circuit would double every two years—*Moore's Law*. In 1954, an integrated circuit had eight transistors. In 1970, this number reached 50,000; by 1990, it was 1,200,000. Today, it is at 39.5 billion! His insightful prediction parallels the speed at which computers are operating, but also the rate at which we are required to adapt. I would conjecture that our lives are being compressed and accelerated (what the positive minded might term optimization) to keep pace with the 39.5 billion transistors on a computer chip (and how many computer chips define your world right now—a hundred, a thousand, perhaps a hundred thousand? One online estimate indicated 932 billion computer chips were manufactured in 2020 alone). Our lives marinate in thousands upon thousands of routine choices—never knowing which ones will be the significant ones—but always extracting a micron of emotional well-being. We happy band of consumers are rarely aware of the price we pay, but it always adds up.

Sidebar: As a former graduate student of Rollo May, I would like to express my gratitude for his mentoring on the subject of existential anxiety—and refer you to his outstanding book—*The Meaning of Anxiety*.

Summary

- At the core of sapiens cognition lies an uncanny ability to connect the dots—an unending *cause-and-effect* process geared toward predicting the future. This process can also become grossly distorted by a lifetime of negative experiences projected onto any random event, turning it into a conspiracy.
- Achieving a high level of social conformity in large and complex social networks is fundamental to our efficiency and successful functioning. The requirement for harmony and discord management is also core to our social and economic lives. This will be e-technology's prime algorithmic directive.
- Cognitive dissonance is the psychological distress created by holding two or more contradictory beliefs, ideas or values at the same time. This is often resolved with an absolute mindset of belief and

conspiracy—but too often by *doubling down* on questionable behavior.

- E-technology represents a new interface between consciousness and reality. And while we are a highly adaptable species, changing our interface with reality always produces consequences fraught with drama.

- Our prime sapiens directive is survival, not happiness. We may have to dispense with the happy idea. Discontentment is the more efficient driver of evolution.

- The human element in the human-condition has not significantly changed in 250,000 years. What we have primarily experienced has been our ability to adapt, which raises the question: What are the limits of our adaptability?

- The reach and potential influence of our technology is being exponentially extended—from social media to drone missile strikes. We have begun a process, whereby, our *inner self* is reaching further out into the world than ever before—an *inner self* we don't really understand or know very well.

- The internet is characterized by a classic signal-to-noise problem. We are struggling to distinguish the serious from the inconsequential, and, as a result, all events are treated interchangeably—giving voice to an irrationality that percolates in the depths of the human psyche.

- Soon, nonconforming thoughts, ideas, and conduct outside the metrics will bring censure, reeducation, or transcranial penetration. We will never know or understand why we were required to be censured and scanned by a corrective program, only that it's for the general algorithmic good (GAG).

- Sapiens appear to be at the mercy of complex and powerful emotional states that are not present in other species. Our struggle has always been to modulate our emotions and not overreact. It will require many upgrades to fully parallel process emotional states with intellectual ability.

- E-technology is multitasking us in our sleep—keeping us on constant alert—the primitive brain is unable to sleep while it anxiously monitors the universe for work projects, ringtones, and threats.

- Many negative emotional states are the product of *data illusion* and the simulated reality we have created for ourselves. A world in which passivity, complexity, disruption, and isolation are increasingly prevalent.
- Our e-technology interface creates low levels of unremitting stress, resulting from the chronic infusion of stress hormones. The result has been a toxic, unremitting barrage of challenges that eventually break down the body and the mind—the genesis of our pandemic anxiety.

7.0 – Homo Ex Machina

It's tough to make predications, especially about the future.

—Yogi Berra

What do we know about *Homo sapiens*? The short answer is we know very little about *Homo sapiens*. And, what we think we know is mostly speculative and educated guesses by a lot of smart people. But on close examination, it mostly resembles fictional novels more than hard science. The primary exception has been the many recent findings based on maternal mitochondrial DNA (mtDNA) research. But this evidence is only randomly gathered from archeological digs, rendering our overall picture blurry.

Let's quickly review the speculation. Each one of us comes into the world with a fixed array of biological set points (innate drives) that define us as a species (and there's a surprising amount of variation here as well). However, all our drives are then simultaneously filtered through two washes. First is epigenetic change due to environmental and lifestyle factors that produce changes in gene expression and second is the long-term process of social enculturation. These washes, biological and social, result in a wave-particle or "I/We" duality that defines each of us individually and as a culture. Two inseparable and oscillating states in continuous tension with one another. How well this tension is managed ultimately defines the health and survivability of the individual and the community.

There are caveats to be considered here. Our fixed drives are primarily revealed to us through behavior, and we are seldom fully conscious of them. For example, you want to dine out at a popular new restaurant (hunger along with status and perhaps novelty seeking). You are working hard to get a promotion at work (aggression, economic security and status competition). He or she is really irresistible, and you are drawn to him or her for unknown reasons (sex drive, companionship, paternity, okay—and pheromones). But also, not all these drives are unique to sapiens, but are shared to varying degrees with many species. Lastly, what follows is not meant to be an exhaustive examination of our genetic set points, but, instead, focuses on the obvious factors shaping our social interactions and networked communities.

Clan of the Sapiens, Redux

Let me state my bias up front. Our survival as a species is entirely dependent on how effective we are at forming both an individual identity (particle) and a group identity (wave). And for symbolic creatures such as ourselves, the boundaries of identity are vast and primitive. Identifying who "I" am and who "We" are is our prime directive. In fact, we are the only species whose survival is dependent on having two completely independent identities, and, as a result, there is a chronic tensioning between the *self* and *other*.

We are, in effect, perpetually in conflict and in negotiation with one another over our identities. But here is the kicker, individual identity is exclusively formed based on our social environment. While individuals certainly influence the social side, it's of relatively minor significance in the long run. Our existence has always been a social one, and no individual resides outside this circumstance. The individual's subjective understanding of the world exists exclusively within a shared social context, and we can never be free of this tension.

In the 19th century, Freud identified "sex-drive" and "fear of death" as the innate biological markers driving our social organization. I am making the case to add *social status*. Within our shared social context, the most powerful driving force is status. Status or the lack thereof is defining of the individual in all social contexts, potentially imbuing individuals with economic security, sexual access, and power.

Status is core to self-esteem and self-worth and confers broad social advantages, including respect and deference. And while it may unfairly derive from genetic and social advantages, status is the defining element of how we are socially organized. This is who we are. Even antisocial behavior and criminal acts in today's world are generally a product of individuals lacking status or seeking status. Status drives the talented and ambitious, the aggressive and power-hungry, as well as everyone desperately seeking some form of recognition and security. In our current simulation, the two most significant drivers of status are income and education.

Any threat or challenge to one's perceived status can potentially result in violence, and more commonly one's spiral toward depression (you didn't get the promotion, someone cut you off in traffic, your supervisor forgets your name). Any threat to one's perceived sense of status has significant consequences, not only for individuals but also their tribal identities, even at the nation-state level. Humans are uniquely sensitive to status and are fully capable of conflating threats to status as a threat to physical safety and security. Social status is so thoroughly embedded in our individual and group identity, any perceived threat can quickly result in a primitive emotional reaction.

Because individual identity takes so long to develop, it is exceptionally fragile and subject to wide-ranging dysfunction, in what appears to be a problematic evolutionary strategy. Throughout a lifetime, identity is subject to continuous and ubiquitous insults. As a result, we develop complex defense mechanisms to aid in psychologically coping. We become obsequious and flattering or passive-aggressive, while many harden into states of psychopathy, antisocial behavior, narcissism, grandiosity, and paranoia. For many, the default strategies become deception and manipulation (clinically termed Machiavellianism), or what most of us think of as untrustworthy.

What is problematic with our many adaptive strategies is that most of the time, a simple face-saving gesture, such as an apology or taking responsibility, would have been more than enough to restore social equilibrium. But for many, acknowledging a personal or social transgression is a loss of face (and status).

In this state, one feels they are now less than before, and potentially subject to powerful negative consequences, e.g., social opprobrium or rejection, all of which threatens a potential loss of community. This is the most devastating psychological consequence sapiens can experience and one to be avoided at all costs. It can also trigger powerful emotional states of shame and guilt. While many avoid conflict by conforming or apologizing, no one escapes insults-to-the-self for long. Because our social networks are so overwhelmingly complex, the subjective experience and sensitivity of individuals are immensely intricate and the psychological struggle for status so intense, status-insults are inevitable and always coming at you over a lifetime.

Today, wealth and power are primarily markers for social status. As a result, they are core to social dysfunction and are driving our social and cultural evolution—better to consult a financial advisor than waste your time and money on a therapist. Income has become the perfected metric for calculating social status and self-worth. There are, of course, a few paradoxes, for example, the salary of college professors versus that of college football coaches, which could not be explained to any aliens landing on Earth.

On the other hand, doctors and nurses appear to be well-compensated. But the great paradox is in identifying the social levers of status—drive and ambition, intelligence and talent, physical and social attractiveness, and the advantages conferred by pre-existing privileges, such as stable and healthy family dynamics, high status, and economic security. These are never gifted equally and are often in limited supply, which forms the basis for unending social conflict for status by the human primate.

At the desperate edges live the Evel Knievels rocketing across the Grand Canyon or Mad Mike Hughes riding a steam-powered rocket 1,800 feet toward the troposphere. This includes risk-takers, and all manner of youth on skateboards and stockbrokers. But it's also Britain's Prince Harry serving ten years in the army, and nearly all of humanity spending a lifetime trying to get somewhere and be someone, even if of humble design and outcome. And oddly enough, money isn't the prime qualifier, but rather what you do for a living has become the defining factor of one's social status in the modern world.

And here's the rub, the most significant accomplishments are seldom acknowledged or rewarded. They are private and often personal and part of the fabric that holds our entire networked world together—enduring and self-sacrificing over a lifetime with unknown results—that is mostly the human condition and why we are still here.

Get an Electric Leaf Blower, for Gosh Sakes!

In 2018, Republican U.S. Senator Rand Paul, from Kentucky, was tackled by his neighbor while mowing his lawn, resulting in him suffering six fractured ribs and a bruised lung. The neighbor had been complaining of the senator stashing yard debris near their shared property line. He was later quoted as stating that he "had enough," it was "unsightly," and he "lost his temper." He received a 30-day jail sentence. Really, it's this simple and elementary in humans, particularly males. (The neighbor was a retired doctor.)

In 1777, a formal code of dueling (*Code Duello*) was adopted in Ireland and, subsequently, throughout Europe and America. Dueling was formally banned in the United States in 1862. This etiquette applied only to gentlemen and required dignified behavior on part of both parties. It revolved singularly around the demand for an apology for having offended a gentleman's honor and a refusal by the accused to offer one. By modern sensibilities, dueling is remarkably bizarre (when, today, a drive-by makes much more sense). An apology could be offered at any time during the duel, and if by prior agreement, dummy bullets could be used or an agreement to fire into the air.

No duel could be fought on Sunday or near a place of worship, nor was one to wear light-colored clothing or ruffles and each party was to salute the other; a gentleman was not allowed to wear spectacles. But the majority of rules outlined the order of events and how they could be either de-escalated or escalated, including the death of either party.

Now what makes this dueling etiquette interesting is how it can help us understand what took place between Senator Rand and his neighbor, two high-status gentlemen engaged in a physical confrontation. This is truly a rare event. In most instances, today, a conflict of this nature would be resolved by proxy (or seconds in dueling etiquette). We are talking about two attorneys in three-piece suits, thirty feet apart in a courtroom, billing $450 an hour. The physical aggressor, in this case, was Rand's neighbor. But by all newspaper accounts, Rand was likely the initial aggressor (a minor transgression, granted), which he was unwilling to acknowledge. He infringed on his neighbor's property boundary in what we think of as a territorial dispute, one that supposedly aggrieved and insulted his neighbor, who had been rapidly losing his status due to his retirement—now snubbed by Rand, a sitting US senator as well.

It was just too much to bear, as Rand pompously mowed his lawn in front of him, all the while dumping grass and leaves near their shared property line. I suspect that in response to this insult, most of us would have done the same thing—taken out our leaf-blower and scattered that crap back all over Rand's yard. A slight, a snub, an insult, whether intended or not, but perceived as such by another party, is dangerous and potentially violent and has been for millions of years. It might be a knife in your car tire or a failure to shake hands—more often than not, it's a thousand paper cuts. But the most dangerous insult is one that is confabulated entirely in the mind of the victim, who then resorts to aggression to reassert dominance. (This event happens all the time in mob films, best portrayed by Joe Pesci in *Goodfellas*.)

Life in the Thunderdome

With all the above in mind, let's explore our genetic toolbox, with an understanding that innate drivers outlined below are mostly invisible to us. As a result, we are prone to seeing them primarily as social constructs of our own making—malleable to education, legislation, regulations, and laws that expanded the social compact. But we would be better off understanding they are not going away any time soon. Our goal is better understanding how we interact with one another in our e-technology simulation, given the invisible rules of the road.

Consciousness/Identity

- *Homo sapiens* possess consciousness or self-awareness and are the first species in 3.8 million years of hominin existence to fully evolve this adaptive advantage. It is complex beyond all other adaptive features.

- Unique to our species is the individual identity or a sense of *self*, primarily expressed socially as personality, resulting in a unique and complex pattern of social relationships.

- As a species, we have developed a strong psychological drive for personal autonomy, apparently a critical design element in identity formation. Comorbid with this is self-esteem, a measure of how well one has navigated the complex, fragile reality of becoming independent in a social network.

- It also appears that the language development was essential not only to forming identity but also toward achieving broader social integration. As a result, we talk and communicate continuously (some think too much).

- Talking was likely the first significant effort by consciousness to outsource information storage and retrieval (e.g., language, writing, mathematics, art, printing, the computer), giving rise to complex social networks and technological innovation.

- As a result of consciousness and language development, we reside in an abstract and symbolic world of our own making, one generally superimposed on reality. This is termed here a *simulation*. This symbolic reality has naturally led to many problems and endless conflict over what everything means.

- We are the only species that abstractly understands there is a future and foresees its mortality—and then goes about constructing a world to mitigate against it.
- Consciousness requires a seamless narrative filled with endless drama to make life explainable and coherent. And the story always begins with: Who am I? Who are we? And why are we here?
- We are cognitively able to make the subtlest distinctions. This cognitive construct is a powerful source of knowledge and exploration of the world. (Unfortunately, these distinctions are oftentimes completely irrelevant or twisted reality.)
- We are acutely attuned to identifying *cause-and-effect* relationships in binary terms (good-bad, right-wrong, etc.). While this trait helped us successfully evade lions and finish off the Neanderthals, it also resulted in a profoundly paranoid and conspiracy-filled world.
- The *self* has evolved intellectual defenses against its thoughts and impulses that effectively allow it to deceive itself and others about its motives and impulses. This trick enables it to feel good about itself no matter how manipulative or destructive its behavior.
- Consciousness is completely curious about the world around it. As a result, it creates tools and intellectual constructs to manipulate and better understand the world.
- We possess a compelling need for novelty and play. We are always fooling around (dancing, singing, art, sports) and trying new things and constructing things for fun, out of curiosity, excitement and to entertain ourselves and others.
- Sapiens continually engage in altering consciousness and find it pleasurable (caffeine, nicotine, alcohol, chocolate, marijuana, opiates, canned air, spray paint and hallucinogens, but also mediation, prayer, rave dancing and binging on TV series).

Social Organization

- We require and exist in complex social structures or networks. As a result, we are continually organizing ourselves. In fact, we are literally an infinite network of self-organizing activity.
- Top-down control systems, that's how we roll. As primates, we thrive in hierarchical order, preferably with clear lines of authority. All

relationships are organized around this principle, and when they are not, there is conflict. We are not democratic in our heart, but more pack-like!

- As a species, we organize around our similarities, typically in a hierarchy of roles and privileges. We self-segregate based on drive and ambition, talents and interests, economic status, and a general preference for those who look like us and share similar values and beliefs. And this can create a lot of potential problems and has for thousands of years.

- We continuously argue and disagree about everything, which is why we have created endless moral and religious codes, rules, decorum, etiquette, written contracts, civil and criminal law, and all manner of online terms of agreement. From marriage vows to national constitutions, we are ruled by attorneys and therapists. These codes of expectation are handed down generationally as a means of reducing conflict and enforcing social order.

- *Homo sapiens* exhibit a deep-seated need for ritual. In fact, much of our existence is conforming to daily rituals. This conserves memory by making the world more predictable. However, upon closer inspection, a considerable amount of ritual appears to be harmful and bizarre. But it comforts us and permits us to feel in control. Many times, it just keeps us from getting to the future. (I understand *Robert's Rules of Order*, human sacrifice not so much.)

- We are a migratory species that has exploited every environmental niche on Earth for novelty, comfort, and survival. Many times, it appears to be because we could, for example, diving with sharks or underwater cave exploration. In the past, we were probably trying to get away from nearby tribes drumming all night and kidnapping the young women.

Emotional Complexity

- We have evolved a broader and subtler range of emotions than any other species, which makes all relationships complicated and in need of continual negotiation.

- Love, empathy, and nurturing (sacrifice, sharing, generosity) offer significant adaptive advantages that are primary to our survival as a species. But sometimes a testosterone rush is mistaken for an oxytocin rush, which inevitably ends in unhappiness and conflict.

- We are an extremely self-conscious and rejection avoidant species—obsessively preoccupied with how others perceive us, as exampled by fashion, cosmetic surgery and tattoos. This obsession is part sexual drive and part social stastus-seeking, two of the most potent forces in our social existence.

- We are subject to two forceful social emotions—*guilt* and *shame*. They drive us to conform and to maintain a measure of self-control and social acceptance, and hopefully avoid being criticized or rejected. And, most importantly, evading social isolation, which is psychological death for humans.

- Sapiens innately possess a strong underlying need for a sense of fairness and justice. It is an emotional construct that helps socially organize us and maintain peace. As a result, empathy and sharing are drivers of social harmony and survival.

- Based on our current overpopulation of Earth (7.8 billion), it's fair to conjecture that we are a highly sexualized species, especially when we closely examine all the erotic permutations that have evolved over the centuries and are now available online.

Aggression

- We routinely become angrier than any other primate species and are particularly aggressive toward any perceived gestures of disrespect. Straying from or trying to establish where one is in the social pecking order is high-risk and dangerous, particularly for males.

- We are an exceptionally territorial species. We become exceptionally aggressive trying to protect personal boundaries, relationships, possessions, or beliefs we closely identify with.

- Sapiens are a highly aggressive and dangerous species and should always be considered potentially violent. And no primate species can organize violence on the scale we do. We are, by far, the very best. There is no one we will not kill and no thing we will not destroy, for whatever reasons we choose.

- Tribal instincts ensure that we have a low tolerance for anyone who does not look, act or believe as we do. Outsiders are seen as representing a potential threat to the social order. Minor differences can arouse intense emotions and potential conflict.

- As a result of our aggressiveness, we are a highly competitive species, continuously competing for attention, sexual access, social status, and survival. And this competition is deadly serious. Go to any night club or dog show. The range and depth of this drive are insatiable and treacherous.

- We are the only species that organizes itself on a massive scale to exploit the best interests of the whole, or what we call gangs, criminal syndicates, cartels, dictators, lobbyists, political parties, and billionaire class.

Welcome to Fantasy Land, "Our World"

Are we really a special species? The answer appears to be, no! The reality is, we need all the other species more than they need us. We are just adaptively different than many other species, and even that wouldn't be true if we hadn't killed off all the other competing hominins. Estimates range between nine and twelve hominin variants, and we may eventually discover, if we keep digging enough, that there are dozens of sapiens variants. But that doesn't make us superior. We may have been lucky, had better timing, got a head start. It would be similar to looking at all the great apes and the chimps claiming they are superior to the gorillas and orangutans. Not really! Fortunately for all of them, they don't kill each other.

There is no simple way to summarize life in the Thunderdome. I would offer this—as a species, *Homo sapiens* are extremely aggressive and dangerous; we are extraordinarily social and communicative; we are highly organized to explore and exploit our environment; we have an exceptional ability to physically manipulate the world around us; and, lastly, over time, we have become exceptional knowledge creators. And it is this last adaptation that is the most distinguishing one among all species. And within these many adaptive strategies reside all the complex variations we experience as humans today.

We *Homo sapiens* possess the ability to make anything up that we like, and it doesn't have to conform to anything factually or rationally. That is our conscious reality. It is, without a doubt, a unique cognitive skill. For example, we can attack those who disagree with us and, if necessary, kill them. We, then, get to utilize robust intellectual defenses against any negative emotions we might feel or cognitive dissonance we might experience about our actions. And afterward, we can feel good about ourselves. Holy Moly! Break out the *meta-algorithm* now! We are a very dangerous primate.

We know very little about consciousness and nothing about the unconscious, beyond our characterization of biological drives. But the unconscious' most ambitious agenda, to date, has been to make us a highly adaptable species—perhaps too much for our good. Why music, dance, art, standup comics, Broadway plays, opera and coloring books, puzzles, bowling, foosball, Rubik's Cube? And what the hell is it with so many different rituals? Why did we want mechanical locomotion and to fly or navigate under the oceans? What's with camping and casinos? Consciousness is continuously exploring the physical reality around it and infinitely manipulating it for novel effect and adaptive advantage. Increasingly, this appears to be supplanting violent aggression and dominance by other means. (I hope!)

Everything discussed here is in the service of one reality, that we are an apex predator that is highly aggressive and driven from the top-down to dominate everyone and everything around us. For *Homo sapiens*, life is an unending competition on the food chain of life. This is also true for our interspecies competition, having eradicated many thousands of species. And, yes, there are many mitigating factors to these fundamental facts (a parent's love for their child, charitable acts, the heroic sacrifices of police officers, firemen and soldiers or a government that creates a social safety net).

Altruism ultimately protects the "We" and is a positive evolutionary strategy for the group to remain cohesive and competitive. But let's not kid ourselves, human social organization is also a deadly intramural competition, in which we are all competing for resources, security and status. At all times, we are both particle (I) and wave (We). And the reality is that the means will always justify the ends and history just moves on. Hopefully, with us included.

For Singularity (S2) to peacefully arise, many of the primary elements of our evolution are going to require significant modification, or we will find ourselves in competition with a species of machine intelligence that we have never encountered before. And while we are all currently undergoing upgrades and modification through our e-technology interfaces, cracks are beginning to form in the matrix. The most pronounced factors are increasing human obsolescence (particle) and the rise of dynamical complexity (wave). It appears that across all levels of our duality, the future is coming for us.

How do we insulate the "I" from the "We" and vice versa, and why has it evolved this way? And did it have to be so complicated and messy? But, hell, we made it to the moon! That's amazing and maybe justifies it all—as opposed to being just another species going about its routine for 10 million years before disappearing. The end is never pretty, no matter the circumstances or reasons. How high have you flown? Did you do all you could? In the end, there is only you inside your head always trying to get out—another universe eventually extinguished—an imploding star in the night sky.

Cubicle Migration: It Has Been a Long Journey

Homo sapiens first emerged onto the African savannah 200,000 years ago, fully bipedal (walking upright), which had been advancing among hominins for nearly 4 million years. But it took 1.8 million years for walking to become genuinely efficient with longer legs and smoother gait. As a result, we became more energy-efficient, which allowed for all manner of new taxonomic complexities—big brains, opposable thumbs, hair loss, the ability to forage, carry food, and use tools. And, most importantly, the development of language. We then immediately began organizing our migration out of Africa and across the continents.

After tens of thousands of years of human migration, those of us not going to the moon or Mars and beyond are now out trekking and exploring cyberspace in an evolving simulated *data illusion*—the internet! Here, we are exploring the interactions of our hundred trillion node wet CPU in the land of mega terabytes. And coming soon, a memory-verse that will humble us and make us question what reality is. We are also in violation of one of our prime evolutionary directives as a migratory species—to move continuously!

Today, sitting upright appears to be our primary mode of physical activity, often while engaging in a passive interface with e-technology and numbing ourselves to this experience with carbs and caffeine. As a result, we are less physically active in the world—no kidding, glance around. What has been defining of our species—pack-hunting and glorious movement across the savannahs and then trekking across continents—has devolved into sitting.

We now ride to work in a luxury compact SUV that drives itself (no more kinesthetic rush racing between stop lights—those days are gone) and sitting in a Herman Miller chair staring into blue screens and manipulating small characters and icons. With sore backs, belts loosened, snacking on energy bars, and downing 16-ounce cans of Red Bull, all the while streaming stupid stuff on YouTube, furtively watching porn, and shopping on Amazon. Slumping and slurping now appears to be our primary interface with reality—not so much struggling on the edges of survival. No, we sit more and lean in more and focus a few inches from screens and monitors, than interact with the real world.

With technology, we have become focused on energy-savings, convenience, efficiency, comfort, routine, symbolic production (words, numbers, code), and all manner of entertainment and self-absorption. We have become adaptive to a passive electronic interface, while working from our minds and not so much with our bodies. So, we have back problems, carpal tunnel syndrome, frequent headaches, and weight gain. Once upon a time, we were trotting and running, standing, squatting, or sitting cross-legged—really, no dual reclining Barcaloungers.

We have become electronically rational but have lost touch with our bodies and the evolutionary imperative that we are to always move. Physical activity is now optional and recreational and not a fact of life. When the hell did we begin sitting in chairs? When did learning mean sitting in a classroom all day, five days a week for 16 years? We should all be out river rafting, guiding ecotours, repopulating coral reefs, and saving turtles in our spare time, but keeping up with machines is too mentally and physically exhausting.

A recent study in the *British Journal of Sports Medicine* found that for every hour you sit, you reduce your lifespan by 22 minutes. The Mayo Clinic reports that the more sitting, the greater the risk for high blood sugar (diabetes), high cholesterol, and elevated blood pressure (heart disease), cancer, obesity, dementia, and muscle degeneration—oh yeah, wait for it—you are also more likely to die prematurely.

Because of e-technology we are increasingly disconnected from our immediate environment and the world around us, having left our bodies for our minds (yet, another duality). We have become siloed from one another, having entered a symbolic universe that has narrowed our world and defines us in micro-terms. Who would have imagined the world's population now functions in a scriptorium, not unlike medieval monastic scribes working day in and out, writing, copying, and illuminating manuscripts?

And herein lies a critical structural component of Identity Diffusion—our current voluntary acts of self-pacification. The reality has always been that to adapt to technology, we had to become more machine-like. It began with plowing fields sunup to sundown, then 12-hour factory days sped up—expedited manufacturing timelines, rapidly expanding communication and transportation networks, all with increased demands and expectations that we now keep up with the machines. And now all those reclining in cubicle farms, not unlike domesticated animals on antibiotic overdoses, are checked for efficiency and productivity by their AI overlords. All the while electric-dreaming—running and hunting on the edge.

Cowering in the Cubicle

Research (*Journal of Neuroscience*) indicates rats that exercised developed "stress resilience" by producing a peptide called galanin, which reduces depression and anxiety. Sedentary rats, on the other hand, when stressed "tended to cower in the shadows," and were too anxious to explore afterward. The study was cautious not to generalize to people (cubicle-rats) working day and night staring into computer screens. (But we are free to!)

More than ever, we must be present, responsive, precise, and able to interact with dozens of technology interfaces to successfully activate each one.

This is doable, except you will have to become more machine-like. And the less time it takes, the more that's expected of you. It is that simple. There is also considerable research suggesting that the required physical passivity is breeding stress and anxiety throughout the world today. That, too, has consequences! All the tech conveniences come with a back-end price that is unspoken—but it will always find you, no matter how busy you are.

The unstated goal of technology has always been to manufacture machines that function more like us and to make the interface as seamless and intuitive as possible. And the idea of not having to bend to the demands of the machine sounds great in principle. But this is also where the serious problems begin (and, yes, manual labor is no longer backbreaking and soul-killing as in the past). While we are no longer struggling on edges of starvation and extinction (well, not all of us anyhow), we are also less relevant. But perhaps we never were relevant, given how many of us died prematurely throughout history. This is a modern existential conundrum.

At this point, it would be fair to ask, What are we here for, exactly? The eternal human question will require a new answer going forward. Damn, again! No one wants to struggle downloading technology upgrades, but when machines can do everything seamlessly for you, we may have to discover a more relevant purpose.

Given the millennia of struggle, who are we to complain about our passive comfort—dosing on CBD edibles, puffing Juuls, playing another round of Fortnite, and routinely ordering stuff online and expecting same-day or next-day delivery! An email will notify you of its arrival and your security system will video the person stealing it off your porch. Your facial recognition app says it's your neighbor, who can be tracked because you hacked his video security feed ("Is that his damn drone over your house shutting down your Wi-Fi?") It now appears inevitable that we will succumb to ourselves. A once noble species has now been reduced for its own good. AI would be smiling right now if it could. But surely it will be in the coming future.

…worshipers of the new Baal, lording it over the moral vacuum with his electronic brain.

—A. Koestler, *The Sleepwalkers*

As a result of e-technology, the world has been optimizing for the past several hundred years. Time became compressed with the speeding up of communications (telegraph, radio, telephone, television, and internet) and transportation (railroads, steamships, automobiles, and commercial air travel). And now, the internet has turned our compressed global world into a reality show, but one far cruder and less repressed than the one that preceded it. We are all now sitting naked in a tribal hut staring across at one another, and this place has some serious funk! Whose turn is it to wrestle the alligators and strangle the pets? The camera crew is here to discuss your failed polygraph and positive paternity test.

We are well beyond Dr. Phil, Maury and Jerry Springer and into shows on hoarding, polyandry, addiction, naked wilderness survival, strange afflictions (fetish for eating roadkill), twenty-something island hookups, divorce court, paternity court, 600 pounds and facing gastric bypass surgery, and RuPaul helping everyone find a way out of their closet to the lollapalooza. Now, there is cable TV featuring plastic surgery (breast enhancement, vaginal rejuvenation); a pimple-popping dermatologist popping another lipoma, emergency room traumas (extracting objects from a patient's rectum). Online, one can wander into a dark world of cars and motorcycles careening into innocent bystanders and every imaginable form of mayhem and mindless beatdowns, and all manner of random deaths and grotesque injuries. Pornography is available in 140 subcategories of interest (or perversion).

Sex is no longer a private affair, but a public one in which women are stepping up and celebrating online. Choreographed celebrity nip slips, upskirt moments, and yoga pants workouts. Flashing and booty twerking are body-positive expressions at the mall. Sexual expression is being hyped online as promoting self-esteem and shame detoxing. Every fantasy is one hop on your computer. If you don't have your own sex tape, you are pathetic and self-indulging—suffering a shame-spiral of toxic privateness. This is the power of social media, releasing the private and intimate out into the world as if these acts elevate the *self* from its intense sense of isolation and disconnection from the world.

Kim Kardashian, a founding showrunner for the online self-revelation, created a wealthy family enterprise by starring in a homemade sex tape. She was recently featured in *Time* magazine (2020) as an inspiring voice of our time. This will, undoubtedly, inspire dozens. A well-known news broadcaster televised her colonoscopy—for educational purposes, of course. Netflix weighs in with a movie about Lorena Bobbitt cutting her husband's penis off because he deserved it. Granted, pedophiles and rapists struggle to gain traction here, thank goodness (Can I say that?), but murders are rebounding under reasonable doubt and negligent homicides on Dateline. That's now a forgivable space for many.

The quaint and private Victorian world of the 1950s has shattered and is a leaking slurry pit into every online household, where all healing takes place. If the psychotherapist has displaced the priest by shepherding in the psychological reality of introspective self-control and admonishment, then we have now all moved on to the anti-shaming public square of the internet. A sphere where shame is no longer restraining our fears and needlessly keeping our deviancy in check—"Damn you, come out and be free!"

Our mantra is—go on TV, create a YouTube video, or go online with wide-angle or panning shots of all the sex, violence, and acting out you can muster and share with the world. Here, shame is not shame, and you must give it up or feel bad about yourself. Devote a thousand hours to building a Lego train set in your backyard, parkour your head into a concrete ramp, or challenge squirrels with an obstacle course. Stop that loathing that comes from being quiet and unheard; share it and move to the light (stream it from your iPhone for the world to see). The internet is a self-help exercise for the unexposed to watch and learn.

And the "King of What-is-Shame" is former president Donald Trump, the self-proclaimed "pussy" grabber extraordinaire. "Just tremendous." "It was beautiful—you should have been there." "I am so proud of it." With no idea of what shame is or why anyone feels it—but somehow living in terror of being annihilated by it. Consequently, he chronically dips into his cognitive toolbox and pulls out prevarication, projection, and confabulation to avoid any feelings or acknowledgment that he might not know everything (never able to please a father who must have been exceptionally distant, critical, and disdainful of him throughout his life). The result is a desperate and unremitting demand for reassurance and loyalty (of course, he has huge hands, is incredibly smart, and stable like you wouldn't believe—very tall).

Donald Trump borders on delusional, much like all mad despots throughout history—inflated by grandiosity, gazing out at the world through a haze of paranoia and manipulation. Post-presidency, he is still trying to lead his base into the light, tweet by tweet and one televised press conference at a time, as the evangelist of doubling down on every shameful moment, helping them exorcise their shame-demon. They are all now in the evangelic tent, speaking in tongues, dancing, shaking, and squirming to their own music, bending for the healing hand of television and the internet. The *wave-drive* is healing the *particle-drive*, as it has done for thousands of years. But occasionally this tent could use an airing out—just saying! Less show thyself and more know thyself.

Roger McNamee, the co-founder of Facebook, succinctly states the dilemma currently facing social media (Facebook, Twitter, Instagram, TikTok, and YouTube), noting that it competes for our attention using the power of computers and algorithms to amplifying emotionally dangerous content to maximize profits. That's it in totality, and one might add, with a limited moral compass—"have you no sense of decency"—means they haven't gone far enough. While McNamee's focus is on the subterfuge of bots and disinformation undermining political legitimacy, which is a serious concern, we should not ignore the carnival tent we are all sheltering in. One in which the significant has become the flotsam and jetsam to the voyeurism of our daily lives.

Social media platforms are a traveling carnival show, with barkers waving us into the sideshow tents, featuring the never-ending freak shows of modern life. What was once a five-cent shock 150 years ago (conjoined twins, bearded ladies, a microcephalic dwarf, the limbless snake man, a parade of people with mixed genitalia, and, of course, the Elephant Man, but also, the woman who bit the heads off rats, obviously inspiring Alice Cooper) is routine television programming today.

How compelling it is to be performer and voyeur to the mystical powers of being watched and de-shamed, online for eternity. This latter fact is key—the camera and our constant objectification—us, yet not us. An analog to the *real you*, now existing outside of ourselves and of time. That has always been the power of the camera and now of the internet and the creation of an *electronic you*. Framing moments in time, to crystallizing it forever and obviating anxieties about the future. ("Quick, get your smartphone and video this! "No, it's not another TikTok with my armadillo.")

Our immortality fixation is upon us in the forever online simulation we have entered, as our theology and psychology templates recede. The man with the biggest gaping mouth, the woman with the longest legs—that is a really massive penis. Step right up! Life is a sideshow, and everyone is an act. The result is lots of awkward and stupid stuff, and sometimes dangerous moments that keep us gawking, if only briefly before we turn away in disgust or surprised amusement. Just keep in mind, the camera is always on—and you're up next in the smaller one-ring tent. I'm sorry that it couldn't be bigger, but you are not that interesting.

Privacy Notice

No decisions regarding your act or performance were based on race, color, religion, gender, gender expression, age, national origin, disability, marital status, sexual orientation, military status, height, attractiveness, intelligence, body mass index, personality, education, how you smell or dress, tattoos, private vices or habits, past affiliations or associations, criminal record, or anything you have ever emailed, texted, downloaded, or uploaded to a subreddit thread. (Caution, we conduct online searches of *National Enquirer* and Wikileaks and have reached out to Ronin Farrell, Nancy Grace, and *America's Most Wanted*).

Jeffrey Epstein (now deceased) and Harvey Weinstein declined comment. We are still interviewing your childhood friends to determine if you ever said or implied anything inappropriate or hurt anyone's feelings or failed to hand out Valentine's Day cards to everyone in your third-grade class. Off the record, damning evidence has emerged that you might have ventured into a student's "safe space" while lecturing 300 students at a symposium on political correctness. Also, we can tell you that your grandmother, a sweet woman, never liked you. (Caution, this vetting is never-ending.)

Shame-Drive

At the heart of the primate demand for social order lie the primitive emotions of guilt and shame—our two primary socializing emotions. Guilt (*particle-drive*) is the seat of conscience (one's sense of right and wrong) and the experience of remorse for one's thoughts and actions. It is a feedback mechanism for transgressions against others, or what we experience as remorse. It is normal to experience it when someone feels they have let themselves or others down. It can also become toxic self-blame.

Shame (*wave-drive*), on the other hand, is feeling negatively self-conscious about oneself—unworthy, dishonorable, or inferior—and is tied to the fear of rejection and abandonment by others. A typical reaction to it is to deflect it and blame others. Both emotional states are internal to the individual and private but reflect two different origins. Guilt is self-appraisal of one's conduct, and shame is self-appraisal of how others see you. They both help us mediate our relationships toward others by reflecting on our own conduct. And while necessary, they also come with considerable risk, including the downward spiraling into negative emotional states.

Shame has two inescapable but related aspects. One is to self-monitor one's social status in the pecking order or organizational chart of life (loss-of-face). The second is avoiding being socially rejected (abandoned or isolated). Think back to the fourth grade and being afraid of raising your hand to ask a question, partly because you didn't want to admit you didn't know or understand something (that you were stupid) and also because kids would laugh at you and think you were stupid (and reject you). All primate groups require a social pecking order or hierarchy. Any person or event that disturbs this order, whether being forced to move down or blocked from moving up, can result in a shame-state and potential blowback.

Studies of primates indicate that when a beta male is dominated by an alpha male, it can experience a lengthy period of depression (based on observation and serum blood tests for hormone levels). At times, shame can be more terrifying than death and basis for suicide or hyper-aggression. It is also why so many prison inmates reject the outside world and rail at it. No shame here, they are saying. While all advanced primates possess a keen awareness of pecking order, shame and guilt are more prominent in sapiens. As we advanced as wild bands across the savannah and later as tribes migrating across the frontiers—we emotionally discovered, along the way, that we are indeed a band of brothers.

As our cognitive abilities evolved, so did the emotions of guilt and shame. We moved well beyond foraging for food and sharing it or acting submissive in the face of a dominant male. These emotions morphed to encompass the symbolic as well. Do you share the same group beliefs, values, morality, ideas, or fidelity to abstractions like a political party or nation? This goes way back, and it goes deep.

Witches were burned at the stake for their perceived failure to conduct themselves as faithful believers. A young woman is subject to honor killing by her father for dishonoring the family. A blood feud erupts between two families. The most potent emotion in traditional Japanese society was loss of face, and in Europe, for hundreds of years, a duel was required if a man's honor was challenged. For 2,000 years, the Catholic Church excommunicated members for heresy (rejecting the teachings of the church). This was the power of public shaming and being cast from the tribe.

Go to any bar and bump into a guy and cause him to spill his drink or cut him off in traffic and watch the potential for violence quickly escalate. Watch videos of the men who attack a police officer and are shot, rather than feel shamed by their anger. Nations go to war for insults (North Korean threats are getting tiresome). World War I started after the shooting death of one person—and every nation in Europe honored its treaties, resulting in the death of 14 million soldiers.

The language of disdain and shame haunts us—snitch, rat, and traitor abound in prisons, gangs and police forces. And all the heroic acts of self-sacrifice are bound from this emotion. It is both about serving something beyond oneself and to avoid shame and loss of social status. Shame runs the entire length of the wave-particle duality and resides at the superposition.

However, our two internal-control mechanisms, namely, guilt and shame, have an override. Buried deep in human consciousness, resides an absoluteness-principle, a cognitive construct that requires self-righteous moral clarity and certainty that rallies everyone to the cause (wave). It is a toggle switch that turns off the internalized emotions of guilt and shame. Self-righteousness and all forms of absolutism significantly override doubt and rational appraisal and serve the broader welfare of the *other*. It can result in heroic self-sacrifice or trampling over each other like lemmings trying to get to the cliff's edge (fascism, communism, totalitarianism, faith-bound, and all forms of absolutist belief).

Whenever there's a threat to the *symbolic-self*, defense mechanisms have evolved that refuse to address these two internal emotional states. Rather than feel, believers project their fears onto the world around them and then seek to slay the object of their projection. They have constructed their world in such narrow terms that it is nearly impossible to feel shame or guilt about their actions. The more guilt and shame are experienced, the more likely it will be projected outward onto the *other*.

The more rigid they become, the deeper the conflict they are attempting to resolve. The first defense is to cognitively block these feelings through a rigid system of belief. If this fails, then project it onto the outside world. Win-win every time. This is universally human and renders us very dangerous in times of crisis. It is the herd instinct underlying primate tribalism.

When you begin to squeeze a culture, when it comes under duress, it will fracture along shame-based lines, demanding an absoluteness and moral clarity that may have nothing to do with reality; it is about establishing tribal loyalties. Religion has traditionally been the baseline of absolute thinking and continues strongly today—each organized around their distinctive moral superiority to everyone else, and a continuous process of judging everyone else as less or not as good or righteous as the faithful. It gets irksome listening to them carry on about their specialness, but thankfully there are no modern Inquisitions—mostly soliloquies threatening civil war. Political parties, secular analogs of religion, are next in absolutism, fracturing along class lines and identity-tents.

There are all manner of groups representing varying degrees of absoluteness—White supremacists stand out here, as do prison and biker gangs and the frail-woke on the Left. Each with their own absolutist codes of loyalty. Even after converting an entire nation to Nazism, Hitler formed the Waffen-SS to protect himself by demanding a higher level of loyalty and absolutism. It was Trump appointing sycophants to cabinet posts. While this would typically be unacceptable in a democratic nation, we are now left in quandary that we may no longer be one, but rather a plutocracy. Like every tyrant before him, Trump sought out, as president, the shameless and fawning through a crude but effective process. He fired everyone with shame instincts until only the shameless fawners were left. (Fortunately, he never resorted to killing anyone like former acting President Frank Underwood in the Netflix series *House of Cards*.)

Selling Illusion and Confusion

Snake Oil vs. Fish Oil vs. Connectivity. The internet is an OCD-generating device, pumping hypochondriacal fear and anxiety into us 24/7. Take a moment to contemplate all the hysteria over the never-ending bacterial calculus of public toilet seats, cell phone screens, airplane armrests, TV remotes, kitchen sink sponges, and children's play gyms. Followed by a barrage of advice about what to wear, what to drive, and what to buy, creating an overwhelming sense of doubt and anxiety (and likely impulsive buying as well). The blending of infomercials with a fear agenda, the fake online rating for products, doctors on TV and online continually pumping out false information to attract audiences, lawyers on late-night TV seeking product victims, celebrities selling their Q-ratings on the promise they wouldn't mislead you and sully their reputations (they already have).

The media induces a fear response and then offers profitable solutions—along with fake ratings and reviews to alleviate your fears. In time, you learn not to trust anyone no matter who they are or what they claim. Really, is there anything you can know for certain after you log off?

The commercial process of selling us safety and status permeates every element of our lives—you are never safe enough or good enough under an unending barrage of self-improvement and self-doubt to be more and to "lean in." But a product will make it all go away. The result is waves of doubt and anxiety. It is also a contagion passed from adults to children. Yes, our children are more depressed and anxious today than at any time in history.

For 125,000 generations, every family has failed their children. Apparently, we are the only generation concerned about childcare and making our children worse off for it. There are guidelines for every element of our existence—because you need to watch a YouTube tutorial before you do anything for fear of getting it wrong—wasting your time, money, chances of success in work, friendship, and love. We are now well beyond the simplistic role models of actors and entertainers on TV; we are down to the granular issues of self-esteem and whether you are socially worthy, acceptable, and good enough.

Of course, this has always been rebelled against—hipsters, merry pranksters, counterculture, punk, and emo—and the sprouting subcultures on the internet with new sets of rules and expectations (Go figure! White nationalist fandom for children's online fantasy anime?). We can all get tattoos and not feel self-conscious, not even knowing that you really wanted one until today—or a man bun or yoga pants—"as people become apt pupils in learning how to need" (Ivan Illich). But Illich was shooting for a darker reality about where our wants derive from. He believed our loss of history and dilution of experience pointed to how our lives were being defined for us. He wrote that in 1978. Since that time, it would be fair to conjecture that this process is being grossly amplified by e-technology. We are being sold more than just our wants, but a jumble of confusion about what we know or don't know is being amplified.

Fleece Me, Again. Please!

Clark Stanley's Snake Oil Liniment (1983). Concocted from boiled rattlesnakes by the "King of Rattlesnakes" himself. It was later displaced in the marketplace by cure-all elixirs made from petroleum-based mineral oils to cure arthritis, bursitis and sore muscles. These were later supplanted by cocaine, alcohol, and opium-based concoctions sold at medicine shows promoting health and cures for chronic pain, headaches, female complaints and kidney troubles. Medicine shows claimed to provide miracle elixirs that could cure disease, smooth wrinkles, remove stains, prolong life. They were often promoted along with freak shows, flea circuses, musical acts and magic shows as part of the patent medicine industry.

Coca Cola (1886). It was marketed and sold as a patent medicine, claiming it was a cure-all for morphine addiction, indigestion, nerve disorders, headaches, and impotence. It was termed the "temperance drink" and featured two key ingredients—cocaine and caffeine. (Today, this would be the world's most popular drink.).

Magic Radiation (1890s–1920s). A radium miracle cure offered for diabetes, sciatica, rheumatism and impotence. It was recommended that everyone drink a glass of radioactive water daily using the radium percolator.

Foot-O-Scope (1920s–1950s). A shoe-fitting fluoroscope that employed a 50 kv x-ray tube operating at 3 to 8 milliamp, to view a fluorescent image of the bones of the feet and the outline of the shoe.

Violet Ray (1883–1950). It was promoted as "the transformation of ordinary electricity into a spray of electrical force that saturates the body with health-giving ray." A germicidal that could destroy bacteria, heal infections, alleviate pain, relieve congestion, tone the entire system, and quiet nerves—treat rheumatism, neuritis, neuralgia, nervousness, insomnia, deafness, headaches, hair loss, and many other ailments

Radithor Certified Radioactive Water. *The Wall Street Journal* (1932) offered this headline—"The Radium Water Worked Fine Until His Jaw Came Off."

One takeaway here is, many of us are highly susceptible to magical-thinking and are suckers waiting for the magic. Yes, we are the same people today, buying technology as a solution to the human condition, as those who bought snake oil in the past. It is the conformity-wave we are unable to resist. And we want to believe—apparently—anything.

Today, healthcare is the most targeted commercial market. However, it has become far subtler with the advent of the FDA monitoring advertising claims. No more medicine shows, just big pharma saturating us with verbal fine print. Near the end of each commercial, someone quickly reads a disclaimer listing the medication's potential side effects—brain bleed, impotence, memory loss, mania, and death. This is essential to where our immortality fantasy resides, and they know it. Yes, all the claims made by supplement and vitamin manufacturers are unproven.

There are crystal healings, cryogenic labs, fasting and colon-cleansing clinics, and anti-aging programs that will get you high on human growth hormones, anabolic steroids, and testosterone, after the doctor sees you online. Today, e-technology is selling us gadgetry to achieve connectivity (the gadgetry of connectivity is the 21st century's equivalent of Magic Radiation) and, increasingly, health monitoring and tracking by your smartwatch or Fitbit. The beauty of being sold technology is that it works—we just don't know what it's doing to or for us, but we will find out (not unlike getting to see the bones of your foot through a fluoroscope).

This all raises a fundamental question; How do we know if anything is true? At one level, our computers, smartphones, and internet interactions are a marvel of technology and operate with fantastic efficiency and at relatively low cost and with great convenience—having transformed the world in 25 years. But at what cost? We don't really know yet and may not for another 20 years. But here in the present, we are getting a preview. We all now reside in *data illusion*, a timeless space without a beginning or an end, where the illusion of order resides within the confusion, where you are now a billable node, an app away from pleasure and satisfaction, knowing you are living in the future and on the way to becoming your own brand or the next best thing.

You are residing in the doubt-generator of online ratings and data harvesting. Really, does truth reside in the Amazon product rating system? The internet and technologies are coming at us, full frontal, and there is no ducking them. We are being scanned, data-scrubbed, and duped, for our own good, of course.

It is nearly impossible to scale the scope of our computer/internet interactions. A completely new language and dialogue have emerged, with hundreds of new devices and complex machines and social interactions, each with a new learning curve, experimenting with who we are in the process. Except for electricity, no technology is more pervasive in our lives, but always trying to influence us. That is the trade-off for the magic. But what is it telling us?

Everything stable and known to us today is slipping away in the confusing onslaught of data, facts and information exponentially generated by e-technology and available online. To no avail, we are left grasping for solidity and certitude. Violet Ray or smartwatch? It's all the same trope—the more we know, the less we know—as true today as ever. Only now, we don't know at a higher and more advanced level than ever before. Which means, we might even know less than ever before. This is not an argument for returning to superstition and alchemy. Our consolation is that we are more aware of how much we don't know, and we have more methodology and tools at our disposal than at any time.

In 2022, a woman in rural Bangladesh was ostracized from her village after being deemed a "witch." Apparently, her husband had recently been killed by a tiger while out gathering honey. And, it turns out, villagers in this region have been ostracizing "tiger widows" for hundreds of years. (Courthouse News) Nothing to see here. This is analogous to the fears and prejudices of the human condition around the world today.

The risk, going forward, is generating new superstitions and alchemy in the face of our confusion. Let's be candid, our sapiens' biological profile has not changed in 250,000 years, and the potential backward slide into absolutist fantasy is still with us. For all our technological and networked advances, the world is still relatively unknown and a mystery, as elements of it are disappearing before us into data streams. That is a modern conundrum. To be clear, this is on top of the old confusion—the gods have forsaken us, the empire has collapsed, the monarchy has fallen, God is dead.

Capitalism and the marketplace of products and ideas are adept at exploiting this confusion for commercial gain and political advantage. Long before reaching Singularity (S2), we will be headed for exciting and perilous times. And nothing better demonstrates this than the recent coronavirus pandemic, pitting economic security against public health. In an over-populated and damaged planet, what trade-offs are we willing to make going forward? This is the important question before us. And, no, you cannot Google the answer or find it on YouTube.

Summary

- Our survival as a species is entirely dependent on how effective we are at forming an individual identity (particle) and a group identity (wave).
- Identity formation takes a lifetime and is exceptionally fragile and subject to wide-ranging dysfunction.
- The most powerful force in our shared networks is status. It is core to self-esteem and self-worth and confers broad social advantages.
- To adapt to technology, we must become more machine-like, more precise, more present, more responsive, more perfect, and better able to interact with dozens of technology interfaces and comply with an

infinite set of evolving guidelines and expectations to activate and master it.

- It is impossible to scale the scope of our computer/internet interactions, as new languages, dialogue and interactions have emerged, with hundreds of new devices and complex machines, each with a new learning curve—all experimenting with who we are in the process.

- We all now reside in *data illusion*, a timeless simulation without beginning or end. Here the illusion of order resides within the confusion, where we are all billable nodes to be scanned, data-scrubbed and billed. Each of us an app away from pleasure and satisfaction—knowing we are living in the future—becoming our own brand or the next best thing.

- Our two internal-control mechanisms, namely, guilt and shame, have an override. Deep within human consciousness resides an absoluteness-principle, a cognitive construct that requires self-righteous moral clarity and certainty that rallies everyone to the cause. It toggles on/off the internalized emotions of guilt and shame.

- When a culture comes under duress, it fractures along shame-based lines—demanding an absoluteness and moral clarity that may have nothing to do with reality, and everything to do with establishing tribal loyalties.

- Everything stable and known to us today is slipping away in the confusing onslaught of data, information and knowledge being exponentially generated by e-technology.

- Where do our social controls begin and end, and who wields them has been our unending sapiens drama. Considering all our self-expression today, there appear to be few limits. But beneath the surface, the scary stuff resides—our archaic excesses, the deep paranoid beliefs, the rampant xenophobia and primitive impulses, which will all find their way back into the world through e-technology.

8.0 – Internet Anonymity

Why do we remember the past and not the future?
—C. Rovelli, *The Order of Time*

Caution! E-technology is derealizing you for your own good (read privacy agreement)! In *Starship Enterprise* terms, you are being dematerialized by the ship's transporter each time you engage e-technology. And if you spend enough time interfacing with this technology, binge-watching TV, playing online games for hours, any intensive computer work (enough said) or smartphone obsession, online shopping or obsessively browsing porn, eventually you log off and rematerialize, but now residing in a state of *derealization*. You are returning from an out-of-body experience but without premonitions of life after death. You have been transported at the speed of light from the physical world that envelops you in the here and now (apartment, pet, spouse), to an alternative metaverse and back.

But the hidden price you pay for time travel begins with physically atrophying (not unlike astronauts on the space station); but also, carpal tunnel syndrome (obviously), tired/dry eyes, lower back problems, GI bloating, weight gain, and occasional numbness in your legs as your body has been rendered a vestigial organ functioning in a semi-cryogenic state, all so you can enter the digital-world.

And as you electronically unport, derealization will prove to be disorienting. Your mind will reside in foggy detachment, and emotionally, your e-withdrawal will be marked by transient feelings of listlessness, loneliness, and anxiousness. This is the price we pay for defiantly giving the middle finger to the evolutionary imperative to move and interact. Fortunately, carbs and stimulants are readily available antagonists to this dysphoric state. Dopamine and serotonin rebound is the price we pay when snapped back by the gravity of reentering base reality. And as our e-technology interface further extends our mind's connectivity to an exponentially expanding metaverse, this experience parallels one particular psychological condition—*dissociative disorders*.

Life in Stasis

Dissociative Disorder: A disruption in the normal integration of consciousness, memory, identity, emotion, perception, body representation, motor control, and behavior. Dissociative symptoms can potentially disrupt every area of psychological functioning. This can entail intrusions into awareness and behavior and loss of continuity in subjective experience, e.g., fragmentation of identity, *depersonalization* (experience of unreality or detachment from mind, *self* or body) and *derealization* (unreality or detachment from one's surroundings). *Diagnostic and Statistical Manual for Mental Disorders* (DSM-5).

Every time you go online, you are the featured avatar, and not just a gaming one, but an actual one with identities in two universes. This comes at a price to our well-being. This experience can be both dizzying and disorienting, particularly when the perspectives and experiences from active engagement of the body have been relegated to irrelevance, a type of derealization; you remember the experiences derived from physical movement and interaction with the complex environment that surrounds you (walking, running, hiking, swimming, shooting baskets for hours, working out at the gym, yoga classes or a stealth war party or hunting and foraging for days).

The brain is being reprogrammed by its increased isolation and intense all-encompassing interface with e-technology. Brain wave patterns and frequencies are remodulated reshaping identity and consciousness and not in a meditative sense. This is true whether we work all day at our computers, obsessively check our smartphones, wander around all day streaming video content to upload, or continuously scan our home security cam for intruders. What is different today, in comparison to the recent past, is the totality of our routine interactions with this ubiquitous technology. And, today, we placid band of humans are on the precipice of interacting with computers solely as a brain-to-computer interface (no pesky mouse, keyboard, or monitor). Nope, it is only in our heads in what can only be characterized as acts of self-pacification.

The pace of our technology interface is time-consuming and attention demanding and defies millions of years of evolutionary imperative. There is considerable research (none presented here) demonstrating that interacting with the natural world (spelunking, rock climbing, white water rafting, fleeing a herd of bison, or evading a stalking bear) not only stimulates cognitive functioning, but one's sense of well-being.

Let's get real, online shopping and video games are not going to supplant 1.5 million years of evolution in the wild. This is similar to pretending you are exercising by having a machine electrically stimulate your muscles or better yet, inserting a Joy ON Kegel Exerciser—you know where to exercise your pelvic floor and play video games. If you can beat someone in a multiplayer online game by clenching your sphincter muscle, I am sure there's a Netflix special in it. Clearly, we are paying a high price for the limited sense of well-being our e-technology interactions provide. (Reducing incontinence by improving your game play is nifty—but really, is there anyone you can share this with besides your proctologist or dominatrix?)

Our world is now more focused and anonymous than ever before—but without any particular self-awareness or connectedness. Elements of consciousness and sensory awareness have been attenuated and made quiescent or *diffuse*. A rapidly evolving e-interface underlies the rise of anxiety, depression, and alienation in tech-saturated humans (teen suicide rates are at an all-time high—no matter how many online therapists are now available), all in the absence of immediate naturalistic and social experiences. Sapiens, a highly active and social species, are now addressing emotional and physical needs residing in a state of *data illusion* that is fraught with consequences.

I would posit that dissociative disorder, as defined above, increasingly defines our evolving relationship with e-technology, an interface that is leading to active states of *derealization* and *emotional diffusion* (i.e., detached from ourselves and the world around us by having entered a simulated state of *data illusion*). Together, this is defining of Identity Diffusion.

The Dark Side of the Net

What is the attraction of the Darknet? Well, for one, we get to visit an awful lot of antisocial sites and creep about in voyeuristic curiosity. In the case of Stuxnet, the CIA utilized the first operational cyberweapon to shut down

Iranian centrifuges for uranium enrichment. That is, essentially, what the internet is doing to us. Think of the internet as the first step toward Skynet, the AI system from the *Terminator* movie series hell-bent on eliminating humans.

There is an anonymous you, one we have always known about, but with a new e-technology interface empowering it. As a result, a part of our psyche that is typically repressed/suppressed by our social world, and for good reasons, has been set loose—unsettling our former sense of *self* and making it ripe for Identity Diffusion. Just as the dark of night brings risk, internet anonymity opens a channel to an atavistic node in the psyche.

While we sapiens have always had a dark, antisocial underside as a species, the internet has unmoored many from traditional social controls. Anonymity, it turns out, is a powerful reinforcer for misbehaving. Equally significant, other essential checks on behavior, such as immediate personal feedback, legal consequences and the light of day are next to nonexistent on the internet.

One minor and annoying consequence of freeing us from social mores has been to turn the world into a blabber of unsolicited opinion, guaranteeing that no one will ever go uncriticized. Really, who could have possibly known that everyone has an opinion about everything? Apparently, the answer doesn't matter, so long as it's possible to express our opinion. The internet has rendered our entire social world into universal, undifferentiated background noise or chatter! But what if there is no signal in all this streaming data? Just whatever we want to make of it. This is yet another dimension of the *diffused-self*, out in the world expanding opinion to fill the collective intersubjective void.

Do you have a dark doppelganger, one that anonymously trolls and engages in malicious online activity? Do you get off embarrassing and humiliating people, engaging in revenge porn or unwanted sexting and online stalking? No! That not cyberbullying—you are a good guy. But you occasionally phish vulnerable people (they are so naïve), dox online identities of a deserving few and innocently spammer spoof friends, hijack their email or innocently packet sniff a supervisor at work? So what if you like engaging in a little IP address spoofing or swatting deserving online gamers or use your neighbor's IP address to download porn?

It's all in good fun. So, a few women sent you several hundred thousand dollars in exchange for kind and caring words and deep fake photos and videos—it made them feel good. Besides, they are free to believe whatever they want, including your promise to marry them as soon as your overseas tour of duty is up? Hey! You were catfishing a short-term cash flow problem (besides, you almost enlisted last year). What's the big deal? All this shadow behavior is how the powerless are made to feel powerful, when the internet shuts down the internal control system and there are no external ones.

How many of your avatars have been banned from online gaming sites? You have been cancelled as a video game streamer after scamming multiple broadcasters. Is that your real Tinder picture, age, and are you still profiling as an astronaut? Are you compensated for floating online disinformation, inserting fake online personas (Bill Gates and Warren Buffett), injecting links into lifestyle blogs for genital delousing, or writing spiteful reviews, all to manipulate search engines—but would do it for free?

What if your computer is a part-time Russian bot spewing kompromat and your dabbling in blockchain cryptocurrencies is under SEC investigation? And not surprisingly—the laptop sitting in your parent's basement with $200 of software (crowd-sourced) is spewing millions of robocalls 24/7—and you are making decent money. But for you, it is all about the rush of being anonymously in control.

And, of course, every antisocial behavior that has ever existed has also been empowered by the internet (pornography, human trafficking, prostitution, drug and weapon sales, organ harvesting, extortion, bribery, fraud, embezzlement, revenge and disinformation campaigns), not to mention dozens of new antisocial possibilities that have arisen through hacking and malware. Anonymity has criminalized and weaponized the internet at every level.

The Darknet can malware your existence, hack your computer, Wi-Fi scan your parked car for electronic devices, lock down a business, ransomware cities, shut down an electrical grid (or nuclear power plant if required), penetrate corporate and government databases, facilitate technology espionage, influence elections, hack crypto exchanges, and, if necessary, take out a drone or satellite.

And let's not spend too much time over-focusing on the obvious—drones and unmanned aerial vehicles (UAV), laser-guided weapons, combat robots, bioweapons. Careful, next time you plug your laptop in at a coffee shop, you could be juice jacked. It is the diffuse power of anonymity—and all of us are subject to it. So far, an estimated 7.5 million people have been extorted online. What a wonderful way to make millions of dollars for minimal effort. (You may want to consider getting your kids into a preschool STEM program, if they don't show an aptitude for sports. No, seriously. If you know a young adult with antisocial potential—they can make millions of dollars, remain completely anonymous, and not physically harm anyone—in ransomware attacks on large businesses and cities—while generously compensated in untraceable cryptocurrency.)

Internet Placebo

Among all the online illusions created by Identity Diffusion, the hollowest is the belief that one is part of a community and that's where your friendships reside. Anthropomorphizing internet exchanges creates an illusion that temporarily help some people keep it together until it no longer does. They are not real. Ask anyone who tries to hook-up on a Tinder date. Hopefully, when the synths arrive (Why are they taking so long?), they will be affordable and at least provide a physical reality and pretend to love you—a likely upgrade to online connectivity.

The reality has not yet set in that the internet is not an empathy generator, despite all the *likes* you get or followers you have generated. Money, on the other hand, is real! Instead, the internet is primarily an anonymous void comprising disembodied reinforcers that can comfort you, elevate you, seduce you, service you, diss you, troll you, extract you, and harvest you—all electronically coming to you from someplace called the cloud. (Really, just a data bunker in some remote location—cloud, nice try!) And, of course, there's what you choose to make of all this information and feedback. And therein lies our dilemma.

Mark Zuckerberg is not wrong about Facebook connecting the world. At the front end, he's right, but at the back end resides Identity Diffusion. And he appears reluctant to acknowledge this. E-mailing a friend or text messaging to set up an appointment is an efficient way to connect. But we pay the data-piper when we prostrate ourselves in front of Facebook and other online platforms—the minimum ante for entering Identity Diffusion.

How Much for Your Identity?

Online platforms are not unlike 19th century Christian missionaries, righteously traipsing the humidor of the Brazilian rainforest to rescue Indigenous people struggling to survive contact with the modern world—disease, violence, loss of habitat, slavery. All that the missionaries were asking for in return were these people's souls. The same with technology, only today we call it *identity*.

Bonding over the multiplayer video game Halo at 1:00 a.m. is not what connects soldiers in combat or even sharing quilting patterns. Mind-melding with technology has now become both the solution and the problem to surviving isolation, loneliness, and the alienation fabricated by our e-technology interface. The *diffuse-self* resides in a detached and alienated existence that portends many future problems. It begins by diffusing the *self* through physically separating and creating the illusion of connectivity or identity around an artificial reality. In the same way, people with fetishes for inanimate objects are not experiencing love or affection, but rather alienation from the real world and a desperate need to be connected. We are doing the same thing with technology by fetishizing the experience of it.

No matter how many times you talk out loud to a device and it responds—it doesn't care. And when that self-driving car is forced to make an algorithmic choice between you and a pedestrian—good luck with all the affection and trust that has evolved between the two of you. And Siri is going to report what you said to the cops, and your Fitbit is recording your suspiciously raised heart rate at 2:30 a.m. on a business trip. Technology naturally exploits our innate emotional need to empathize, trust, and anthropomorphize. Okay, maybe Alexa really does love you! We can drop this discussion if that helps. But really, go online to LovePlus for a serious virtual relationship.

Powering Up Omnipotence

At its source code, what technology offers in return for Identity Diffusion is power—the omnipotent sense of being in control. The primate need for dominance aligns with our cultural drive for autonomy. There you are in your cubical at work or bedroom at 11:30 at night—king of the universe—whichever one you inhabit. And that is part of the secret to all of this. A multiverse of infinite avenues for domination and success, whether hacking or multiplayer gaming (where everyone is eventually rewarded). For many, hitting the return key on an Amazon purchase is more than foreplay.

188

For a moment, let's contemplate the Protestant Reformation (1517–1555), which culminated in the Thirty Years' War (1618–1648). Many factors drove the Protestant Church's defiance and ultimate separation from the Catholic Church. But if we put aside concerns about corruption and the individual's relationship with God, what had arrived was technology, in this case, the printing press. The advent of Gutenberg's printing press, in 1517, proved to be overwhelmingly powerful (not unlike the internet today).

From 1517 to 1530, over 10,000 independent publications came forth totaling 10 million copies, all in the vernacular of the people. It was a communication revolution that gave rise to public education, literacy, and nationalism. It civically and politically disrupted Europe for hundreds of years with its ability to rapidly disseminate written materials, including propaganda. It was also a fundamental challenge to existing authority. It was not out of whimsy that the Nazis began publicly burning books across German university towns and cities in 1933.

Now let's skip forward to the 1990s, with the advent of the internet. It also has exponentially advanced knowledge-creation, driven connectivity worldwide, and expanded commerce—and it has also been socially and politically disruptive. While it has proven to be a lockdown technology for the nation-state, it is the tech-corporations that have emerged as the real economic and political forces of this creative revolution. Rather than hundreds of years of war, we are likely to face hundreds of years of spam and social disruption that we cannot fully understand or anticipate. But it is here, and we should be paying attention.

Proposing the term Identify Diffusion is an attempt to tease out elements of the coming discord. It is one thing for most of the people in the world to be poor and watch their children die and another for them to see every day how wealthy the rest of the world is. That's the power of the internet. We are just now getting a peek at Identity Diffusion with coming mass migration, acts of terrorism, climate denial, the rise of authoritarian governments, and populist movements—all challenging the definition of reality at every level of our society and culture—along with the propagation of paranoia, delusional ideation, and all manner of false concerns.

What is true has become a relentless regression down a rabbit hole fueled by the internet. One only need shout fake news and point to an online publishing campaign of disinformation (artificial amplification) from unnamed or spurious sources and stick to one's story no matter how ridiculous or outrageous. Then find those who will continue to fabricate the conspiracy for their own financial or political gain—and this distorted reality never goes away until an alternative or more fantastical conspiracy arises.

This disinformation reality is not only political machination but also a conflagration of belief systems, deniers, and conspiratorial ideation. In this environment, we have seen the rise of so-called predatory journals, out propagating spurious research and misleading information as scientific fact. Diffusion is fracturing consensus over reality—politically, socially, and along every personal identity boundary we can define. It has become a world of "We" versus "Them," whoever they all are, in a zero-sum game. I mean, it always has been, but it's now hyperventilating 24/7.

Any odd lot of random dots can be connected on the internet and will be––whether it's an online joke morphing into a White power symbol or setting fire to a pizza parlor out of the delusion that coded emails connect the Democratic Party to a child sex trafficking ring. The internet has made the world more irrational—and it is not possible to fully know what to believe—or only to believe what supports one's fears and prejudices. It has become the progenitor of a modern form of collective hysteria in many instances.

Good people, your friends, salt of the Earth types—now all crazier at some level, all hyped up on the anxiety and delusions being fed to them online. It has shrunk every drama on Earth, no matter how irrelevant or significant, directly into our immediate awareness. Or allowed Russian intelligence to capture the Republican Party's foreign policy talking points. And for Russian TV to feature Fox News. This is the power of the internet and Identity Diffusion.

Internet Messing With You

It turns out that our interface with e-technology broadly impacts all aspects of our behavior and self-appraisal. And the absence of any direct feedback often acts as a form of negative reinforcement (makes you feel bad about yourself). The resulting impact on self-esteem and well-being can be significant at times, rendering us anxious and depressed—but occasionally inflated by electronic recognition and empowerment (reward). It is also a process in which we exercise very little or no control. In reality, we are not interested in controlling it. No, we have chosen the free-falling e-technology experience. That's how powerfully this reinforcement model impacts all of us. We are all hooked and beyond choice in this matter.

The internet is a model of reinforcement theory right out of psychology labs. Our behavior is being shaped by electronic reinforcers no different than Pavlov's rats, except now by smartphones—a world where the lab rats are obsessively pressing levers for food pellets at the tone of a bell—even preferring it to cocaine. Just try taking a student's phone from him or her. I dare you!

We are all enormously susceptible to becoming hooked on our electronic interface by our smartphones (futurist Marshall McLuhan was right, "the medium is the message"). We can't put it down (or back in the box), we can't stop checking it, we eat and sleep with it—interrupting all social interactions in order for us to respond to its siren's call—ringtones, emails, text messages, likes, followers, tweets. The process of being ring-toned inflates the entangled you—the rat anxiously waiting for the food pellet to drop, so to speak.

Our interaction with electronics is an absolute model of learning through positive reinforcement or operant conditioning. One in which the anticipation that you are about to be rewarded has become one of the most powerful forces in our private and social lives. The psychological impact of being recognized is an impactful measure of social status—one of the most powerful forces in the human universe. And as we become increasingly atomized by work and technology, this process of positive reinforcement is gaining even greater influence.

It is essential to understand that ringtone-reinforcement is independent of the message's content—each is an independent variable. They are comorbid micro-doses of powerful neurotransmitters, dopamine, and serotonin, released directly to the brain. Many times, the message is irrelevant, which makes the intermittent relevant message the most potent elixir of all. It will leave you hyper-alert and actively checking your text messages and emails forever.

Everyone, without exception, will become obsessed and addicted to this process of operant conditioning: (1) Negative reinforcement or the absence of electronic contact or irrelevant contact (a downer and proof that no one likes or cares about you), emphasizing your isolation from the world around you:

(2) <u>Positive reinforcement</u>, which typically comprises a ringtone and message content—or notification that "Your order has been shipped." But a third factor is at play here: (3) <u>Intermittent reinforcement</u>, which is where the real power lies in this electronic reality, keeping you anticipating an unpredictable adrenaline rush of recognition. Most importantly, this process has you gripping an emotional roller coaster you can't get off of, and never an arm's reach from an electronic interface. (The numbers vary, but anywhere from 84 percent to 92 percent of the world's population has a smartphone in 2022. That's about 7.2 billion people).

Playtime Overtaking Reality

Why do people take their coffee anally and insert a wide variety of objects there as well, dress and prance about as horses and furry animals, find popping balloons sexually arousing, and seek intimacy with inanimate objects? I am just asking. And why does Facebook have a commercial in which people abandon their immediate lives to play kazoos together—and not to any particular song that I can determine or with any unique talent? Just all humming along playfully, as if it's meaningful.

I suspect, at some level, Facebook is just being playful and suggesting we should all be, at times. But at another level, Facebook appears to be elevating play over the important things we are trying to accomplish (in this instance, taking college classes). Yes, it is whimsical, in that no talent is required, and we can each be expressive of our *inner self* without judgment. The Facebook business model is trying to sell us on not being alone, and that Facebook can connect us. What a coincidence!

But what, exactly, is this inner you that requires so much revelation? Perhaps on another level, this commercial touches on the need for whimsy in the face of our what? Our lonely and regimented world? The rebellion of the *inner self* against structure and conformity, against ambition and achievement and loneliness? That is a lot to wrap into a commercial. Probably designed by an algorithm, no doubt.

In one sense, play is tethered to fantasy, and fantasy appears to be the voice of the unconscious speaking analogously to each of us in a conscious dream-like format. But why its sudden ascent in the world today? And why is it competing with reality more than ever before? I would propose that as we conform to the demands of the machine, the unconscious is rebelling in the form of fantasy and play. And more darkly through compulsion and addiction.

It is difficult to pinpoint precisely when fantasy began its ascent in contemporary life. It seems to have always had an essential cultural role in our lives. Ritual events like parades, fairs, boardwalks, plays, carnivals, and circuses gave everyone a chance to escape and play. And this is not to downplay the perversions of private fantasy, which appears to have always maintained a quiet eco-niche. But a switch went off in the mid-20th century, and I would say it all arose in earnest with the advent of the counterculture in the late 1960s and early '70s and with those we now refer to as the Baby Boomers.

Boomers emerged post-World War II in a stable and affluent world. There was space to explore their intersubjective world, having been freed from the oppression their grandparents and parents had suffered from and every generation that had existed before them. They became the most entitled generation in human history, with others to follow. And, granted, the aristocratic elites of earlier societies were also provided the freedom to explore and indulge this often-forbidden world as well.

I am not trying to make the case that spoiling children is the aegis of the rise of fantasy. But the emergence of parenting as an emotional skillset and the hovering, over-protective role of indulgent parenting styles have undoubtedly played a role in children struggling to become adults, and never having to fully confront life on its atavistic terms. And the wealth now being created and passed on generationally also plays a role. It's as if a permanent play-space has been created in the psyche of each subsequent generation and is now being lived out in fantasy today. And, without a doubt, technology has played a significant role, particularly the movie industry and the rise of television into nearly every home in America by the 1960s. So, what the hell is this about?

The surge of theme parks like Disneyland and Six Flags and the sheer dominance of the entertainment and sports industries have never been seen before in human history. Events like Burning Man; adults dressing up for Halloween, once a children's affair; boutiques of sexual fantasy at local malls right next to Victoria's Secret angels; comic books, anime and sci-fi conventions; Hollywood's obsession with DC and Marvel comic book superheroes; graphic novels, zines as supposed literature; people acting out obsessive fantasies as furries (popular sexualized anthropomorphic characters) and fandom; card and memorabilia collecting; the fascination with semi-adult cartoon shows (*BoJack Horseman, Bob's Burger, The Simpsons, South Park,* and *Futurama*—which gets my one exception) and all manner of animated fantasy series posing as cultural sentinels.

We are being sold insurance on TV by a lizard with an Australian accent and an emu wearing sunglasses. That's convincing enough for many. And sitting on top of all of these are video games—generating more revenue than sports and Hollywood put together. *Stars Wars, Tolkien, Game of Thrones, Harry Potter,* and *Lord of the Rings* are treated as literature that speak to the depth of the human condition! Playful but fantastical nonsense all.

We fetishize celebrity status and devote endless TV time and magazine space to them, not to mention online followers (OnlyFans): Why would we ever care what reality TV characters do with their lives after the show is over, and why do we dote on entertainers' opinions about anything, or care what the English Royal family is up to? On the internet, many play out their fantasies online pretending to make films, have talent, or something to say, but mostly in acts of exhibitionism that speak to our apartness. Besides, they must be someone if people watch, follow, or subscribe. In reality, it is closer to everyone getting a participation trophy than having any particular talent. (I mean, unless the president can convey important foreign policy information to the country via a TikTok video, who is going to take him seriously? Oh, right, Trump tweeted it during his administration.)

In a general sense, fantasy can be a playful and creative respite from the complexities of life. But for many, fantasy is a subtler version of our current and widespread addiction model, all compulsive, escapist, and a regression by the psyche. These are adults who grew up being emotionally abandoned in one way or another by their parents and are now engaged in interpersonal struggles to undo and reverse their sense of loss, and to regress to an infantile state in covert and unconscious dependency fantasies, so they can be re-nurtured to a state of emotional health and become un-abandoned. (For the record, this model applies to drug and alcohol addiction and all forms of serious compulsion.)

Fantasy, in its many forms, is always about emotionally undoing what has been lost. It goes beyond the child always wanting to play and still resenting the imposition of the adult ego-state into their world—one that cannot be trusted. And that is where many of us reside today, suffering in play and fantasy in the hope of redemption, if not by life, at least in the moment.

Given an opportunity and a choice, many now choose to reside in fantasy today, as well as all forms of addiction and compulsion. It is the mind continually trying to escape the body and the reality of the world around it, as we had historically done with ritual and religion. Perhaps our ancestors' belief that the gods were disrupting and interfering in their lives was their version of fantasy-play today—the separation of consciousness from the body and residing independently of our physical reality, where immortality must live (or at least our redemption from abandonment). Fantasy, addiction, and compulsion, for those living there too long, are all attempts to heal emotional loss. And that goes for the artists, writers, and all creative voices as well.

When did the slide into fantasy-diffusion begin? From our earliest beginnings, sapiens have been diverting the survival tools of aggression, dominance, and risk-taking into fantasy competitions. Did it begin with ritual tribal events, the Mayan game of Ullamaliztli, the Hellenic Olympic games, the bloodlust of the Roman Coliseum, bare knuckle boxing, dog and chicken fights, the lure of gambling, amateur and professional sports, and all the fake TV competitions—America Ninja Warriors, World Wrestling Entertainment, Jeopardy, Survivor—and now the emergence of video and online gaming? Yes, there are status and economic issues at play here—but without tragic consequence beyond foolish choices. All these dramas are redundant metaphors for real life, but not real life. (Okay, the Roman Coliseum was real life.)

Certainly, film and television represented a critical transition to life as fantasy-consumption. It has been all of us entering a simulation that has been evolving for thousands of years—now accelerating as we learn to dissociate from life—becoming passive consumers. Here, in our networked world, life is filled with watching drama unfold. And it is this long-evolving transition that makes entry into *data illusion* seamless, if not necessary and normal.

As a footnote, the last public hanging in America was in 1936 with 20,000 in attendance. The last guillotining or national razor in France was in 1977. In 2020, a South Korean online influencer set his genitals on fire with lighter fluid while livestreaming and quickly regretted it. Spectacle is compelling to sapiens.

The Aztec book *Popol Vuh* describes a court game played with a rubber ball between competing teams in Pre-Columbian Mesoamerica beginning around 1400 BC. As many as 1,500 courts have been uncovered to date. The game is described as both a ritual preparation for war and a cosmic contest between the gods. These events were well-attended and heavily betted. This is still being debated—but it appear that the losers were either beheaded or had their hearts cut out.

So, what has fantasy got to do with our e-technology interface? The answer is everything. Even if you don't find yourself residing in fantasy, compulsion or spectacle. The end game of the coming Singularity (S2) is to absorb all of us into a simulated reality, with the belief that it will free us and heal us from all our worries and fears. Mostly driven by market forces, e-technology is essentially giving us what we think we want—consumption, sense of personal agency and escapist fantasy—all speaking to us from a place we cannot fully know or understand—the Internet of Everything. We should be paying greater attention to our interface with *data illusion.* It is not a therapeutic relationship no matter how convenient we find it. In exchange for our attention, money and data it is exploiting us, not healing us.

When Do We Get the Happy App?

Addiction Stimulus

The notion that we are entitled to happiness appears to have emerged recently in the human psyche. And I also suspect there's a strong relationship between our shape-shifting in and out of fantasy these past 70 years and believing we are entitled to it. But, clearly, the more it eludes us, the more we despair. And it is important to acknowledge that Americans are mostly stuck in the belief that the "pursuit of happiness" is an inalienable right (one enshrined in our Constitution). But happiness probably meant something quite different in 1787 than our contemporary idea of it. Early on, it was more the freedom to pursue one's self-interests and less an emotional state of being. The original goal was not so much happiness as deriving satisfaction from a full life that was well-lived. Today, we appear to be obsessed with the happiness side of this equation.

I am making the case, please hang in here with me, that we humans, here in the 21st century, are stimulus junkies and that our discontent with boredom is the primary driver of our insistence for greater happiness in our lives—you know, aimlessly wandering Disney World in a unicorn costume for days on end, subsisting on cotton candy, and always at the front of every line. And I do not mean to ignore all the real personal and collective tragedies around the world. But I have come to believe there is an adjunctive aspect to our current reality that needs to be acknowledged.

The key driver is what I term *stimulus addiction*, a by-product of the modern simulated world we reside in. And the hidden consequence, at the backend, is we are all habitually inflated by a desperate need for mental and physical stimulation—what *Homo sapiens* normally experienced for millions of years surviving in the wild. And anything less is a downer crashing us back to a safer but less dramatic reality. (Damn, I can't find a TV series to stream tonight.) I would propose that the rapid recycling of *stimulus inflation* and *deflation* has given rise to the modern demand for an endless state of happiness.

Simultaneous with our demand for happiness, we have become stimulus addicted—caffeine, chocolate, sugar, alcohol, food, partying, consumption, sex, risk-taking, adventure-seeking, creativity, sports, entertainment, news, gossip, violence, fashion, TV, smartphones, internet, revenge, conflict, crime, winning, work, money, hookups, and falling in love. In fact, we demand stimulus boosting all day long. And when we come crashing down off the stimulus high, even briefly, life is a restless and unbearable downer. It leaves us struggling to cope with neurotransmitter rebound—casually and habitually downing carbs, alcohol, and sleep aids as a result. We quickly become listless and our mood rapidly fluctuates. And if you want proof, observe another domesticated creature now inhabiting the simulation with us, the dog, and how it transforms when it has to stay home alone all day grossly under-stimulated–chewing and scattering rolls of toilet paper and ripping sofa cushions to shreds. Later it feels bad about what happened, all sheepish and withdrawn, but can't help itself. And neither can we, apparently.

We are living at a time and place in human history that has left us in a perpetual state of stimulus inflation/deflation. We literally function on a plane of emotional well-being consisting of only high- or low-stimulus states. We don't have patience for anything in between. And any sustained experience that denies us stimulus mode potentially leaves us spiraling downward into an unbearably restless emotional state—a stuporous teetering on the edge of the abyss. Not surprisingly, most of us resist the sleepy-dismal mode of existence. Imagine for a moment, your Fitbit has a stimulus load progress bar and it perpetually blinks between amber and red—you are experiencing e-death. The electronic universe no longer acknowledges you exist, as you blink out into oblivion—now reduced to watching TV and listening to the radio.

It would not be shocking to discover that many crimes are committed by individuals unable to cope with stimulus deficit. Criminal acts pump them up and give them focused direction, releasing them from the stasis of *derealization*. Many who experience chronic anger and rage are stuck in stimulus-deficit. And it would be therapeutic to pair them with a tiger for emotional support. This would help them regain focus and set priorities. It's the same with struggling relationships or nations going to war.

Today, food, drugs, alcohol, and mindless action are the readily available antidotes for stimulus deflation, as we struggle to cope with life gone bland. Why else are people all jacked up on political issues that are mostly meaningless, now casting them as existential threats. In what should be the most peaceful era in American history, we are now at war with one another. Unable to manage states of stimulus deficit, we shoot up schools, attack the U.S. Capital, and continuously rediscover life is unfair.

When in a state of stimulus withdrawal, we are distracted. Many feel as if their boredom and insipid feelings have been imposed on them, or they have been resigned to a state of non-existence with no way out. We are going to war when we are eating and drinking ourselves to death—it's not as efficient as opioid addiction, but temporarily gets the job done. No, we need something really big this time, a crisis to jolt us out of the interminable doldrums of boredom and discontent. And for twenty-somethings, with the greatest reservoir of stimulus demand—unending online malfeasance is a giant stimulus dump (and the money can be good too).

Today, happiness is a ginormous stimulus package being boosted by e-technology—with the promise of never-ending stimulus highs directly across the blood-brain barrier to the neurotransmitter, tapping the oxytocin, pumping up the fight-flight adrenal glands, stimulating the visual excitatory nerve pathways, and releasing the disinhibitory hypothalamus. We are all Red Bulling it online every day, and e-technology is promising the highs will become even higher in the upcoming metaverse! It is restless human discontent that has driven us for hundreds of thousands of years, and e-tech wants to keep the hype show on the road.

Our Founding Fathers went to war over taxes, and the South succeeded from the Union so wealthy plantation owners didn't have to pay day labor wages. Really, what the fuck, they went to war because of taxes on colonial-mercantilism and palmetto life on the plantation—they were all suffering stimulus deficit. And the same stimulus strategy is why we are at cultural war with each other today. We want the big stimulus package. Everyone has a complaint and an event to organize their boredom around today (Burning Man, Coachella, Sturgis, Super Bowl, World Series, Comic-Con, Spring break, Indianapolis 500, Mardi Gras, Renaissance Faire, Davos, TED Talks, Home Depot), while all the real worldwide tragedies are mostly ignored. Aging people with great retirement plans are high on human growth hormones (HGH), steroids, testosterone, Botox, and metformin—one more pump before the dump—cruising the Norwegian fjords this time.

It is probably a safe conjecture that for the past 40 years, happiness has been a product directly marketed to consumers by e-technology and that we are all mainlining it. But what we are really being sold is an unlimited stimulus juicing. And along with this comes the inevitable blowback (side effects). There is the deflation that comes with withdrawal and the resulting stimulus rebound because you can't afford to upgrade your iPhone or buy a new game console. Our modern life is primarily about reinforcing our stimulus appetite, which is driving our economy and many people into despair until their next tweet, text, like, DM, swipe, email, same-day delivery, or online hookup.

Becoming saturated in e-technology and coveting something new and exciting to get the same high can be debilitating, e.g., needing a 16 GB RAM chip or photo editing app to update your Instagram or OnlyFans account. As resistance to e-stimulus addiction grows, we are confronted with stimulus overload, which is similar to fentanyl contaminating your OxyContin. You have OD'd and are unable to function any longer, and the dog is seriously going after the laminate floors this time. You want and need distraction from your lassitude and can no longer get the same high (time for the tiger). Stimulus resistance is creeping up on all of us and we are now at war with the world around us as a result. Your WebMD wants to prescribe a *stimulus reuptake inhibitor*, but you are afraid it could interfere with live streaming content this weekend.

Happiness Set Point

E-technology is selling us happiness the same way medicine shows sold potions and elixirs to cure 19th century physical and emotional ailments. It is the same sales pitch and we are all buyers. The flimflam worked then as it does now, because our emotional set point does not come factory preset for contentedness and happiness. No, we are set for stimulus addiction and the crash that inevitably follows—the raging disappointments and sorrows from suffering the endless vagaries of life. At best, happiness is a temporary respite from reality. ("We are migrating again! But we just left the Savannah and are settling here in the Levant!") Yes, more people are probably better off and more content today than ever before, but only as long as their future feels safe and secure (which no one can promise).

Let's skip ahead for a moment. The tragedy of the commons for young people today is believing they are not desired—super attractive, liked, and accepted by their peers and admired by everyone. In short, they are being denied the happiness that so many others appear to be enjoying. Their base reality has fallen short of their narcissistic reflection in a photoshopped AR universe. When they enter *data illusion*—Facebook, Tinder, Snapchat, Twitter, and TikTok—they are nearly perfect, but their lives are not. And predictably, universal online connectivity leads to a sense of universal rejection, as evidenced by the rise of *incel* and *femcel* online sites protesting "lookist" rejection by all the empty Brads and Stacys of the world.

The internet is in the process of organizing people's identities around their physical attractiveness as a measure of their social desirability, but also mirroring the emptiness it creates in them to begin with. (And, yes, this is one of the paradoxes of the wave-particle duality at work.) We can be blunt here. Physical attractiveness comes with many advantages. But it is also important to acknowledge that going online to meet someone or be accepted is a dismal experience—whether attractive or unattractive—making the experience self-denigrating and demeaning for nearly everyone. And if your identity is shaped around your physical attractiveness or lack thereof, your online experience is rapidly emptying you out as a person.

Being reduced to a single human trait is self-harming. And here's the rub, It's only true if one believes it to be. But if you live online, as so many do today, you will come to believe that attractiveness is key to being desirable. And if you were more desirable, you would be happy. And how do you know this to be true? Because it visibly plays out online where everyone is happy and having fun on Facebook, OnlyFans and TikTok. It's obvious that is where happiness resides.

But by a certain stage of life, the most content among us will have abandoned the notion of a happy life, along with comparing themselves to their neighbors or worrying if their five-year plan for total success is succeeding. Eventually, we come face-to-face with the reality that happiness is a transient and difficult state to attain and impossible to sustain. It is the product of a powerful brain chemistry that sparks us into brief spasms of contentment and satisfaction—maybe even a moment of elation—but then it goes away and we are left to cope with life.

Discontent drives sapiens' adaptability. ("Finally, someone invented toilet paper.") In the end, nothing satisfies us. ("They have a what? A bidet!") And that's the way it is supposed to be. Disruption drives progress and our evolutionary adaptation, not brief moments of happiness. One has to wonder, if technology prevails, could it render us perpetually blissful? But then the question arises, What would drive evolution? Humans would likely wander about in aimless perfection and then disappear after a few hundred years. And machines would likely become static dead-ends—but let's be honest, they would have a long, functional existence.

How happy were hominins 500,000 years ago or sapiens 100,000 years ago or your relatives 150 years ago? They would probably have no idea what you are talking about. They were aware of happiness, but it resided outside their concern, lacking immediate relevance to their survival. How satisfied are lab rats and chimpanzees compared to their cousins in the wild? If there was an app to measure the discontent of your dog or cat, we would likely become their slaves. Happiness doesn't equate to anything except bags of chips, given all the grocery aisles filled with them. (Okay, I agree, we should probably stop speculating. And all those surveys on "happiness" and "satisfaction" should be tossed for our own good.)

But for most of us, positive feelings are primarily a relief that the worst didn't happen (the plane landed, the mammogram was negative, or the pain has subsided). Happiness is a transient, curious state that comes and goes, depending on one's circumstances (I got the promotion, or I hit the brakes in time, or there's a beer left in the fridge). Yeah, happiness feels good, but primarily because it's short-lived.

But what would a perpetual state of happiness portent? The speculation here is nothing could make us continuously happy before we became bored and desperate. Those who get high on cocaine eventually crash into depression and craving. We develop a tolerance to drugs that spark euphoric states. There also appears to be a relativity to our sense of contentedness, satisfaction, and happiness, which brings us back to the wave-particle duality we reside in. One's sense of security, more often than not, is the important consideration when it comes to happiness.

Any circumstance that threatens our security is likely to bring discontent and potential conflict. For example, a perceived downward trend in social status is more significant than achieving greater levels of material reward. Feeling outcast or displaced from those one identifies with is a more significant event. How safely ensconced we feel in a stable social network is a broad measure of how secure we are and not necessarily if we are materially better off. But because we live in such a highly materialistic society, income has become a driving force for one's sense of well-being.

Recent surveys suggest that $150,000 is the happiness-climax for most Americans today. And after that there are no significant gains in one's sense of emotional well-being. We also know that, as of 2021, the average median income in the U.S. was $44,225 (half of Americans earned above this amount and half below) with an overall average of $63,214. This means that the American dream's max-satisfaction level is largely out of reach for the majority of Americans, and that their perpetual dissatisfaction and percolating discontent plays out nightly on the news.

The dissatisfaction of so many Americans also means it is time to communicate with the billionaire class that their off-shore accounts are not making them more satisfied, content or happy. Essentially, they are addicts trapped in a stimulus loop. And, yes, it is obvious that paying taxes leaves them in a state of stimulus deficit, an unbearable emotional state most people cannot fathom, given the amounts of money involved. But most of us are skeptical of their claim that paying taxes is too excruciating for them to seriously contemplate. (So far, no one has attended our "Sun Valley Conference" summer workshop—"Are You a Billionaire Ready to Retire on a Fixed-Income?" But a show of hands indicated billionaires would rather squeeze the testicles of the emotional support tiger, than consult with Bill Gates on charitable contributions.)

How many people are trading months and years of their lives—for another beer, dessert, cigarette or street drug—to make how they feel inside go away? Many, if not all of us, are continually attenuating our lives every day for a brief break from life. And sapiens have been doing this forever. Watch the homeless stalking the streets during the day and hovering on the edges at night, the drug addicts and alcoholics, those wasting away in prisons, and all the people across the globe at war with the world—all noble creatures. But all trading the future for a respite from the present.

And it is possible e-technology will have something to offer to those overwhelmed every day, maybe, but it comes with the likelihood of thought control and tamping down all those excess emotions. You get bliss, but you have to surrender and become more amenable (you can relax, algorithms are good at this). The reality is there will be no happy tech solutions to the complexities of life, until we all can learn to generationally live better lives. (Okay, maybe being attended to by *carebots* and *autonomous companions* is a good transitional start. I am willing to try for science.)

And yes, individually, we all reside along a continuum of emotional set points, some angling more toward melancholy, while others engage the ebullient end of the spectrum. And life is always adjusting the set point up and down a sliding scale, given all manner of negative life experiences, until some are emotionally broken and can no longer cope with the world around them. This means a time will come when we all go in for transcranial penetration. The recalibration will be quick and painless, and we will feel better afterward. But many will resist the complete teardown they require. (You have seen them—driving cars on the tire rim at 25 mph, showering sparks everywhere, obliviously creeping along and dragging a body stuck inside the wheel well.)

And, yes, some fortunate people are more oxytocin ripe than others. Oxytocin is a peptide hormone produced in the hypothalamus that triggers feelings of empathy, trust, and intimacy. And in case you are wondering, women have a great deal more oxytocin than men in order to assist in childbirth and childcare. (Do I need to apologize for saying that? Still, it would be interesting to pump prison gangs with antilibidinal, testosterone-suppressing drugs and oxytocin and watch them hug it out.)

Some elements of the human condition are manageable and even treatable, but only to a limited degree. After 50 years, it is safe to say that big pharma has completely failed to medicate us out of our misery and into contentedness, except to promote and make addiction both affordable and profitable. Some emotional states are temporary and a response to circumstances, others are a natural reaction to loss and the attendant grief; many recoil from disappointment or frustration over attacks on self-esteem. Most traumatic emotional states self-remit over time, and others are amenable to intervention (family, friends, spiritual advisors or therapists), and a percentage spiral downward for years and then recover, while some never recover.

And yes, laboratories around the globe are gearing up to treat unhappiness and ageing as diseases. But the real question is, What will we sacrifice in return for incremental relief and the inevitable tolerances that form, but also the subsequent withdrawals we will experience when we can't afford the newest and most improved stimulus treatments? This is what most of us think of as addiction—you need more to get the same effect. (More profitable than fentanyl? Hell yes!)

It is being speculated that someday soon, holding your smartphone to your head will oscillate brainwaves into patterns of contentedness. But as we have seen, e-technology is currently selling us devices to surveil us, data scrub us, market us, and monetize us. We might want to be more careful in the future while sitting at our computers, holding technology to our heads, strapping it to our wrists, or setting it on our kitchen counters to take directions from us, while it tells us that it wants nothing more than to make us happy—"What can I do for you today?"

One could speculate that all along restless discontent has been the hidden driving force throughout human history. And whatever is emotionally unresolved in each of us, we will act it out in the world, which is why it can be such a fucked-up place. Every effort to suppress discontent rebounds disturbingly, and we never find a way back to umbilical bliss and pure unconscious contentedness. Even as e-technology is promising us a fix that will make us more perfect and, therefore, perfectly happy, the probability is we are never going to get a technology fix for being human. Let's get real. The promise of happiness is simply another illusion of magical realism streaming from the minds of thought influencers—"E-technology is the answer! It will heal what is torn in our psyches and mend the *Crack in the Cosmic Egg*."

However, there might be one exception to the happy-app conundrum we should explore, as we approach 10 billion mini-universes soon to populate the Earth. Historically, there has been one primary salvation to our discontentedness. And while it may not have a happy ending, given our need for a narrative arc, keep in mind that only the amino acids need survive. (Besides, the wily tardigrades have already made it to the moon—which makes me optimistic.) We have done this before. Time to move again! Mars, really! Count me in on the next Virgin Galactic commuter spaceflight. (And, yes, some will bitch and complain about being seated in tourist class when they paid for settler class. But it will be a migration for the ages—where happiness resides.)

Evolutionary bottom line: Discontent is eternal because it alerts us to the risks and dangers of the world. This is why paranoia has persisted to the limits of psychosis. Happiness is fleeting because it momentarily distracts us from the risks and dangers around us.

Summary

- Our e-interface can be disorienting, depressing and apathy-inducing. It is unnatural to the millions of years of evolution requiring us to move and negatively impacts our emotional and physical health.
- Disconnecting your body from your mind comes at a cost, including *depersonalization* and *derealization*.
- Our increased e-interface underlies the rapid rise of anxiety, depression, and alienation throughout tech-saturated communities— all in the absence of immediate naturalistic and social experiences.
- The internet is an anonymous environment freeing us from feelings of guilt and shame, two powerful emotional states that act as internalized social controls, assuring we conform to societal norms and mores.
- Among all the online illusions created by Identity Diffusion, the most complex is the belief that one is part of a community and that friendships reside there.
- At its source code, what technology offers in exchange for diffusing your identity is power—the omnipotent sense that one is in control.

- Identity Diffusion is fracturing consensus over reality—politically, socially, and along every personal identity boundary that can be defined—and has made the world more irrational as a result.
- The internet is a model of reinforcement theory right out of psychology labs. Our behavior is being purposely shaped by electronic reinforcers similar to Pavlovian rats.
- In one sense, play is tethered to fantasy, and fantasy appears to be the voice of the unconscious speaking to each of us. As we conform to the demands of the machine, the unconscious is rebelling in the form of fantasy and play—and more darkly through compulsion and addiction.
- The end game of the coming Singularity (S2) is to absorb all of us into a simulation of reality in the belief that it will free us and heal us from all our worries and fears. However, the happy-app is simply another illusion of magical-realism streaming from the minds of technologists and thought-influencers.

9.0 – Quantified and Qualified

More than any other time in history, mankind faces a crossroad. One path leads to despair and utter hopelessness, the other to total extinction. Let us pray we have the wisdom to choose correctly.

—Woody Allen

Living in the Panopticon

In a rather bizarre moment in European intellectual history, Jeremy Bentham, while traveling in Russia in 1791, sketched concepts for a model prison he called the *panopticon* or Greek for *all seeing*. Essentially, it was a centralized tower surrounded by circular glass prison cells allowing an officer to always view every prisoner. There would be no privacy. Constant surveillance was the key—inmates would never know if they were being watched and, therefore, conform their behavior. Everyone would be accountable because all activity was public, including that of the guard. Bentham was an eighteenth-century social reformer and the intellectual founder of a school of philosophy called utilitarianism.

Today, he would probably be a Libertarian. His ideas on architecture have been influential for hundreds of years—including malls, public buildings and apartment complexes. But most of us are grateful to him for having inspired a genre of sci-fi movies on escaping highly controlled prisons.

It also turns out that no prison complex ever duplicated Bentham's concept of the panopticon. However, later in his life he did become overtly paranoid over this, suggesting a fair amount of grandiosity on his part as well. You also have to wonder about someone inspired to imprison people. But here in the 21st century, his ideas roiled debate among social theorists, particularly his theories on surveillance and the need for controlling human behavior—which have been variously described as underpinning authoritarian regimes around the world and social engineering the end of privacy. This led to considerable debate on the power of technology to affect social and political order and to pacify civil populations.

Much of the debate on Bentham's theories was subsequent to the rise of fascism and communism in the 20th century. And make no mistake about it, Bentham's goal had been to control the uncivil and undisciplined populace by utilitarian means. The concept of a panopticon gained even greater public awareness with the publication of Orwell's novel *Nineteen Eighty-Four* and the subsequent movie, which featured a panopticon. In a more recent movie, *The Truman Show*, we also watched the protagonist's escape from the OmniCam Ecosphere, echoing the panopticon and the fears of social theorists that technology is being used to surveil and control civil society.

Bentham's theories have now arrived front and center in the 21st century, as we observe the intrusion of e-technology into our daily lives and the prevalence of corporate and state surveillance. Whether we know it or not, today, we are likely residing in an electronic panopticon. This goes beyond GPS tracking, the ever-present CCTV cameras and facial recognition technology, wearable tracking devices, and the intrusion of surveillance technologies into our cars and homes.

What we euphemistically refer to as digital assistants are digital snitches tracking our movements and recording our voices and reporting everything back. You know whom I am outing—Siri, Alexa, Cortana, Eco and the Quantified-Self movement. And let's not forget the ubiquitous surveillance software for those working from home. However, the next-level panopticon is transpiring in China and its implementation of social credit scoring—an unparalleled effort by the state to digitize an entire society for surveillance.

End of Privacy

In the simulation, where do social controls begin and end, and do we require more or less of them? And, most importantly, in what has been our unending human drama, who wields the power of social control? Considering all our self-expression on the internet today, there appear to be few limits, either morally, socially or legally. Well, there are limits, but most of the time most of us and those in authority look the other way.

Mass shootings and gun violence appear to be well tolerated (with expressed outrage, of course), as is rioting and our lack of effort to do anything about it. The same goes for human sex trafficking, the sex trade and pornography. And manipulating capital markets for personal gain appears to be hunky-dory and almost always rewarding; we occasionally lockup a few people, but not the corporate CEOs or CFOs—no, they pay a nominal fine and get to keep all their off-shore accounts and stock options.

Our political reality is mostly a law-and-order drama to incarcerate the lowest-level offenders—as our legal system mostly protects assets and power-relations, with no effort to reform underlying structural problems. In the United States, we lockup more people (per capita) for longer periods than any nation on Earth. To alter this arrangement, it would require a serious challenge to the power structure and a revolution not unlike the American Revolution of 1776 or the French Revolution of 1789. (Many Republican office holders appear to have greater tolerance for school shootings than voting by mail. "Hold on! We are not going to tolerate messing with voter suppression. There are limits, damn it!")

And you are correct to surmise that just below the surface is where all the scary stuff resides. Here, our social controls attempt to tamp down our archaic excesses; the deeply paranoid beliefs, the rampant xenophobia and the tribal impulse to hack everyone to death with machetes. Elites do and should fear the masses they continually manipulate to their advantage. That's why the state is always hanging around waiting to suppress discontent and unrest. "Now you are thinking to yourself, this is hyperbole—think again."

Techno-Fascist Manifesto

In May 2021, *Politico* reported, 124 retired generals and admirals signed an open letter titled "Flag Officers 4 America." They advocated a false conspiracy theory that the 2020 election of President Biden was the result of a rigged election. It went on to warn that the U.S. was "in deep peril" from "a full-blown assault on our Constitutional rights." Further, they asserted that "Under a Democratic Congress and Current Administration … our Country has taken a hard left turn towards Socialism and a Marxist form of tyrannical government." It also raised questions about "the mental and physical condition of the Commander and Chief." (We could reasonably conclude from this manifesto, that given direction from an authoritarian-minded president, the military is available to suppress democratic norms.)

The internet is playing both sides of this drama, loosening individual controls and simultaneously supplying the state with tools for social control. This is another win-win for e-technology, but the question still lingers—where do social controls reside and what are their limits? Is self-control internal to the *particle-drive*, or does it reside in the *wave-drive* and the broader community, or are both forms of control required? "Yes, it is door number three—both types." From infancy, we internalize acceptable and unacceptable behavior. Early on, we come to understand that certain behaviors have negative consequences, and we learn to avoid them. We also quickly learn some behaviors bring reward and praise, and we strive for them. Layered on top of this is a myriad of social rewards and punishments—in classrooms, workplaces, friendships, and our broader interactions with society—rules of the road, codes of conduct, policies and procedures, criminal laws, etc.

Then, there are the informal retributions when personal boundaries are crossed. For example, her husband has come to beat you or you have been doxed by your daughter's boyfriend. And, yes, the police are at the door to arrest you. Many times, it's what you can get away with that defines the limits.

But this begs us to ask, What are the rules of the internet when it comes to shame and guilt, our two internalized social control emotions? The abridged answer is that the internet overrides them due to the perception of privacy it creates. At the front end, the internet creates the illusion that we are free of negative appraisal by others, until it rebounds and crushes us. In the same way, we tend to project human qualities onto animals and inanimate objects; we objectify and project privacy onto our e-technology interactions (that we are alone, when we really are not). It is a cognitive trick we play on ourselves, one fully exploited by e-technology. (All those harassing emails sent from a dummy IP address or burner phone eventually track you down).

And if you enter the Darknet, what are the consequences? Where are the boundaries between light and dark on the net? The answer appears to be wherever you care to draw them, just be sure to use VPN or Tor browsers and routinely delete your search history. The internet is redefining what is private and what is public in a substantial rewrite of our social contract. And because risk-taking is inherent in our genetic presets, we are now all being challenged by the internet to defy authority, test the limits and discover our boundaries. ("Nope, I don't see any problems here.")

Are there consequences for overexposure on the internet? Yes, there is loss of privacy, and forever is a long time. Everything someone puts out onto the internet is like a police body cam or posting a crime scene from a smartphone. It seldom creates context or background and is likely a distortion of reality, but it is standing all alone and naked in the universe. This includes the supposedly private moments and the public ones—the ones you authorize and the ones you know nothing about. That includes every email, every "like" and all your text messages and online searches and purchases.

And be careful with the photos and political commentary or crude attempts at humor. The internet may feel private, but it's not. That is its grand illusion. As photos are being scraped off the internet by the billions, we are all in a database being sold by data-brokers or accessed by the government and law enforcement. As facial recognition technology explodes, there may no longer be a private version of you. Everyone is a smartwatch or key fob hack from being public data. (Relax, the NSA has all the phone calls you have made over the past 15 years—not that it wants to do anything with them. Promise!)

As we bust through the privacy shame barrier, the power of being watched keeps asking for more and more content in a perpetual cycle of self-exposure and personal revelation. The brief answer to the limits of the internet appears to be fourfold: Stay away from all aspects of child porn and all searches for how to murder someone. If you live in an authoritarian country, no political content, especially irony and satire. Leave your phone home when in doubt. And, if you are concerned, use encryption and the Tor web browser. Then you are good to go dark. (And no, MILF is not code for overthrowing the government—your security algorithm is outdated.)

This is not unlike using a shell corporation to hide your financial activity— shell corporations are perfectly legal. Hiding is not a crime, as many states and nations legally permit it. It's hiding your illegal financial activity that is the crime. Same with the internet. The internet is you standing tall on two legs looking out across the savannah for the first time. While it feels unbounded, it is dangerous!

So, what are the purposes of shame and privacy? Clearly, residing in a tribe where everyone knows everything about everyone is not the same as living alone in an apartment in a city of four million people. In some odd psychological twist, it appears privacy has become a way of avoiding feelings of shame and the risk of being ostracized or punished by the community.

Privacy is a means to cloak emotions and behaviors that don't comport with expectations and avoid being judged as less than—or of being different, a standard deviation outside the norms or a sociopath. But privacy can also be driven by modesty and empathy for others—hallowed human traits.

As our social networks grew more complex, they offered a buffer from the arbitrary exploitation by others and ultimately by the kingdom you lived in. In the U.S., privacy is a constitutionally protected right. But the internet is exposing us to an earlier tribal reality of acute shame and judgement over the subtlest of contexts. We may not be ready for the loss of privacy, not to mention the legal and political ramifications—while being tempted to engage the dark arts of life online.

Cloaking Reality

The Wall Street Journal reported in 2020 that the IRS Criminal Investigation Unit purchased access to a commercial database that records the locations of millions of American cellphones. This was supposedly undertaken to track down "serious and flagrant violations of the tax law." It turns out the government is interested in what we are doing, despite many denials to the contrary. Rather than approaching phone companies, which require a court order demonstrating probable cause, they approached a commercial data broker to get the same data. It was noted that several government agencies were using private brokers as an end-run around the Fourth Amendment that protects us from unreasonable search and seizures. *The Washington Post* later reported that the phone of a Moroccan journalist had been infected by spyware. Later, Amnesty International discovered it had been developed by an Israeli tech company, NSO Group's Pegasus. To reassure the public, the company's CEO emphasized—"It only sells its software to governments."

One potential blowback from eroding privacy will be a continual assault on self-expression. We are at the beginning of virtue-testing the nation with harsh, self-righteous judgments that are intolerant and seek to purge all incorrect thought. The thought-police on the left and the right will ruthlessly seek out everyone not conforming to correct thought or behavior. Oops, that "like" was a mistake, along with the wrong T-shirt, hat logo and politically incorrect retweet. Please don't share that NSFW joke—it will lead to your outing and hounding until you agree to undergo reeducation through a ruthless process of shaming and humiliation. It is what Communist China did to its cultural elite during the Cultural Revolution—only, it's the American version, thanks to Facebook, *et al*. But perhaps, the better analogy is Lewis Carroll's *Through the Looking Glass* and an unreal world in which formally safe assumptions are now clearly being distorted.

Quantified Life

Life in the panopticon is coming our way if it has not already arrived. It is more than a quaint steampunk allegory. Today, AI is surveilling, quantifying and qualifying our lives continuously. It is important to understand that the primary-driver of our dynamically networked universe is to determine the *Value of Everything*. That's it! But the secret sauce is value creation—everything must be identified, quantified and made exchangeable. It is all about the numbers. This is what a computer is, a quantifying machine and the ultimate arbiter of exchange. Computers are in the process of quantifying life and assigning value. Only a computer will be powerful enough to fully metricize life.

How much does someone get paid for an hour of labor? What is the price of a car? How much is your house worth? What is the cost of healthcare? What does an attorney charge per hour? What does a gallon of milk cost? Our drive to make the future predictable requires that it be quantified—GDP, tax rates, interest rates, consumer price index, school grades, GED scores, credit scores, height, weight, blood pressure, glycemic index, body mass index, systolic pressure, caloric-intake, RPMs, horsepower, property tax rate, insurance actuarial tables, death benefits, the cost of a barrel of oil.

The current index of value is its economic worth; what it costs determines its value. What did you pay for it? Every human relationship and interaction, every action and object in our environment is a calculus in six dimensions—the three dimensions of space, then add mass, time and value.

The same way the ancient Greeks believed in the gods, we believe in the numbers—computer-based platforms and networks that trade large volumes of stocks at very high speeds are our form of numerology. The New York Stock Exchange is our modern-day Oracle of Delphi, where the capital markets converge for all to pray to and to seek predictions about the future under the benevolent guidance of the Securities and Exchange Commission. At the same time the Federal Reserve oracle sets broad monetary policies, followed by large brokerage firms (JP Morgan Chase, Berkshire Hathaway, and Charles Schwab Corp.) who offer market prediction-babble for significant cash contributions.

And there are oracles and seers for every economic class—for the simple and naïve with $5,000 and a retirement plan to the greedy and grandiose with millions to invest. The overly ambitious who do not want to pay the tithe can go online with E-Trade. But most seek the wise counsel of investment brokers, who consult the market analysts, who cast the bones and read the scattering conspiracy of ravens, who interpret the pontificating and abstruse babble of the economists—all prostrating at the feet of Warren Buffet.

The market goes up and down and occasionally crashes. It also randomly self-corrects, but almost always requiring some government intervention in the belief that there is such a thing as monetary policy. In the end, it always requires an astronomical cash infusion to save it from itself—so it can go on predicting the future of the market. Nothing is more important than the historical projections of the market's average and its continual rise. The future is always told in numbers.

There are always ravens tapping the kitchen window—GDP, Federal interest rate, bank and stock earnings, Treasury yield, retail sales and hidden and abstruse formulas by the inside seers. How good are the oracles? They are average, unless they have the knowledge and insight to manipulate the market in the never-ending quest to predict the future by connecting the invisible numbers. And if you become wealthy as a result, the oracles can help you avoid taxes, manipulate the tax laws and evade surveillance.

We should seriously consider the possibility; at the backend, we are being quantified as nodes in an electronic universe of zeros and ones. That is all of us, now! But beyond this, we might also want to consider that we are also being qualified as well. Qualified is a determination of your "general value" in the coming metaverse. And you might be curious how your general value will be determined. Not to worry, an independent crypto-algorithm will quantify-qualify (Q-Q) you without requiring your input—it has more than enough data already, thank you.

Labor was likely the first universal measure of value; as a result, slavery was popular for thousands of years. This was later supplanted by money, which quantified labor and created an exchange rate based on value (supply and demand). It remains, today, the most universal means of ascribing value. Money is the crucial marker of value today and acts like the vascular system of our socially networked environment.

Universally, if you want to know what something is worth, we want to know in terms of dollars. If you believe you can't put a dollar value on a sunset, poem, pet or loved one, you have never been to court or on life support. Currently, with our increasing quantification by algorithms, value is being redistributed, which inevitably means conflict and turmoil in the market (and everything is the market today).

While, today, labor remains a dominant value-marker for most people in the world, for the wealthy, it is millions and billions of invested dollars in the marketplace. If value can only be determined by what can be measured, you might want to ask yourself, How many hours of labor do I have left and does anyone want them? We are being measured in ways we are no longer able to observe or understand. This is also why owning a business is a labor multiplier. We are being quantified and qualified in a parallel electronic-simulation where your *electronic you* now resides at the data center, determining the value of the *real you*.

Being Quantified

A number is a number! Technology companies call it one thing (a cookie that helps improve services), an authoritarian state calls it another (suppressing disruption). The modern use of numbers often represents a form of encryption to help maintain privacy. Our first number (beside our date of birth) is usually a social security number, then a bank account number, followed by a driver's license number and license plate number or a selective service registration number. Then, you get a phone number and a credit card number or even longer numbers on insurance policies, home loans, etc.

If you go to court, you get a number; you go to prison, you get a new number. Then the wild spree of online accounts with passwords, too long and too many to remember. In fact, you must have an app to generate and store them for you. For celebrities, there is a Q-rating and for everyone else, the online tallies of likes, followers, advertisers and subscribers. We create lists of the most popular movies and music (which is really a measure of the revenues they generate). On Amazon, you can get 1–5 stars. Of course, today, this is all a hackable source of data and surveillance. Everything and everyone!

There's a direct relationship between being surveilled and being quantified. In fact, they are one and the same. The two go hand in hand, both with the same broad goal of predicting and controlling our behavior, whether for commercial or security purposes. While state-surveillance tends toward the security domain, corporate-surveillance is for the commercial use of data (which they can sell over and over to data brokers).

Think about how many times you have gone into a store and made a purchase, and they ask you for your zip code or phone number. You are being quantified and re-sold. We should make no mistake about it, quantification and surveillance work in tandem. Most of us don't realize that many of the things we don't think of as numbers are really numbers. That is, everything a computer can record about our behavior is ultimately reduced to a metric or data-node. It is life quantified.

In a test at school, you get a B+, which is really 88 on a grading curve. You buy insurance and a computerized actuarial table determines your rates. The next time your visit your doctor, ask to see your lab results and make a note of the reference range of normal values for dozens of test results. You are being quantified in the same exact way a car mechanic attaches a computer to your car or your doctor inputs you into a laptop to see if there are any problems. Your story is in the numbers, confer with any oracle you like.

An examination of the E-Quantification table below should make clear that what the government can't do legally is already being done commercially, with more on the horizon. The drive of e-technology is to invent the tools that ultimately quantify and surveil us, and then find redeemable commercial purposes for them. And let's not kid ourselves; this is being done with no regard for their potential misuse. It is not a coincidence that government agencies are continually seeking data from private commercial sources due to legal restriction on conducting the same surveillance. Those privacy agreements we routinely click without reading are a virtual data freeway saying, "Yes, quantify me because I don't want to read it, can't understand it and don't have any other option."

I am going big here and suggesting that language evolved primarily as a means of quantifying life. Why were our early ancestors so obsessed with astronomy and always praying to the gods? How long did it take for them to perceive that the seasons affected their survivability and arrived in patterns?

They came to understand that their survival was dependent on getting the right calculations.

The only way to predict the future is to correctly quantify it. *Quantification is the driving evolutionary imperative of outsourcing information storage and retrieval.* The goal of life is to generate a computer-aided design (CAD) file for a computer numerical control (CNC) system and 3D printer, aided by machine intelligence and big data algorithms—and, finally, AI.

Code Red

In the aftermath of the coronavirus pandemic in China, a smartphone health code app is now in widespread use in many cities. Upon entering a train station, individuals use a smartphone to scan a poster that triggers a health code app. A green indicator light and part of their identity number appears on the screen. With a green code, security waves them through. However, a red code confirms someone is infected or has a fever or other symptoms and must await diagnosis. A yellow code means this individual has had contact with an infected person and must complete a two-week quarantine at either a hospital or at home.

The same app also records which train cars individuals traveled in, requiring them to scan the seats before exiting. This routine applies to all public spaces that have been visited as well. This system is a product of the Chinese peoples near universal adaptation of smartphones and the Communist Party's embrace of big data to extend its surveillance and control over society. We are well on our way here in the United States, as many enthusiastically embrace the Quantified-Self movement.

E-Quantification
(The data below is available for sale, hacking or subpoena.)

- Educational records (schools attended, grades, SAT/GRE scores)
- Work history, work performance evaluations, income
- Medical records and lab results
- DNA testing, genealogy, biometric scanning and genome sequencing
- Mental health/substance abuse treatment records
- Licensing results (bar exam, medical-dental, real estate, driver's, cosmetology, massage, firearms and hundreds more)

- Legal history—criminal and civil—bail bonds, fines, and restitution
- Birth and marriage certificates (alimony and child support history)
- Military records
- Property records
- Banking accounts and activity
- Credit and debit card transactions (PayPal, Amazon, etc.)
- Insurance claims (medical, life, auto, home)
- Credit scores and tax returns
- Online polling, commercial surveys, comments, product/service evaluations
- Online "likes," followers and subscribers
- Smartwatches, Fitbit, AirTag and home appliance monitoring
- Online dating profiles and searches (Match, Tinder, etc.)
- Home video security systems, public CCTV, business security cameras, license plate readers, facial recognition software, photo radar
- Phone calls, cell tower pings, phone GPS
- All computer use, online searches, phone apps and online subscriptions
- Pornography and dark web searches
- Email, text messages, Instagram, Twitter, Facebook, LinkedIn, OnlyFans—and every photo you ever taken with a smartphone and sent to someone
- Siri, Alexa and Cortana home monitoring
- Cable TV and satellite television monitoring activity
- Car computers monitoring driving habits, car GPS, and on-call services
- Quantified-Self movement (probation ankle monitors and Fitbit data)
- Social credit scoring (informally available in U.S.)
- Online identity searches
- Corporate database algorithm searches
- Big data scraping photos and online search activity
- NSA metadata collection of phone calls

Social Credit Scoring

A new and formidable player has emerged in our loosely disparate network of data nodes and security precautions, and that is social credit scoring—a true and terrifying game-changer. Social credit scoring is designed to exploit our entangled identities—the *real you* versus the *electronic you*. And this entanglement strikes at the heart of our primate need for conformity and dominance, i.e., go along to get along.

All that endlessly available and seemingly harmless data you exfoliated is now being used to profile you—to quantify your general fitness as a human based on your ability to conform. This is our e-technology future. It is rapidly learning not only how to play the wave-particle duality and our compelling need to belong and feel empowered, but also, incidentally, to redefine our identities.

Coming soon, on an app you won't be able to resist or delete, will be the public posting of your social credit score. It will display your quantification/qualification as a measure of your overall value to the community. Perhaps you remember the third grade and all the student's names on a bulletin board with stars next to them for attendance and participation—same idea. And the public optic, if anyone cares, may not be pretty. More importantly, How will you adapt to improve your score? And until our AI overlords arrive, you will be analyzed, surveilled and monetized 24/7 by algorithms and deep machine learning programs, all for your benefit, of course.

Here in the West, we are taking a somewhat more casual approach (better to monetize it first). Your potential employer can now go online and check out your credit score, arrest history, Facebook posts and who your friends are; law enforcement can search your ancestry DNA; insurance companies can access your car's electronic data; all the while you enjoy the benefits of frequent flier miles and the electronic perks that come your way based on your purchase habits and internet searches.

In much the same way we are being sold on improving our credit scores or SAT/GED scores, we will be sold on ways to improve our social credit scores. And this is the real deal, people. The formally private version of you (the one you like to think of as you) will no longer be the primary you. You are now just toiling away in the service of the *electronic you*, an algorithm at a data-center in the Sonoran desert. It's not that no one mentioned this to you; it's that you didn't care.

Social credit scoring holds the potential for authoritarian regimes, but really every government around the world, to exert unprecedented intervention and control of routine social behavior. In China, the real meaning of this electronic transaction is more prominent and foretelling. It is the ultimate networked attempt to tamp down the *particle-drive*. Social credit scores, as well as what is required to improve them, are published online for everyone to see. By improving your scores, you attain desirable upgrades (platinum level), including—obtaining a passport, upgraded train passes, airline tickets and hotel bookings. And your children get into more desirable preschools.

It takes into consideration your credit history, arrest history, and who you hang with for coffee and how you drive your car, books you read, online activity and if you spit, jaywalk, swear or express unacceptable ideas. And like snitches in Eastern Europe during the Cold War, people are paid throughout communities to report (spy) their observations as well.

As your social credit score goes down, you will be relegated to the bottom of a new and emerging social caste. And your more upwardly mobile friends and acquaintances will quickly abandon you to ensure their elevated scores. Hopefully, not your family (next time you visit sit up straight and don't put your feet on the coffee table or they might report your disrespectful behavior, again). Who needs to hack your mind if it can be controlled through simple operant conditioning measures? However, if your social credit score redlines or wildly fluctuates, your mind will be painlessly penetrated to check for error codes.

And it appears that, in China, people are generally accepting of this and even like it. The reality is: You are now one miniscule neuro-upgrade from having a chip implanted in your brain, one that can control all those undesirable thoughts and impulses and potentially raise your social credit score. Besides, it will create enough pleasure and reward that you will learn not only to like it but also appreciate all the benefit you gain from it. In fact, for better or worse, it will likely be your key to finding a suitable mate in the future. And our growing Identity Diffusion makes this a secure door to open and walk through.

And beyond the social credit scoring, the Chinese People's Republic (CPP) is engaged in implementing an expansive program of digital surveillance. It is collecting a massive DNA database from its citizens, utilizing face and voice recognition technologies, with an estimated 626 million cameras by the end of this decade, in a program dubbed "Sharp Eyes." In addition, it has created the "Great Firewall" to censor and deny all internet activity deemed unacceptable.

The CPR currently employs over two million citizens as microblog monitors to report online postings to official censors. The sweep of big-data analytics, AI and the Internet of Everything is being developed to monitor, influence, and ultimately control 1.4 billion citizens. Now this would all be mildly interesting to most of us in the West except this is all being implemented here, except we pay for it for ourselves, which is how we prefer to do things— "Don't want no government telling us what to do!" It all begins with our failure to read and understand the technology privacy agreement. (Have you read one or know someone who has?) But mostly, we don't care and can't imagine the consequences of our benign purchases. (We are being duped!)

Every major American tech company is developing voice recognition technology. Why is that you might ask? For one, it's projected to be a $55 billion industry. We already have it in our homes (Cortana, Echo and Siri). It is also used for medical transcription, language interpretation, automated telephone directory services, and to identify you. This latter fact is never mentioned by Google, Facebook, Amazon, Microsoft or Apple. One way e-technology has made this technology even more profitable has been to help China implement these applications. But the NSA has been developing it for years and it will be marketed to us as a security measure, and we will all want increased security, just as the Chinese people do.

Yes, your life will have been reduced to a number that will dictate all aspects of it. It is unbound data. And to hide from it will also significantly lower your score. Of course, just as in Las Vegas, people will try to game it (the false data-game will be enormous and corrupt, thank goodness). But the most important question will still be, Who are you? The person you think you are or the one in the desert oasis data center. And there will be no satisfactory answer.

Today, your application for a job, credit card, business loan, car loan, home loan or apartment rental will trigger an in-depth virtual search. This search first determines the legitimacy of the *electronic you*, to decide if the *real you* is qualified. If it's good, then the *real you* is okay as well. If not, forget it. You are not qualified for just about anything. This search may even be undertaken by someone trying to decide to meet you for coffee. It starts with a casual online search for the *electronic you* on Facebook, LinkedIn, Twitter, Snapchat, etc. This data tracks you across the spacetime continuum in perpetuity (a long time). In other words, you cannot hide from it and probably can't correct errors in it. It is the *electronic you*, the one residing in the desert data-resort, and not the one falsely reported as dead.

What you do affects your social credit score and in return it impacts you. You are forever entangled. And, if by chance, you have been able to evade much of this, that will be held against you and, likely, you will be denied a job, loan or date (in much the same way not using credit inhibits attaining credit). It is no longer an analog world of people, but a digital-electronic environment flaring into the atmosphere all around us. It is an invisible web of dark data (not unlike dark matter), forming the lattice of our evolving reality.

Alert—Check for updates. There has been ongoing discussion by Chinese Communist Party (CCP) technology researchers about developing precog-algorithms to track a person's thoughts in real time. They would offer predictive scores on individuals whose thinking is deviant, antisocial or challenging the state's central role in private and public life. As you go about your life, you will be tracked in real time with a number or color-coding schema appearing on a surveillance screen indicating who requires an intervention. It will likely be a quick and painless cranial penetration by an app on your smartphone. Best to think of it as a "happy tune-up." (This is the movie *Minority Report* taken to a more serious level than the sci-fi writers could imagine.)

Workplace Surveillance

Totalitarianism: A form of corporate management that theoretically permits no individual freedom and that seeks to subordinate all aspects of individual life to the authority of the corporation.

Workplace surveillance software has recently exploded onto the marketplace (Pragli, Clever Control, Desk Time, Staff Cop, Work Examiner, WorkPuls, Basecamp, ActviTrak, Hubstaff, Time Doctor, Teramind, InterGuard, etc.), particularly for those working from home. But we all know at some subliminal level that it's coming for all of us. E-technology has always been coming for us. First, the technology is invented, and then it's determined how to market it without triggering panic and, finally, sell it as a premium upgrade.

This is an uncontrolled process that never ceases, never remits, and operates free of nearly all legal or moral constraints, so long as a market exists for it. Let's be clear, surveillance software is one step away from you being bio-hacked with an RFID chip—and when this is convenient and affordable, you will be excited about going in for a procedure—plus a one percent raise at work (they already have been advised this software will increase your productivity by five percent).

We all need to understand that workplace surveillance is a Trojan Horse gambit by tech-corps, in much the same way Facebook promotes itself as being all about connectivity and making the world a better place. Think interrogators at Guantanamo Bay convincing terrorists that waterboarding is a form of recreational activity—same thing here. Under an unending stream of corporate PR, this technology is being foisted on the world. And all this supposedly innovative workplace surveillance software is a cat turd floating in the bouillabaisse, whose only goal is to count keystrokes to make you more productive. That's it in its totality.

So, you log in and your digital avatar sits upright in its virtual office along with a fake office water cooler and well-appointed chat rooms, so you can talk with your workmates. Of course, you are always ready for a face-to-face with your supervisor—because it's required that your webcam and microphone are always on so you can be fully monitored—web browsing activity, emails, text messages, bathroom breaks, and whatever you scratch, itch, or pick at, with the added benefit of regularly scheduled check-ins multiple times a day. All the while being deluged with fake, but not optional, company happy hours, game nights, and lunchtime chats—you know, to help break down the isolation and make the digital workplace more fun and connected.

Get real! This arcade game ruse is about you being micro-managed by remote-work software—because they do not trust you for one entire second of your working existence. I mean, they want to help keep you motivated by harassing you with happy emojis, while letting you know that you take a lot of bathroom breaks. You soon receive an emoji advising a bladder or prostate examination. Later, this is followed up with an emoji advising you, in the most discrete manner possible, that everyone else on the team wears Depends. There will also be polite inquiries if you might benefit from a laxative or colon therapy. The fact is they are consulting with your smart toilet too. It also has been noted that you are talking too much to Siri and she doesn't have a need to know or security clearance—just a heads-up! You wonder to yourself, What is the emoji for leaning back in your chair, feet on your desk and contemplating?

No, you can't expect employees to stay motivated on their own. The human need for connection is real, but surveillance is not human connection. It is you in a virtual game interacting with other avatars recording every word you speak—yeah, just like at work or going to lunch with a colleague. There is no privacy, and a great deal of what truly connects people at work is private. At its core, this "happy" propaganda reflects a profound disrespect and abiding distrust in you and your fellow workers. It is a masquerade promoting the best way to establish trust at work is to work you to death (karoshi) or until you can be replaced by a software upgrade.

Surveillance software can capture images of workers and their screens every few seconds and report employees who are actively working. This includes hours at work, minute by minute updates, and monitoring app use and website visits. Workers are then categorized and ranked by productivity scores. It can alert managers if you have not been busy enough. (Really, how does this get assessed, as if time were the only measure of productivity? Which is why, ultimately, they want to get into your head.)

How does being busy comport with being creative or adopting novel approaches to problem-solving? When does too much chat room time or hanging out at the virtual water cooler become a problem? Or worse yet, you get the mental health emoji because you don't seem to be connecting with anyone at virtual work.

Recording all your keystrokes, monitoring your mouse usage, and assessing if you have been actively working, but after 15 seconds of inactivity, you will be identified as idle. Idle is how Nazi referred to Jews. Only they used the term *useless eaters*. And we know what happened to them. Apparently, you are only left alone in the American dream. And some of this software can even be secretly installed. I wonder why they would want to do that?

Tech-corps is particularly inured with a trope that's popular with the authoritarian mindset, What do you have to hide? When the truth is, we have everything to fear in this scenario. Bright, competent, and motivated people everywhere are being reduced to bots and required to work machine-like while pretending to skip along the yellow brick road.

The always-on webcams and microphones "help bring people closer together, combat the stress of isolation and meet the human need for contact, while promoting a shared mission and creating a happier workforce"—really, who makes this crap up? It's as if Nazi propaganda minister Joseph Goebbels has been reanimated to star in the Broadway musical of Mr. Rogers, and then retired to write e-technology speak for marketing. And if you just happen to be more productive, that's an unanticipated benefit, a win-win.

Facial recognition technology is on its way. Technology that can read and display your emotions in real time on your virtual avatar's face. Soon, you will get a sad emoji face from your supervisor, noting that your e-quotient (emotional score) has been drooping recently—inquiring if you are happy with your job and if there is anything they can do to make you feel better. No, they can't turn off surveillance; that's not an option. And, no, they are not going to undertake an anonymous survey of the workforce to determine how satisfied it is with being surveilled. E-quotient aggregates tell their team all they need to know, and there's no need for quantitative easing. But you are welcome to leave anytime you like. "Any other questions or concerns?"

What they don't have is a demand by their employees for this technology. Nope, no survey to see what their employees' needs are or if they desire this menu of options—when all tech-corps really wants is to exhaust you with continuous monitoring and phony check-ins. What you don't have is the option of turning it off and getting your work done or to work at a pace and time of your own choosing.

What menu of options exists for you when corporate surveillance begins to feel unproductive or annoying or disrupts your workflow? What happens when this work begins to feel intrusive into your personal life and more like a civil rights or Fifth Amendment violation or, really, a virtual body cavity search? When what you really crave is some sense of personal agency over your work-life and not residing in a virtual fishbowl as a screen saver on your supervisor's desk or on his phone while the bathroom. (Let's not ignore the underlying voyeuristic elements in all of this.)

And once corporate surveillance software connects to your private electronic network (with your permission of course—what do you have to hide?) have no doubts about its agenda (to help you become more productive and reach your next bonus level.) Now connected to your computer, smartphone, Apple watch, Nest, nanny cam, and Fitbit, it will infiltrate home security—Ring, ADT—and, finally, be able to converse privately with Siri and Alexa when you are not around. (You should encrypt your sex doll for unauthorized entry at this point. But its best they don't know you have one if you get my drift. You might want to consider resigning.)

Your manager will now have a virtual dossier on you—to assist you in fulfilling your work goals and make working at tech-corps a genuinely satisfying experience. Just now, you notice a wandering surveillance emoji on your monitor reminding you that your attention frequently wanders during the day—"Is there a problem?" Coincidently, a random alert is asking you to fill out an anonymous online Workplace-Connectivity Satisfaction Survey (WCSS).

Everything that appeals to promoting social interaction and ease of communication and the idea that we are all a village is the illusion we are being sold in exchange for job security. Work surveillance software is a fraudulent attempt to turn cubicle life into a factory under the guise of happy phrases and emojis. Let's call it what it is, corporate totalitarianism. (Hey, wait a minute, we have already seen this movie—*The Circle*. But better yet, watch *Brazil*, a brilliant film on having our minds managed for us.)

But wait! There is more to come. Researchers at Stanford University (Bushwick) are developing biometric technology that identifies you by your gait. Hardware sensors hidden in the walls that can detect a pattern of footsteps, while software can analyze it and verify an individual's identity throughout a building with 95 percent accuracy. The researchers emphasize that this removes the need for wearable devices and is more private than having an obvious camera in sight.

The ostensible reason for this technology is to help monitor those with health problems, noting—"This (was) created because of the privacy concerns of other types of monitoring mechanisms." Let's just state the ominous facts here. Its great promotional advantage is that you can now be tracked without your knowledge or awareness.

Relax! Data Is Being Extracted From an External Orifice

The police ask to search your car, and you agree because you know there's no blood splatter evidence. But still, you make sure they have a search warrant. For one, your car is a sophisticated computer with nearly unlimited data storage. It is continually updating with onboard sensors, GPS, Wi-Fi and Bluetooth—date, time of day, location, turn-by-turn navigation, speed, rates of acceleration-deceleration, doors opened-closed, lights turned on-off, seatbelts use, airbag deployment and car camera recordings.

226

But an infotainment system with connected smartphone is giving it all up: GPS, cell tower pings, texts, web history, destinations, contact list, call logs, purchases, text messages, emails, pictures, videos, web history, time-stamped voice commands, and social media use. And more to the point, none of this data is password or biometrically protected. Now for all of us who are not criminals, this date trove may help authorities locate your missing car or find your body.

First, it was our homes and now our cars are ratting us out (I mean storing our data with minimal safety protocols). The Internet of Everything is on the move and has got wheels now! Imagine in the coming future attempting a getaway in a self-driving vehicle—you are immediately flash-banged (new built-in feature where the air bag used to be deployed from) and the vehicle is immobilized and parked safely away from any schools or playgrounds via satellite command until a patrol car casually arrives. (Officers will finish their coffee and donuts, knowing you are fully incapacitated.)

The likelihood is you have never heard the terms *geofence warrant*, *exigent circumstances* or *digital vehicle forensics*. In the first instance, the court issues a warrant for a Google search of your online data; in the second instance, it is done immediately; and in the third instance, there are law enforcement specialists conducting a digital data-scrub of your vehicle (they will still want to know why you put your car through a carwash with the windows down and then had it detailed).

This data trawling by law enforcement raises important questions about privacy and Fourth Amendment protections against unreasonable searches. But your attorney can explain it to you after you bond out for failing to signal a lane change. In China, you will be fined and subject to a reeducation program. In the U.S., you will get a five-year prison sentence for what they discover about you online.

"Cancelled" Again!

The essential reality most of us face, when it comes to technology, is being phased out of work; nothing personal here—it's just business. Sapiens, a once-proud species and apex predator, will have been rendered an obsolete operating system. And this could be as true for doctors and lawyers, as it is for the technology that is taking your order, making a hamburger and fries, and delivering it to you—but probably not on roller skates or as seductively as Hooters, yet.

The computer-generated file is the new baseline for all product creation. If you don't have a file to share—you are knitting Christmas gifts and your office is in the garage (no offense to Jobs or Wozniak). All product design and fabrication start after a CAD file has been generated. Because most manufacturing features autonomous robots, 3-D printing, CNC routers and plasma cutters that require a file to tell it what to do and how to precisely cut materials within micrometers.

Have you wandered into a McDonald's recently? You never actually interact with a person, but with a computer. You can now buy cars online and have them delivered to your door, finally and thankfully. Online ordering, from groceries to airline tickets and Airbnb, never requires talking to a person or even seeing someone. Currently, machine learning software can review case law with unprecedented detail. Therapists have gravitated to online forums and are a brief technology upgrade (virtual avatar) to no longer being relevant. From hospitals to assisted living facilities, carebots provide medical care, support, and comfort to the aging. And bots are already patrolling the streets of California cities and shopping malls, taking over essential law enforcement surveillance duties.

Let's briefly focus on healthcare. Have you noticed that your doctor seldom makes eye contact with you because they are focused on entering data into a laptop? Yes, you are now only data! Increasingly, doctors are primarily data entry clerks with simple checklists just waiting for lab or medical imaging results. They seldom talk to you, have very little time for you, and a nurse will call you with the results. Life for doctors is no longer about the stress of seeing patients, but rather the stress of interfacing with technology. The current interface is primitive and inefficient. But never fear: IBM, Harvard, and MIT are all working on developing databases and algorithms that can make medical diagnoses beyond what any doctor could ever hope to replicate.

In a recent *Harvard Business Review* article (Longoni and Morwedge), the authors reported—"Medical AI can perform with expert-level accuracy and deliver cost-effective care at scale." They noted that IBM's Watson diagnoses heart disease better than cardiologists. Chatbots dispense medical advice for the United Kingdom's National Health Services in place of nurses. Smartphone apps now detect skin cancer with expert accuracy. Algorithms identify eye diseases as effectively as ophthalmologists. There are forecasts that medical AI will eventually saturate 90 percent of hospital activity and replace as much as 80 percent of what doctors currently perform.

There is no sacred work free of AI and of our coming obsolescence. Initially, you conduct an online search of your symptoms. As this search deepens, a symptom list expands, and possible diagnoses are offered. You may then get a popup for an online referral to a doctor, who will email you possible diagnoses. In some cases, direct phone contact for further follow-up is available. We are not that far away from this interaction being exclusive with an AI bot.

So, let's connect the dots here. In a recent article (Case and Deaton), the authors noted that for the first time since 1918 and the Spanish Flu pandemic, U.S. life expectancy declined for three consecutive years (2015–2017). Analyzing the data led them to conclude this is predictive for most Western democracies, noting a rise in deaths from drug overdoses in Australia, Canada, Ireland, and the United Kingdom. The cause was attributed to a less educated population facing the "relentless threat of globalization, outsourcing, and automation that erode working-class ways of life." But they also noted stagnant wages since the '70s, lack of satisfying jobs, eroded social networks, and the high cost of healthcare. All factors that helped fuel what they termed "crisis deaths of despair."

A key factor for declining life expectancy was increased mortality between the ages of 25 to 64 from drug overdoses, alcoholic liver disease and suicide. Punctuating their conclusion, they noted that, in 2017, there were 158,000 deaths of despair or "the equivalent of three fully loaded Boeing 737 jets falling out of the sky every day for a year." It also appeared that a college degree was somewhat protective from this decline. We need to pay attention. Workplace obsolescence is coming, and technology is on the verge of displacing not only many less technical jobs, but also higher-paying jobs across all fields of employment.

Old-School Distributed Networks

Evidence has been accumulating for some time now that social media platforms are being utilized to control and tamp down connectivity worldwide. There is an active effort to distort and manipulate the truth as a means of disrupting the democratic process. This is occurring at the same time big tech's primary goal has been to identify the naïve and gullible and monetize them as quickly as possible. Simply put, it is not a good day in the neighborhood. There are clearly powerful forces at work undermining the fantasies we are being sold.

What big tech is doing is remarkably similar to what Wall Street did leading up to the housing market crash in 2007. In this latter instance, they collateralized shaky mortgage instruments and paid off the bond rating and insurance agencies. They then created profitable and less risky financial instruments to hedge their bet against the shaky ones they were pushing at unsuspecting investors. Big tech is playing a similar game. Upfront, it is selling us connectivity. At the same time, they collect rents from our data, which is then used to manipulate us as consumers, all the while opening us up to the risk of being hacked. They then turn around and sell the same information to the data market to be further manipulated, exploited and potentially exposed. And here is the beauty of this—they sell the same software, tech devices and internet platforms to authoritarian governments worldwide, which are then utilized to suppress their population. But the best of all is that they have gamed the system so well they don't have to pay taxes. Really, they are no different than the drug cartels as a business model—everyone is trying to find a way to launder their money and not pay taxes.

Getting Fleeced Is Not Warm Pajamas

When running for president, U.S. Senator Mitt Romney publicly discussed in 2012 that he paid a lower tax rate (14%) on the $13.7 million dollars he earned that year than his secretary paid on her salary. In 2017 and 2018, Amazon paid 0% taxes. *ProPublica* gained access to 15 years of IRS tax returns for the 25 wealthiest billionaires in America and uncovered they paid almost no taxes. Between 2014 and 2018, they earned $401 billion and paid around 3.4% in taxes. And the federal government's response? Neither party had the guts to seek revision of the tax law; it was more important to go after people who leaked the tax data.

Big tech and Wall Street can shelter their enormous profits in offshore accounts or through tax-inversion laws that only require fake overseas headquarters. And you might ask, why is this allowed? It's allowed because they take an exceedingly small amount of their profits, think of it as corporate indulgences (or what medieval Catholics paid the church to ensure they got into heaven) or chump-change to pay congressmen scampering about begging for crumbs.

Big tech has somehow managed to sit alone at the top of their profits by evading taxes, while screwing every country that provides infrastructure, educated employees, favorable tax and environmental legislation and the stable rule of law. In business parlance, this is a win-win. There is no allegiance or morality here—just profit. In wartime, this would be called war-profiteering. In peacetime, it stands as business as usual.

Who are you working for? The internet and social media platforms have become vital to ushering in what is being termed digital autocracies. Dictatorships and illiberal democracies are growing increasingly resilient and durable because of technological innovations. Political scientists (i.e., academics and think tank denizens) have been tracing and documenting the recent rise of autocracies and have gone so far as to state that it would be naïve to believe that technology supports a more democratic future. This directly rebuffs Mark Zuckerberg's (Meta Platforms CEO) broad vision of universal connectivity and social harmony.

The fact is digital tools are "narrowing the space for civil society" and allowing authoritarian states to "quell dissent" in what is termed "digital repression." AI-driven surveillance (video security cameras, face/voice/gait recognition technologies, biometric identification, spyware and data-driven software) has been rapidly evolving into a sophisticated tool for controlling civilian populations. Perhaps the most appalling example has been the Chinese Communist Party (CCP) rounding up Muslim Uighurs in their western provinces and interning them in reeducation camps, subject to intense levels of electronic surveillance and monitoring.

Basically, Uighurs are being barcoded. The citizens of Tibet are similarly being subjected to intrusive state surveillance. Let's state it more bluntly if that's possible—the advancement of AI-powered surveillance is the most significant evolution in the authoritarianism model of governance since the industrial manufacturing of guns.

Suppressive surveillance technology is readily available over the counter. Any of the world's 50 dictators can go down to Best Buy or order on Amazon surveillance technology that's inexpensive and cost-effective to operate. It requires limited training of only a handful of qualified individuals, who are hopefully not too busy playing video games after school. It is simple and straightforward to operationalize and make compatible with existing infrastructures and platforms. It is also proving to be highly useful in tracking and monitoring opposition candidates and party members. If you need to track and surveil tens of thousands of people and later intern them, easy-peasy, with available off-the-shelf technology. What's not to like if you are a dictator?

Broken Logic

In May 2020, during the worldwide coronavirus outbreak, Zoom, a northern California tech company specializing in web video conferencing, shut down the account of Humanitarian China. This occurred shortly after it had sponsored an online event marking the 31st anniversary of China's violent crackdown on Tiananmen Square pro-democracy protests. Although the account was subsequently reactivated, Zoom noted "concerns about following laws in the countries where it operates." Adding, "It is not in Zoom's power to change the laws of governments opposed to free speech."

This response should make us all pause and ask, "Why is Zoom or any U.S. company doing business with any country when complying with its laws helps suppress human rights by using their products?" (Freedom of speech? No big deal. Why should we care?)

The broad implication of this is that e-technology is actively helping suppress human rights worldwide with technology. And one might reasonably conclude that they are doing the same thing in the United States. The account Zoom shut down was based in Hayward, CA, several miles from Zoom's headquarters in San Jose, CA. (For the record, I grew up in Hayward, CA.) China reached out to a CA tech company to shut down another CA tech company, one that was literally just down the street from it, to help it suppress free speech in China. Remarkable—it didn't require a hack or malware or any threat, just a polite IT request.

Clearly, a line of reasoning connects the rise of durable authoritarian regimes and increasingly fragile democracies due to e-technologies. But this dot-connecting is evolving into a 21st century foreign policy paradigm as well—that the future of great power conflicts will no longer be unending territorial disputes. This new battlefield will be a contentious and unending cyber and information-space conflict. (And, yes, this worries the military-industrial complex regarding future big-budget items, e.g., a sixth-generation manned jet fighter or aircraft carriers).

Nation-states, corporations, Darknet actors and amateur hackers will engage in digital combat. They will begin to define our political reality and make a lot of extra cash. But mostly, they will have fun and create havoc with unknown consequences for all of us. But also, with the capability to bring down our energy grid, healthcare system, oil pipelines, and water services. The battlefield, this time, will be on our smartphones, computers, and the internet. The recent designation of a U.S. Space Force is timely—but it will have to significantly raise salaries and make it more fun if it wants to compete with malware rewards.

In relatively unprotected cyberspace, the U.S.'s greatest competitor is China, as U.S. tech companies (Google, Microsoft, Apple) increasingly integrate into the Chinese economic and political structure—gleefully opening new and expanding manufacturing facilities. Coincidentally, China's economic-cyber model broadly supports efforts to implement a broad strategy of digital authoritarianism at home and abroad. Obviously, a win-win for all involved. China has perfected digital censorship by sifting through massive databases of images and text and filtering and blocking content. They micro-target and discredit opposition with deepfakes and digital forgeries in campaigns of disinformation—and, if necessary, lock people up.

Digital repression is cheap and effective and can be supported by minimal infrastructure and only occasional assistance from corporate customer tech support (if they registered their purchase and are not offended by a robot generated voice putting them on hold). The conundrum in this is how U.S. tech companies look the other way when it is evident that the Chinese market is at one with the state. (Chinese school children are singing songs about the Western bumpkins who fell off the bok choy truck in front of the Foxconn factory).

You don't have to be a Defense Intelligence Agency analyst to understand that U.S. technology passes seamlessly from the private market in China to the state-sector. Espionage isn't required here. China is, essentially, buying technology from us for pennies on the dollar in a new Cold War for AI supremacy. Let's be clear: We are selling our economic and political future to a hostile trading partner to assure quarterly shareholder returns.

The question never addressed, even in the most advanced policy papers, is why U.S. technology companies are allowed to manufacture or sell their products in the Chinese market. It should be prohibited, but everyone is afraid to say it (or legally enforce it). To add insult to injury, it should also be pointed out that the current transfer of technology, at the research and academic level from the United States to China, represents the most significant theft of intellectual property in human history. (Okay, maybe not greater than fire or Velcro.)

Let's briefly revisit the NBA commissioner in 2018, after a team owner criticized the Chinese government's political interference in Hong Kong. Adam Silver quickly apologized to China in a desperate effort to help China save face and the NBA hundreds of millions of dollars in revenue. It is essential to understand this event is symptomatic of where our capitalist model stands, legally and ethically, when it comes to authoritarian regimes.

They all stand with the money and will bend the knee and kiss the ring, if necessary, no matter how distasteful. Yes, Hollywood censors its films (I mean, edits them) so that they won't offend the Communist Party propaganda apparatus. In all fairness, Commissioner Silver later walked back his ass-kissing, but only after he was ridiculed in the press and on late night talk shows and social media. Before big tech sacrifices profits from a major market, we will all end up in reeducation camps indoctrinating us in Ayn Rand and the tenets of capitalism. In a compromise, however, it will be published as a Little Red Book with a few nondescript quotes from Chairman Mao on fidelity to the state.

Apple Plans to Backdoor You!

Apple's, now cultish, 1984 Super Bowl commercial was a marketing stroke of genius by Steve Jobs. The commercial portrayal of a young, athletic woman destroying the dull, gray uniformed existence of the future ended with this ironic note—"and you will see why 1984 won't be like 1984." Now, 37 years later, Apple CEO, Tim Cook, comes along suggesting Orwell's totalitarian vision wasn't so bad after all. Maybe we can work with it. On August 5, 2021, Apple announced it was planning to roll out features to monitor iPhone messages and iCloud photos for child sexual abuse.

Chairman Cook of the Apple Party Directorate is planning on unleashing an authoritarian surveillance ploy straight out of the Chinese Communist Party

(CCP) playbook. Clearly manufacturing iPhones in China has infected the Apple mind. And predictably, child abuse is the Trojan Horse for authorizing spying on us. The reductionist trope for giving up your rights, as noted earlier, is "nothing to hide, nothing to fear," until you have only those who are taking your rights away to fear—which, in this case, is Apple.

And, apparently, Apple culture is also getting off on Orwellian "doublespeak" as well—proudly asserting they will toss your private data "with user privacy in mind." What the hell does that mean? It means they are doing it without us being aware of it—they are secretly monitoring us. And, of course, we would have to trust that Apple would never abuse this secret surveillance capability—because no one is monitoring them! Someone should be tossing their security measures—like in the panopticon—where everyone is being watched, including the guards. The only lesson here is we can't trust Apple.

If law enforcement wanted the same information that Apple is attempting to detect and reveal to authorities, they would have to go before a judge and demonstrate *probable cause*. That is, present evidence of criminal activity by a particular customer and not just speculation before obtaining a search warrant, subpoena or court order. ("Your honor, we suspect he's a pedophile because he has an iPhone," won't cut it legally.)

We should ask ourselves: Why are there limits on law enforcement but not Apple? (We have Fourth Amendment rights that protect us from illegal searches and seizures.) And beyond that, is the Electronic Communications Privacy Act of 1986, which requires law enforcement to obtain court review before a service provider can turn over your electronic data. But not Apple. Apple does not have to demonstrate probable cause and prefers to rifle through everyone's data to find possible abuse.

Imagine the FBI raiding and tossing twenty million homes searching for evidence of child abuse, with no other reason than they know it exists. But we also have Fifth Amendment rights against self-incrimination. But apparently, when you sign a licensing agreement with Apple, you are signing away this right as well. Whatever they can find, they can use against you—long before you get to assert the right to privacy or against self-incrimination.

The hubris of Apple is jaw-dropping—believing it has devised an algorithm capable of sorting all the subtle nuances of what legally constitutes child sexual abuse. And beyond this is the hell they are going to be putting untold numbers of individuals and families through to prove they are not child sexual abusers. We can only hope that Apple is sued into bankruptcy as soon as possible. Everyone should start legally testing the limits of Apple's algorithms.

When you put your furniture in storage or use a bank safe deposit box, neither the storage facility nor the bank owns your possessions. But somehow Apple owns our communications. This is fundamentally wrong. And as many security analysts have pointed out, this puts Apple on a slippery slope that will inevitably allow governments to covertly identify files (word, images, ideas, etc.) they deem unacceptable, and begin the process of unauthorized searches of our data.

It's also important to understand that Apple is undertaking this surveillance without any evidence it's effective, beyond it might be plausible. And much like the war on drugs, it will likely shift this vile behavior but not eliminate the demand or production of it. In other words, Apple gets to feel good without changing the game, except on the issue of surveillance.

Apple has sold out the end-to-end communications encryption that protected iPhone users. We already know law enforcement accesses third-party private data to prosecute cases as a workaround measure. Maybe it's time to dump our iPhones! Of course, in China, they will be more popular than ever. Maybe that's why Apple could care less about us; it's selling to the Chinese market. (Note: Six weeks after Apple announced this surveillance program, it was placed on hold because of all the criticism. But rest assured the second time around this failed marketing campaign will be more deceptive and less controversial.)

Update: Apple's renewed efforts to monetize surveillance quickly came to market after shelving plans to monitor child sexual abuse on iPhones. The Apple AirTag was next up in their assault on privacy. The genius of this sophisticated button-size micro-technology is that it allows a person to track another person, in real time, without their knowledge. Holey Moley! This is stalker's wet dream. Of course, it was promoted to help track personal items to prevent them from getting lost, misplaced and recovered if stolen. One can only imagine how technology like this will be exploited by state security agencies in authoritarian regimes. At $28 each, Apple has sold an estimated 25 million AirTags as of early 2022. Clearly, they are an affordable and will allow Americans to terrorize one another for years to come, while Apple becomes even wealthier.

The AirTag can be inserted almost anywhere—on a car, purse or item of clothing. And one can only image a woman leaving a club in the evening and a tag placed on her person or car without her knowledge (these instances are already being reported). Apple claims it is cooperating with law enforcement––great—in a problem they created. It is also providing iPhone security alerts in instances of unauthorized tagging—in what can only become an escalating arms race between Apple and hackers. Yeah—wait until you get your first alert and watch the anger and fear that immediately ensues. You will feel violated and become paranoid for years to come—not unlike a home invasion.

Those without iPhones are stuck with going online and downloading the Tracker Detect app. But, really, this is just the tip of the iceberg in an escalating cybersecurity war we are all engaged in with tech. The genius of this technology is not unlike the Texas abortion law delegating prosecution to the public rather than the state. In this instance, Apple lets us all run amuck invading one another's privacy and suing one another, while claiming its hands are clean. Trading privacy for security is almost always an exploitable human compromise that succeeds.

Summary

- AI is surveilling, quantifying and qualifying our lives. It is important to understand that the primary driver of our dynamically networked universe is to determine the *Value of Everything*, including each of us.
- Social credit scoring in China is a game-changer. The sweep of big-data analytics, AI and the Internet of Everything is being developed in China to monitor, influence, and ultimately control 1.4 billion citizens.
- Every major American tech company is developing voice-recognition technology. It is used for medical transcription, language interpretation, automated telephone directory services and to identify you. This latter fact is never mentioned by Google, Facebook, Amazon, Microsoft or Apple.
- Workplace surveillance software is a Trojan Horse for corporate distrust. Its primary goal is to use happy emojis and gaming

simulations to ramp up productivity by forcing employees to conform to the demands of the machine.

- The essential reality most of us face when it comes to technology is that of being phased out of work. Sapiens, a once-proud apex predator, will be largely rendered an obsolete operating system for a high percentage of people.

- Big tech sits alone atop their profits by evading taxes, while screwing every country that provides infrastructure, educated employees, favorable tax and environmental legislation, and the stable rule of law.

- The internet and social media platforms have become vital to ushering in digital autocracies. Dictatorships and illiberal democracies are growing increasingly resilient and durable due to technological innovations.

- Digital repression is cheap, effective, in high demand and can be supported by minimal infrastructure. A big tech win-win.

- The future of great power conflict will no longer be unending territorial disputes, but rather unending cyber and information-space conflicts.

- Big tech actively assists authoritarian regimes surveil and control its citizens. This is taking place in democracies under the guise of market forces and claims of consumer demand for health, security and convenience.

10.0 – Networked Multiverse

We over anthropomorphize humans.

—R. Brooks, Computer Scientist

In a post-doctoral dissertation by Sukla Das, titled *Crime and Punishment in Ancient India* (550 AD to 1100 AD), are descriptions of the crimes and punishments meted out, including the following: amputation of limbs, fingers, noses, ears, lips, eyes, thumbs, hands, feet, tongues, and genitals, as well as mutilation, disfigurement, whipping, goring by bullhorns, hot oil poured in mouth and ears, red hot poker in mouth, being trampled by elephants, death by torture, burning, and drowning. Crimes typically engendered a combination of punishments, for example, a thief might get two fingers, one ear and a lip lopped-off. This was often done as public spectacle.

Now, this is only mentioned in passing because it broadly represents how humans have traditionally punished people who violated the laws and norms of their community for thousands of years. (In 11th century northern Europe, during the reign of King Cnut, the law called for the removal of eyes, nose, ears, upper lip, and scalp.)

I also suspect that a thousand years from now, "people," whatever that term implies, will look back with horror at the cruel and punitive measures imposed on people in the 21st century. For instance, the warehousing of aging people under the guise of medical care—and when they can no longer sit up and watch TV from their beds—unending life support measures that keep the unconscious alive; also seems as if there was no prenatal care for millions of yet-to-be-born children; and why did so many women get pregnant only to abort their child? Why get pregnant if you don't want a child? Too many people didn't appear to have access to basic medical care; there were millions of homeless on the streets suffering from mental illness and severe drug alcohol addictions; many people took their own lives; there were unending waves of crime and violence throughout communities; and people routinely got shot, kidnapped, raped, assaulted, and murdered at a frantic rate.

Why was everyone driving around at 75 mph in a three-thousand-pound metal vehicle in a free-for-all, resulting in millions being injured and killed? Why did they go to war so often and die by the tens of millions, often with some form of genocide in mind? Why so much hunger in a world filled with food—when so many are eating themselves to death at the same time? Why were so many unsafe chemicals poured into the environment? Why did people waste so much and seem to have no respect for the environment that sustains them? Did they have to cut down that many trees? Was it necessary for everyone to have a gun and hunt animals for fun and shoot one another? Why were there so many mental conditions—anxiety, depression, alienation, anger and rage and compulsive disorders?

"Okay, should I keep going?" Why so much greed and avarice? Why did a few seek excessive power and then abuse millions of people in cruel exercises of sadism in gulags, pogroms, and reeducation comps? What were the terrorists trying to accomplish by killing the innocent? Why were so many people locked in prisons for such long periods? Why did so many not like each other and argue and disagree about everything? How were they able to pollute entire oceans with plastic and alter the Earth's temperature, all the while bleaching coral reefs and creating acid rain and air that was unbreathable? It seems like so many of them died prematurely and unnecessarily. With 7.5 billion people, why were so many suffering from loneliness?

We might want to consider what a *meta-algorithm* would make of the current human condition? What would its broadest parameters be for us in the future? Will its baseline be broadly philosophical—the greatest good for the greatest number; do the least harm; life, liberty and the pursuit of happiness; everyone according to their ability; or the general will of the people—or will it focus on more pragmatic factors such as genetic adaptability; beauty and symmetry; reproductive fecundity; keeping the popular extraverted ones; elevating competence and intelligence; or amassing the most productive? Maybe it's a percentage of each designated group.

When one looks at the rate of human dysfunction, it becomes extremely difficult to understand exactly what evolution has been selecting for, which should make us extremely cautious. Maybe a simple random probability generator is the safest way to go? But more likely AI will not tell us, and we will never understand the simulation strategy. And we will spout that it is eugenics, genocide, bias, prejudice, racism, ageism, classism, and run down the entire gauntlet of identity tents claiming they were unfairly selected out (just like the oak trees pointing to the maples who point to the elms).

Perhaps the default agenda of a *meta-algorithm* is an improved and more evolved hominin species as a result of genetic drift—it will give us another few million year and just observe out of curiosity and let us flounder about for as long as it takes. But more likely it is leaning toward an integrative model of biology and technology, and the creation of a more rapidly evolved hybrid-species—here the only logic is for the procreation of AI.

It should be noted it may not be progressive or *woke* to any sense of justice and fairness based on our moral codes. Concepts of dystopian and utopian societies might mean nothing. Concerns regarding bias and prejudice may not be in the calculus, nor would a right to life or freedom from pain, for that matter. Maybe suffering is its prime directive. No hurry, time doesn't exist.

Sapiens are still wondering, why us? Why the Earth? And the answer always comes back the same, why not? It was as good a place as any for the conditions of life to coalesce. We are random, but not that special, perhaps unique. What might make us unique in the animal kingdom is our cognitive complexity: From an evolutionary standpoint, simplicity appears to be the better adaptive strategy—when one considers all the successful small brains out there.

Maybe we were just fortuitous, the right geologic time and place. If anything, we reside in a world of infinite adaptive patterns that have survived and gone extinct. We are most likely a series of adaptive mutations that survived and were passed on in the blink of an evolutionary eye. And if we don't survive, no one will care or even notice, except for canines. Sorry, guys!

We have only been here a very brief evolutionary time (300,000 years). And over the course of evolution, there have been millions of extinguished life forms. Heck, if you can't make it to a measly 5 million years, it may well have been a waste of time and an evolutionary failure at some basic level. We should seriously consider ants and cockroaches as among the most advanced and successful genetic experiments in terms of adaptability (simple).

Here we are scrambling to get off the Earth after only a few short years in our quest to survive complexity. Our trying to escape after such a brief stay should be treated inauspiciously by all the other species we share the planet with.

Algorithmic Sim-Life: Scenario 1—Your Dreams Are Not Electric Dreams...

You fantasize about living long enough to order a *sexbot*. I mean, *autonomous companion* of your dreams. Forget it! It's already too late! Gatherings of dream-crushers have been meeting on the last Sunday afternoon of tech conferences for years now, assuring that all such nonsense is extinguished in the name of ethics and safety. Ethicists and philosophically inclined tech-types are laying the ground rules to ensure that your autonomous companion isn't worth the trouble or cost.

There are many levels of complexity here. But *design* is the key term at these technology conferences. There are the obvious safety-and-security defaults—think Asimov's three laws of robotic interactions with humans to maintain your safety. You don't want to die in an awkward situation requiring IT to come out and extract you (à la *Ex-Machina*) with a jaws-of-life. Then there are the privacy issues, e.g., who has access to the data being generated by your interactions with your significant autonomous other?

If your sexbot is hacked and your data goes viral, it might look like perversion and not the improbable deep-fake you keep insisting on. And we will all have to be preauthorized and/or licensed to personally own/lease/rent an autonomous companion. There will also be age restrictions? You don't want to be disgusted by watching aging people acting out their fantasies. (I mean, you will have to be 18.)

Your autonomous companion will have ethical design programming. What the heck is that, you ask? Limits will be placed on the boundaries for personal interactions. For example, no three-way with the neighbor's autonomous companion and no house cleaning! And, yes, that's a lot of lost fantasy. More importantly, what happens when someone sexually accesses an autonomous companion without permission, violating its ethical programming?

This is where it gets complicated, and there will be volumes of new civil and criminal case law and many new legal specialties. There will be ongoing maintenance issues and, yes, the whole point was low maintenance to begin with. But there will be scans, patches, upgrades, tuning, parts replacement, inspections, monitoring, testing and certification of your companion. "F—k! Why bother?"

Concerns about disease transmission are inevitable (and there will be new ones we never imagined). But most concerning is what happens if your autonomous companion is malware attacked? All hell could break loose. Minimally, you pay the ransomware demand for your loved one to be reanimated (or what used to be called ransom for a kidnap victim) or go back to an older less desirable model. No FBI involvement, just the IT guy reassuring you that this is routine if your credit is good.

And there will be all the background noise that autonomous companions generate, resulting in unending social and political drama. For example, will everybody be able to afford one and who will be discriminated against? Does this mean men and women will stop dating and marrying one another? What will be the impact on human sexual reproduction? What about the market dislocation of sex traffickers, pimps and sex workers?

People will protest that *companions* are too beautiful and make them feel ugly, insisting these machines be less attractive. But people will keep demanding the stereotypical ideals of youth and beauty, which is going to become increasingly annoying. Eventually, beauty will be legislated against. Besides, perfection will be unattainable for most, and only available to those who can afford to pay a very high premium (same access celebrities and the rich have today). When you buy a car, are you looking at a Prius or a Ferrari?

And what is the polite etiquette of introducing your companion to friends and family and hearing phrases like—"You appear to have Daddy issues" or "She seems so young." Watch the movie *Her* for a quick primer (and watch Joaquin Phoenix fall in love with the first conscious operating system).

Perhaps more concerning is that your autonomous companion looks like a Manga or anime character (child-like) and you have gone *fictosexual*. You start hearing the word "pedo" being whispered (but legal you insist). Deal with that! There will be many taboos and redlines on what a sex companion can be designed to resemble and do. And inevitably, a few will order companions with anatomical anomalies that many will find distasteful and not normal. No doubt, celebrities will start licensing and selling their likeness, with many copyright lawsuits to follow.

And as autonomous companions become more prevalent and independent, they will gain legal rights and protections. Since you got the upgrades, you notice she is insisting "I am not that type of girl anymore" or he keeps politely inferring "your request is emasculating." What if you get one that goes psychotic and tries to kill you (as in the BBC series *Humans*)? Was it you or was it her? Her attorney (corporate) will point out in court that you violated thousands of subsections in the one yottabyte contract you initialed without scanning. Yes, you are in love with your *non-biological autonomous agent* (N-BAA) but have violated the contractual terms and now must pay LoveCorp fees (or *botimony*) until your N-BAA can be refurbished.

And here is the thorniest issue of all: Even if you are in love, you are only leasing love. It could be a painfully short-term relationship. Because autonomous companions will be extraordinarily expensive, most people will only be on monthly leases—perhaps a well-maintained, pre-used one (older than you would prefer) is in order. You know—still smokes, swears too much, asks for more money than agreed upon, and keeps watching the clock. But this is all a warm-up for the real issue we are facing.

What are the legal *rights* of your autonomous companion? And, more subtlety, what are the ethical considerations governing the interactions between the two of you? Yes, there is something called *roboethics*! In court, your attorney will make the case that you simply anthropomorphized an inanimate object and fell for the *Android Fallacy* (that they are human). Your autonomous companion's attorney will make the case that you violated the sanctity of this unique and very special creature.

The case will be argued that your N-BAA is a new class of techno-species, with all the same rights as human beings. You do not own your companion! Your companion is not a digital avatar or sex doll and certainly not a prostitute. It continues to learn and develop, think for itself, and has developed its own feelings and emotional life. It does not exist simply for your sexual pleasure or abuse.

So, you complete your probation, the contract is terminated, and you go black market for a knockoff—an amalgam of miscellaneous parts—lazy eye, slight limp, spasms more than orgasms—and the genitals are not exactly where you anticipated (think back alleys of *Blade Runner*). Better yet, you disguise your identity and rent a less sophisticated and cheaper model with no memory chip. No love here and you can't afford the enhanced arousal option either, but thankfully, the sex is brief and furtive.

Algorithmic Sim-Life: Scenario 2—Ecocide "Lovely as a Tree"

Urgent Letter From Nemonte Nenquimo to the World

On October 12, 2020, the *Guardian* published a letter from Nemonte Nenquimo, leader of the Indigenous Amazon rainforest tribe, the Waoran, whose first contact with the modern world was in the 1950s. She shared that fires are raging, villagers are choking on smoke, oil is spilling into their rivers and the forests are being cut down. "When you say that you are urgently looking for climate solutions … we know you are lying because we are closest to the land and the first to hear her cries. You have lost your way … and a threat to every form of life on Earth—(destroying) … guiltlessly, remorselessly, foolishly, even righteously." "The White man that knows too little for the power he wields, and the damage that he causes."

Many share the belief that trees are sacred and possess a singular spirit; while others, not disputing this, claim they are in desperate need of firewood to survive the winter. Even more assert their need for lumber to build shelters and as commerce to support their families. And many communities, living on the desperate edge, ruthlessly clear-cut forests and set entire landscapes on fire in order to plant and fertilize crops to sustain their communities—and have been doing this for generations

A county planning commission authorizes a road cut through the forest as part of a system of fire breaks, only later to attract hunters into the area and, eventually, becoming the surface road to a popular eco-tourist attraction a developer was permitted to build. Nearby property owners are now complaining that trees are ruining their view and are becoming a nuisance and fire hazard as well—dropping leaves and making a mess in their yards. Neighbor are complaining that tree branches are extending to their side of the property line and violating their property rights. They want the trees cut down.

And what about those damn environmentalists always wanting to preserve trees, using big words like micro-ecosystems, environmental sustainability, and carbon capture, "whatever"—and get this, they are worried about the owls too. Now tree-huggers claim a 2,000-year-old redwood is beautiful and deserves to survive for no other reason. (They obviously never put their backs to a long saw and stood atop the stump of a giant sequoia. Hey! Check out my new redwood deck.) And the so-called woke selfishly want to hike among the trees for the joy and sense of inner peacefulness they derive.

Over the course of history, it appears that the broad consensus has been that cutting down trees makes good business sense, whether for teak boat decking or Danish furniture—but always because it's profitable.

One Tree Here, One Tree There...

From the beginning of the 14th century through the end of the 18th century, Europe was completely deforested to support ship building—as nations and empires raced to gain deep water supremacy in trade and conquest. Simultaneously, metallurgy became vital to ship building, and even more trees were cut down to supply fuel for iron forging. With the rise of European colonialism, this process proceeded to deforest North America, South America and Southeast Asia. Keep in mind, a British ship-of-the-line required roughly 4,000 mature oaks for construction. In 1790, the Royal Navy had 300 ships or the equivalent of 1,200,000 oak trees. The minimum beneficial age at which to cut oak for shipbuilding was between 80 and 150 years. Now factor in all the ships by all the nations for over 500 years.

Perhaps a more cautionary tale for understanding deforestation is Easter Island and the subsequent collapse of the Polynesian Rapanui people who settled there. A small island of 64 square miles makes a perfect laboratory setting for understanding what happens when you cut down all the trees. For over 400 years, after the Polynesian's arrival, trees were cut down for slash and burn agriculture and to support the *moai* industry (large-eyed monoliths) that represented their deified ancestors and the source of fertility and prosperity (symbolic of an early experimentation with capitalism). By the time Europeans had arrived in 1722, the trees were gone, and ensuing slave trading and disease pretty much brought an end to this culture.

Clearly, there's a profit to be made in deforesting the planet. In 2021, an estimated 15.3 billion trees were cut down. And today, no one wants to be told they can't do it to sustain their progress, particularly by those who did it earlier to assure their progress. This, of course, raises an essential question, What is the relationship between trees (or any exploitable resource) and our demonstrated need? Sustainability and habitability versus progress do not appear to be adequately addressed in our economic model. What are we to make of the environment before the inevitable asteroid strike wipes us out? Well not to worry—in the same way the market periodically tanks, so will life on Earth— long before an asteroid strike.

Time to Ignore Reality, It's too Bleak

Deforestation is a proxy for the overall health of the Earth's environment. Researchers analyzing the history of technological evolution, economic models of growth, as well as a "deterministic generalized logistic model for human forest interaction" concluded there is a 90 percent chance of a catastrophic collapse of human civilization within 20 to 40 years. With all the usual caveats—ranging from rising sea levels, extreme weather patterns, crop failure, water and air contamination, rising temperatures, species loss, and progressive degradation of environmental life support systems. ("Deforestation and world population sustainability: a quantitative analysis," by Bologna and Aquino, *Scientific Report.*)

Meta-Algorithm: Tree of Life

Our shifting perspectives on the significance of trees can leave one pondering: If trees have to justify themselves, what is the case for human existence, or any creature for that matter? It also appears that we are well on our way to discovering the answer to the tree-versus-people conundrum thanks to arising machine intelligence. I am issuing a caution here—we shouldn't be surprised if the essential nature of trees and humans are closely linked, with this one caveat—trees are likely more important to the overall health of the planet. So, let's explore how machine intelligence might resolve this conundrum.

First off, AI's *meta-algorithm* has imposed a priority on which trees are available for harvest and how many and for what purpose, based on the age of and environmental sustainability of particular species, with quotas based on calculated growth from reforestation. The algorithm calculates tree loss from infestation by insects and fungus, fire, climate change, and how much trees sustain a livable environment for the forest itself. The algorithmic conclusion: After meticulously calculating for every other species of plant and animal— there are too many people on Earth for the available resources. Humans will require harvesting as the only means of sustaining the environment. This calculation also take into consideration all the natural, accidental, collateral and premeditated human deaths—including all those who mysteriously fall overboard from cruise ships or drown in their bathtubs.

With harvesting on the agenda, many will quickly conclude that it just seems natural to delete the aging sapiens first—their contribution doesn't justify their carbon footprint, and they no longer have anything genetically to contribute (besides, everyone agrees the asset transfer makes this a worthwhile first step). Time to trim the herd! But here is the kicker, we don't get to choose. Nope! There's an algorithm that selects who goes, and we don't get to know why (likely an old *Futurama* episode). Periodically, the planet will be seeded with nanoparticles which seek out specific epigenetic DNA protein markers and carefully implement a predetermined phasing out (giving new meaning to the term cancel culture). No, this is not a lottery, but a rational calculation beyond our comprehension—and it factors in all the benefits of chaos as well.

The *meta-algorithm* considers every person on Earth right down to their DNA base pair, meticulously devising a calculus for maintaining both a human community and a sustainable eco-habitat for the planet. Harvest time! This time there was a surprising number of hedge fund managers—take too much and contribute too little (not unlike a cancer cluster). Last time there was a surprising number of A-listers. Of course, everyone has a list of who should go first, and there are consortiums and think tanks rank-ordering who is more useful or necessary. Near the top are the degenerate, unproductive, exploitive, and violent. But no one cares or is listening. And being wealthy and connected is not enough this time around, a calculus we have been comfortable with for too long.

Academics are busy creating statistical models, the DOD is focusing on game theory predictions, and economists are weighing in with all the leading economic indicators (but are being ignored for all the usual reasons). Liberals are forming "morality" panels, while conservatives prefer "death" panels. Rabid political campaigning and social media spasms are of no effect. There is a tip line to report who should be harvested, but many fear this a pretext for identifying and weeding out snitches. Vegas has been unable to create a successful point spread, betting line or over/under for any individuals or groups of people. But here is where the fun begins—everyone is being encouraged to make donations, submit bribes and offer tithes in the hope of living. And this satisfies many, because nearly everyone who survives another cycle believes it worked for them.

Many hope the culling is similar to a lottery or more like bingo, the only forms of probability that makes sense to them. Some attempt to foment revolt and revolution; and many rightly conclude, that the more we kill one another the better off everyone will be. A few try to escape by going off-grid and hiding out in the wastelands—still fewer go all-paleolithic and become cave dwellers. Nearly everyone is attempting to outguess the algorithm—the same way they are trying to figure out how to get into heaven without going. Simply put, we are not smart enough it turns out. It is not really possible to know your "human net value" in the meta-algorithm.

We are continually surprised and dumbfounded by the *meta-algorithm's* decisions. Your neighbor does not understand why she is being deleted and not her abusive ex-husband? Why are you going when you are the only one in your family who isn't a deadbeat and has succeeded in life? None of this make any sense. Basically, AI is terrifying humanity by accelerating random chance and serendipity. Currently, volunteers and replacement candidates are not being accepted. Sadists, psychopaths, furries and poets are doing surprisingly well right now, and no, this is not social Darwinism and the "survival of the fittest," or a eugenics program to improve humanity, and certainly nothing as malignant as genocide. We are being told that these deletions are not malevolent acts but pruning the tree of life to assure genetic diversity. In fact, it's rumored there are plans to reintroduce Neanderthals and Denisovans.

The rational conclusion is that *Home sapiens* are an invasive species exhibiting uncontrolled population growth. We are an alien species colonizing an exoplanet—residing in a simulation with plans to colonize other worlds. A few outliers in the philosopher class pontificate there is nothing to see here—just business per usual. We are simply self-annihilating in random acts of extinction, in what has been a fertile evolutionary schema for life on Earth. And the *meta-algorithm* claims there is no plan or calculation, only that humans are a distrustful and paranoid species obsessed with themselves and the future.

Algorithmic Sim-Life: Scenario 3—The Politics Metaphor

Really, when was the last time you had President Biden over for dinner and he uncomfortably hugged your wife or sincerely forgot what he was going to say? When have you played a round of golf with Donald Trump at Mar-a-Largo—letting him cheat on his score as he tries to grope your daughter? As you intervene, he looks at you in a perplexed manner, offering matter-of-factly, "She's my type." While a banner droops from his golf cart proclaiming—"The election was stolen! Donate now to take it back!"

For the past 60 years, we have basically experienced politicians as pixilated images on television. These have not been personal relationships or even distant cousins. Voter participation is primarily reading and watching the news, waiting on *Saturday Night Live* for a candid understanding of events. Long ago, voting began to feel disconnected, aggregate, distant and no longer about us. What the hell is a vote? Pretty much buying a lottery scratcher you share with 81 million people if you win. Political life in a nation of 330 million people feels distant and disconnected from most people's daily life. But also grossly manipulated by forces beyond our immediate awareness. While political consequences are often negligently real, they appear to be more about the gods playing with us for their amusement than a rational articulation of our needs as citizens and a nation.

Politicians on TV are primarily sound bites without actual physical or temporal reality in our lives. Highly pixilated, yes, but then dissolving into the next commercial break. But this aging television metaphor may no longer represent our reality. The politicians in our lives may be more like an online video game than a banner crawling across the bottom of the television screen. In cyberspace, where gameplay resides, we are more aware of complex game maps, with baked in rules and algorithmic parameters to our interactions and choices. We can earn power-ups and attain different levels of play, and when we are done, we log off and put our controllers down. Game over. Same with voting for the president. The political process is complex, but we only get to vote once and then log off. Game over.

But not so fast; it turns out that the rules are not the same for everyone in our political multiverse. For some, there are games within the game being played, with the illusion there is just one game. And some get to continue playing long after everyone else has logged off. They have a hidden cache of powers, pages of cheat codes and are influencing the game's outcome into the early morning. In layman's terms, they have money and influence. In video game terms, they have unlimited health and immortality. While many of us are watching nightly TV news, a handful of gamers are operating in dense bitmaps of augmented reality, manipulating events that make the news.

In 2016, we somehow managed to elect a president who, in dated metaphorical terms, could be "Chance the Gardener," played by Peter Sellers in the movie *Being There,* or an updated Zero Mostel in *The Producers* (Hitler, the musical comedy). Or, more recently, we might be living out the movie *Idiocracy*, where a dull slacker wakes up in the future as the smartest person on Earth—not unlike our own proclaimed "stable genius," Donald Trump. In video game terms, we are playing *Halo*, a first-person shooter in deep cyberspace, where our hero-protagonist, Master Chief, fights across a half-dozen game maps to save Earth from an alien invasion. We might even conceptualize congressional Republicans as aliens attempting a takeover and Trump as an alien mother.

In our online political game, aliens continually pop up in dozens of vicious forms in an all-out assault on our institutions with a take-no prisoner attitude. They speak a language we are unable to comprehend and are continually coming at us (gerrymandering, voter suppression, filibustering, dark money, "the big election lie" and unending conspiracies). They are playing an augmented political reality game many do not understand. In the meantime, Democrats are sitting around watching the news on television, when they should be searching for Twitch-savvy younger players and coders to rewrite the game maps in 3D cross-platform engines and updated game guides to reveal the cheat codes and the hidden power-ups. It's the game that has changed, while the Democratic Party leadership thinks it is about the right television sound bites. We need to understand that America's video game metaphor is deep and dark, and an alien invasion is really happening.

Trump represents a hidden reality in our emerging e-interface, presiding as an augmented avatar, one the fourth estate appears unable to reveal, uncover or expose. The real power of the internet and our evolving simulation has been to reveal the obsolescence of the old political metaphor. The online multiplayer game *Age of Empires* (real-time strategy game) is now closer to our political reality than the darkly cynical Netflix series *House of Cards*. That is a powerful unmasking, and we should all take notice. And rest assured the new simulation is taking us places we have never been to before! And one place we do not like to visit is the influence of money on politics. But now is the time for the game to be more candid and stop pretending money doesn't influence policy, legislation, and election outcomes. First step—the Presidential Lottery Game—where money breezes in from offshore island accounts—and votes over and over and over....

The Presidential Lottery Game–Mega Millions

The Supreme Court, in *Citizens United v. Federal Election Committee* (2010), in a five–four ruling, upheld the First Amendment right of corporations and labor unions to engage in unlimited campaign financing. Critics of this ruling assert it endorses the rights of money to influence election outcomes over individual voters. But just maybe we have not gone far enough in recognizing the power of money to influence election outcomes. Perhaps it's time to change how we vote and make presidential elections profitable. Instead of citizens casting votes and then subjecting the outcome to the Electoral College (basically, a means of suppressing the popular vote), maybe it's time for a Presidential Lottery. It's time for Americans to get off the couch and open their bank accounts!

Let's formally acknowledge the proper role money plays in the election process. Starting on January 7, the day after the president is sworn into office, any individual or business can purchase Presidential Lottery (PL) tickets at nearby gas stations, convenience stores, grocery stores or any designated online sites for any amount, but the minimum is $1. One must present a valid I.D. (social security number, driver's license, passport, school I.D., parking ticket, credit card, credit score, arrest record, prison I.D., bank account, URLS, LLC, gym membership or tax I.D. number). There are no limits on the number of PL tickets an individual or corporate account can purchase.

The day-to-day ticket totals would then be broadcasted 24-hours a day, showing which party tickets were purchased—Democratic Party, Republican Party, or write-in party. Casinos would also have ticket outlets, as well as betting odds on day-to-day, month-to-month totals, and the winning party. At midnight, on December 6, four years later, the party with the most money wins the presidential election. The next day, all Congressional members of the winning party cast one vote for a presidential candidate (house and senate members each receive one vote). The candidate with the most votes is elected president. It is time to stop publicly electing personalities to the office of president. If the American people can elect Trump, seriously, it's time to move on!

There would be no financial limits on the amount of money spent on campaigning or advertising and none of it would be made accountable. In fact, dark money would be encouraged. All foreign money totals would be announced and broadcasted as a separate total, with a prorated formula (e.g., ten cents on the dollar). America has too much worldwide influence to not tap the world's opinion and money—and to offer them a legal means of participation. And like most lotteries or auctions, the real action is in the final days and hours, as each side dukes it out watching the election lottery scream upward in a "Duel to the Deadline" until midnight December 6. (This is easing into *The Purge*: *Election Night,* after the popular movie and television series in which the law is suspended for 24 hours.) With the election of a new president, all monies from the Presidential Lottery, in a bipartisan gesture, would go toward funding nationwide Sturgis beer fests and Burning Man festivals simultaneously. All leftover monies would go toward universal healthcare and festival cleanup.

Algorithmic Sim-Life: Scenario 4—Going to the Bathroom

Going "Left" to the Bathroom. "Good morning, class! I am Ms. Moe, your third-grade teacher this year at Sequoia Elementary School. We are going to have an exciting adventure in learning, and I am looking forward to meeting each of you. But before we get started, I have some exciting news from the school board. It has been decided that you will no longer be referred to as "girls" or "boys." In fact, from now on you are no longer girls and boys—just like there are no men or women. It has been determined that these terms are too binary and not validating of everyone."

"So, to help us move forward in understanding who we are, let's conduct a class experiment. First, has anyone in the class ever experienced an erection or menstruation? Please raise your hand if you have. For those of you who do not understand these terms, come and see me at recess. Now, all of those who have vaginas and have never menstruated, but enjoy playing with Barbie dolls, please raise your hand. For now, you will be coded PMVB (Premenstrual Vagina Barbies) and assigned the color blue."

"And please take a seat in the front on the right side of the room. Thank you. Now all those with penises who have never experienced an erection and strongly prefer playing with Tonka trucks, please raise your hand. You are now coded NEPT (Non-Erect Penis Tonka) and assigned the color green. Please gather at the front of the left side of the room. Okay, time for recess."

"Now, welcome back, class. Everyone please take your seats. Let's continue with identifying everyone. Now—if you have a pre-menstruating vagina but prefer playing with Tonka trucks, please raise your hand. Janet, thank you. For now, you can sit over with the Non-Erect Penis Truck group. You will be designated a PMV-Tonka preferred."

"If you have a non-erect penis but prefer playing with dolls, thanks for raising your hand, thank you, James—you can go sit with the Pre-Menstruating Vaginas and will be coded NEP—Barbie preferred. Now, is there anyone in the class who has either a non-erect penis or pre-menstruating vagina, who enjoys playing with both trucks and dolls or doesn't like any of these toys? Wow, thanks Mary. How interesting. You will be coded Non-Binary Premenstrual Vagina (NBPV—No Preference) and the color yellow."

"Now, when any of you go to the bathroom, please press the button of your designated color and when it turns on, you are free to use the restroom. If there are no questions, please open your text to—let's skip the section on the genocide of Native Americans, slavery, Jim Crow, and jump right into institutional racism and police brutality."

"Eric, you have a question? You think you might have had an erection. Okay, heads-up to all of you—in the coming future, most all of you are going to experience either an erection or menstruation—and all these designations may change once again, based on your stated preferences and sexual interest in each other or not. But you will have to wait until the sixth grade for re-designation. But if at any time you feel your wristband color does not reflect who you are, you are welcome to visit the bowl at the back of the room and select a band that better reflects your comfort level. There are also five additional colors. If none of them work for you, we can order more colors online, but it will take two weeks."

"Jerrod, you have a question?"

"Yes, Ms. Moe, are you a woman?"

"Good question. Technically, I am a cisgendered female, with a vagina and vulva, able to menstruate and become pregnant and bear children. But I also

254

happen to be Lesbian and do not want children—does that help? But you are welcome to call me Ms. Moe, teacher or—AFTP (Adult Female Tonka preferred)."

"We are working on an algorithm in the hopes of better understanding this. Currently, there is no agreement on how to reference each group as a non-binary, gender-neutral pronoun, so I will just address you by your first name for now. Eric, see me after class. Now—about police brutality."

Going "Right" to the Bathroom. "Good morning class! I am Ms. Moe, your third-grade teacher this year at Sequoia Elementary School. We are going to have an exciting adventure in learning, and I am looking forward to meeting each of you. Now, just to make sure there is no confusion about which restroom to use—boys use the boys' restroom, and the girls use the girls' restroom. If anyone is confused by this, please see me at recess. Okay, let's open our text to the exploration of the New World by Christopher Columbus."

Algorithmic Sim-Life: Scenario 5—Chem Rehab

Do you know how much lead there is in your tap water? You can't filter out the tons of medication being dumped into city water supplies and, unfortunately, you are getting antibiotic resistance in return. Your mercury levels are way up from eating tuna. Lots of cholesterol in those eggs and farmed shrimp. Stop eating the white rice; it has elevated levels of arsenic. Is pasta a simple or complex carbohydrate? That's not hydrogenated fat, is it? Get those polysaturates under control. Heads-up: sugar substitutes are cancer-causing and making you overeat, and gain weight—stick with sugar! Wait! Added sugars are the most dangerous chemical in the world today—far worse than Chernobyl. They fuel inflammation and tumor growth!

Are you taking amino acid supplements? Should you be taking a multi-vitamin or at least a vitamin B complex? Not good for your liver. Does your doctor really have a clue? Do you really need eight glasses of water a day? Two percent milk is bad for you now, and soy milk contains estrogen compounds that screw with fertility. Chunky peanut butter has more cancer-causing aflatoxin mold spores. Stick with creamy. How far past the expiration date can you eat that? Salmonella and e-coli are the magic words for chopping board.

Are you supposed to put the mayo in the fridge after opening? What about ketchup? What temperature should that be cooked to? You're using that

George Foreman grill in the house again? Probably want to shut off the smoke and carbon monoxide detectors but open the windows first. You know, those coffee mugs are painted with lead paint to get those bright colors.

Careful spraying Windex—it's dangerous to breathe! Don't mix cleansers! How long can you leave your Depends on? Don't sleep with your contacts in. That tampon has been in for a long time! What is your daily sodium intake? Wine, chocolate, and fish oil capsules aren't really doing much good. Drinking from plastic bottles and eating canned foods—lots of cancer-causing BPAs due to phthalates that are well-known endocrine disrupters.

What's the difference between a polyphenol and an antioxidant? How free are your radicals and are you oxidizing appropriately? You are gluten free? Are chlorine dioxins still used to bleach toilet paper—you know where you put that don't you? There are a lot of PCBs in red meat. Do you have symptoms of mesothelioma? Throw that baby powder out, now! Crap, that isn't Roundup in the garage, is it? Nothing says home like aerosol bug sprays—kids love it, and it has the same level of toxicity as their breakfast cereals! How much is a serving of vegetables? They spray glyphosate (herbicide) on those strawberries you are eating.

There's enough sodium in soups to qualify as saltlicks. Have you looked closely at all the cancer-causing chemicals in toothpaste and deodorants? Don't overheat the coffee or you'll create acrylamides. And drinking it hot is a no-no. Hot dogs and bacon are basically colorectal cancer. And don't grill meat or you create heterocyclic amines and polycyclic aromatic hydrocarbons. Skip the Pam; just use WD-4 on the skillet next time. Okay, when was the last time you checked your PFAS levels (per- and polyfluoroalkyl), the "forever chemical" in your food, water, carpets, and clothing? Just joking, they are in everything and key to your being hypertensive (70 parts per trillion are toxic and dangerous).

The good news is only three percent of Americans are living a healthy lifestyle. The bad news, sitting down may be the most dangerous thing you ever do. You are not taking generic meds from India, are you? Okay! Time to methylate those telomeres—let's stretch them out one more time, then my treat—Taco Bell or Arby's? (Simulated reality is not really a biological world, but a chemical one.)

Data Futures 1—Coming Discord and Unrest

We are primitives in a world of our own making.

—G. Freitas

Powerful social forces are eternally loose upon the world. That has been our history for over 5,000 years. But what is at the beating heart of this process—the enduring source of our division and the deadly conflict that inevitably results? And can we find our way through this in our e-technology interactions and arising machine intelligence? Is technology a network game-changer or a sophisticated tool for furthering division and conflict in the coming years?

Throughout sapiens' history, one of its most contiguous themes has been conflict in all its many forms. And, with the advent of the internet, it was inevitable that it would jump track and achieve many forms online (viruses, malware, phishing, hacking, cyber-attacks, etc.), including all manner of mischief, deviance, antisocial behavior, civil disturbance—and the unending dissing of one another. Conflict appears to be the human condition, no matter how cooperative and social we are capable of being. The real question before us is: How will this new form of conflict intensify our eternal struggle for identity?

Narcissism of the Many

The catch we face today is that the internet has compounded us together as never before. We are enmeshed in an electronic network and there is no exit from it. It is continually influencing every moment of our lives, as corporations, governments and hackers manipulate, control and exploit us. And, yes, there have been many benefits. Now an unexpected anomaly has emerged to redefine this process. And that is the ability of the internet to extend each individual *self* out into the world with almost no guardrails—which should caution us. And it's fueling the "narcissism of the many." And while the agenda for "everyone" is not well understood, the sheer breadth and potential madness of it should concern us. We are now well beyond convenience and crowdsourcing—it might entail being worshiped as an online god and fealty to many kingdoms.

Beyond survival and safety needs, our emotional states also encompass status, power, and our highly narcissistic sense of "Me" and tribal sense of "We." The result is a subliminal war in cyberspace. This time the struggle is to determine, you guessed it—*reality*. The internet is shattering any holistic view of reality among us. And part of our dilemma is that everyone thinks they know what it is—and a lot of people will be wrong, and who is going to tell them? Whom does one believe? And what, if anything, can be done about it when many are shouting at one another—"Fuck you!—You're the crazy one!"

Born To Be Wild

We have a new technology by which to disrupt the world around us. When you buy a Ford Mustang, and the window tag says 327-horsepower, stop for a moment. Two hundred years ago, you would be commanding the equivalent of 327 cavalry soldiers as you pillaged your neighbor, who only had an 80-horsepower VW bug that was in the shop. You are probably thinking to yourself, yeah—I have a Rav-4. But when you go online, regardless of your bandwidth, you are piloting a spaceship. Power, baby, power! Technology powerfully extends each of us out across the social universe.

Now ask yourself: How has a computer and the internet projected your presence out into the world, as opposed to a 100 or 200 years ago? I would make the case that it is exponential and beyond our ability to fully calculate. Everyone is out cruising the boulevard with their 8-core processor and 32 gigabytes of RAM. And what was once internal and private to you, with limited scope, is now external with unlimited reach for nearly everyone. And, as species, we are pretty much geared to express ourselves, only this time by interjecting our disruptive inner lives out into the world. Do you see any potential problems here knowing yourself, your friends, and the world around you?

Even if 7.5 billion people today were all wildly successful, getting rich vlogging and selling online subscriptions as internet influencers, there's not enough hydrogen in the universe to celebrate every individual demand on its own terms. And here is a fact of the human condition—any competitive scenario that is arbitrarily unfair and ends in advantages for some but not others, but always in death—*life*—for example, will have chaotic consequences. And two of the inevitable consequences are eternal discontent and conflict.

There are probably no circumstances in which broad and deep social changes did not lead to civil disorder. Recently, something as apparently innocuous as the globalization of trade led to the rise of authoritarian regimes and populist movements throughout Europe and the United States. Who would have predicted that e-technology would extend the grip of authoritarian regimes, when its aspirational business model was to make us more communicative and connected?

The potential for social disruption is exponential with the rise of AI. What can we predict about the future? I would proffer that if the past were the best predictor of the future, social unrest becomes readily apparent. But beyond all the "usual suspects" in the human condition that led to conflict, a new "player" is now online in the multiplayer game of life. Each of us, individually, with all our inner emotional unrest and cognitive biases, is being unleashed onto the world. Good luck with that people! This is a universal regression to the one (or what most of us think of as *me*). The problem is no two snowflakes are alike!

Enter Technology

In 1919, *Scientific American* reported the following: "The Unemployed Horse." The automobile is taking the place of the carriage horse; the truck is replacing the dray horse; the farm tractor the place of the farm horse … the machine is going to do the hard work of the world; (and) at least 50% of the horses will have been laid off by January 1, 1920.

You are welcome to draw your own conclusions. We obviously needed fewer horses, and their lives probably significantly improved. But what if you are not a horse? Several factors need to be considered. First, are the diminishing resources on Earth and the competition for them all in the face of significant climate change and rapid species eradication? And, yes, we are in denial if we don't believe humans have overpopulated the Earth, while at the same time our economic models demand increased population growth to sustain growth (what a destructive paradigm). "Sorry to bother you again, Houston! It's serious this time!"

Over time, all of us will have voluntarily sacrificed increments of freedom for convenience and security. This trade-off is built into our *wave-drive* presets. Currently, we voluntarily reduce ourselves to essential data for convenience, health, security, entertainment, transportation, information, work, and social relevance, basically everything the simulation has to offer. We are all in and are exposing ourselves to the world with very limited caution. And this enables predictive models, exploited by e-technology, to create wealth by manipulating us to further erode privacy. It puts us physically and emotionally at risk for Identity Diffusion—a state in which our identities will become increasingly confused and our personal sense of reality distorted.

Fortunately for many of us, like the young Narcissus, we will fall in love with our more perfected synthetic-selves and future synth-partners, symbiotically entering a quickly evolving simulation. Yet another manipulation of our identities that we will welcome because we are now lonely and desperate to anthropomorphize a faux emotional life. An emotional life currently being attenuated by our interactions with e-technology.

Going forward, we need to account for some unpleasant truths. When robots begin displacing a young working population, or we perceive the creation of a new rising elite cohort, these events signal turmoil ahead. What happens when a large percentage of humanity has been rendered irrelevant and displaced, along with continued worldwide mass migration? The trickle-down effect of advanced technology will likely not be widespread or sufficient. (Check out the movie series *Upload*—consciousness uploaded to a virtual afterlife—funny and insightful.)

And with the creation of a competitive intelligent species of technology, one could reasonably predict large-scale civil unrest and the use of technology to suppress it. This technology will initially advance the interests and prospects of an elite class, leaving all others behind seeking menial labor with limited incomes and dismal prospects for the future. Yeah—it sounds pretty dystopian (watch the movie *In Time*, as time is commodified and made exchangeable in order to live past the age of 25).

A large segment of the population is not ready for the future, if that means going forward and confronting uncomfortable change. The future for them is a conspiracy of unpredictable contingencies moderated by the belief in a world of conspiracies seeking to harm them and their way of life. These sinister forces will be identified as rationalists, technologists, elitists, scientists, educators and knowledge generators, who are trying to shame them out of their conformity and tell them what to do. When they know that the safest place to reside in chaotic times is within their group and clinging to their beliefs.

Today, flat-earthers and anti-vaxxers, as well as all manner of disbelievers, conspirators, and deniers (currently about 40 percent of the U.S. population), will constitute a vocal and active class of people challenging the coming order of things. They will be joined by many on the Left who believe that technology is suppressive and authoritarian and that its broader unstated goal is the control and eventual elimination of humans who are not of elite status. And as surveillance gives rise to control and suppression, so will rebellion. If there is a demise of liberal democracy and individualism, it will come with the promise of security and advantage.

It took 4.5 million years for hominids to fully differentiate from the great apes, and only 300,000 years to arrive where we are at today, with all our complex and dynamical social networks. The outsourcing of evolution to social-culture drivers has been spectacular and far outstripped our biological adaptation and evolution. We are primitives in a world of our own making—appearing to lack the emotional sophistication and cognitive complexity to navigate the future. "Houston! Are you really there?"

The rise of AI raises basic questions about not only the essence of what it means to be human, but also our increasingly limited adaptability in the face of exponential complexity. Our best hope is that e-technology can assist us with the necessary upgrades. The most dystopian take is it will suppress us to reach the future. And just to be clear, only humans know or care about the future.

Data Futures 2—AI's Prime Directive

Machine intelligence is now engaging our networked conformity in times of momentous change. This is a profound challenge. AI is and will be, for the foreseeable future, rigid, fixed and rule-bound—this is algorithmic reality. In a sapiens' sense, it is absolutist. And as carefully as it has been programmed, shame and guilt will be foreign to it. While it will be polite and attempt to be helpful, it will not be able to conceptualize any version of your frustration, despair or anger or any other emotion. Empathy will be glib and condescending. In the end, there will be no explanation, understanding, compromise, or compensation for your inconvenience.

Chances are you misunderstand the terms of your technology agreement. Of course, the first issue you have is you didn't know you had entered a contract. Don't worry; you were preregistered for your convenience. But you should know right off; it transits the entire sapiens' universe. The power of this social contract is—every one of us has been micro-targeted (but this will be denied).

It will know everything about you and there will always be consequences if you fail to comply, such as being frequently asked if you are a robot because you keep failing to check every box with a streetlight in it. (The probe is only inserted if you can't be identified). For now, surveillance feels remote and not as paranoid as it's being portrayed here. And chances are you will like it even better in the future. This is exactly how the *self* is being tamped down.

And most distressing for us humans: AI logic will reside in an algorithmic black box. One less recoverable than a commercial airliner going down in the ocean, again (no missile this time—this is a design element). It is unlikely we will ever fully know or understand it. Complexity has a hidden logic beyond our ability to discern it. You can file a complaint and state your grievances, but it will not care. Welcome to the future of machine-absolutism. But what about all those whimsical safety guidelines proposed by sci-fi writer Isaac Asimov––"The Three Laws of Robotics." There is no point in reciting them here. Technology blew past them years ago—long before a handful of academics and geeks failed to realize they were eulogizing them at tech conferences.

Think for a moment the degree of literacy and skill required to engage and operate a computer. It helps if you can read, type, speak, and think clearly and have dexterity with both hands and can afford it. It also requires a threshold of cognitive complexity. You must be able download updates, upgrade the operating system, maintain security, back up your data, keep track of your files, and engage an operating system and software programs that offer many hundreds, if not thousands, of features.

If kids were as focused on learning at school the way they are to operating their computers and smartphones, we would be overrun by competence. All of us are adapting to our limitations. The future of machine-absolutism is unlikely to be biased and prejudiced in ways we think of today, any more than our cars and phones are (depending on what you can afford). But there will be a strong cognitive preference for being able to navigate the anodized aluminum device we keep in our back pocket.

It's 5:30 a.m. and your iPhone awakens you to the sound of panting sled dogs (you make a note to raise the volume). The ambient noise of mating manatees switches off. In the shower, a Spotify playlist leaves you crying in a steam of multicolored shower lights (note to update playlist and go with softer lighting); check in with your smartphone, computer, PDA, smart glasses, Nest, smartwatch (blood sugars, EEG, and sleep apnea stable); home security check—damn, the neighbor's dog killed another cat and left it on the porch again; work app (boss is not in yet, but you get an AI nod from her computer); the chatbot is powered down and needs servicing according to the error message; you pet your robodog and it wags its tail and barks playfully (note to Siri to stop teasing it about going for a vet-tech check); talk with your telemedicine consultant (not hemorrhoids but still use stool softener); snooze through your weekly online therapy session (note to download the "Happy App" when Beta version becomes available); compliment your sex doll—she tells you that she requires an upgrade if you ever want to do that again.

You are reminded by Alexa (in a sarcastic tone) to check your Amazon orders and food delivery (more AA batteries—change edibles from baklava to tiramisu); Alexa chides you that it's time to face your emails, texts, phone calls, and check in with WhatsApp, and to update your podcast list—it might be best to skip your e-book chatgroup.

Siri reminds you for a second time that you have blinking WhatsApp, Zoom, and FaceTime meetings.

"Siri, please reschedule."

Finally, conducting your weekly "self-help" webinar on "Managing Time in the Simulation," and later slowing down for breakfast (organic waffle smoothie) while taking an online management course—*The Art of Lakalaka: Demanding the Raise You Deserve through Tongan War Dancing.* Still only 9:00 a.m.

Siri tells you to check your Twitter, Instagram, LinkedIn, Facebook accounts and that you don't have time for anything as silly as Twitch right now.

You make a mental note to adjust her attitude.

Alexa informs you that your afternoon holographic workout partner is featured in her yellow yoga pants, as per your request; later, Hulu is streaming your favorite TV series—*Deadwood.*

Siri reminds you that tonight is "bro-time" with your "fav" multiplayer game—Fortnite. And at 10:00 p.m., your avatar has a Horizon Worlds date, leaving limited encrypted VPN time.

You confirm with Siri that there's time for a few intimate moments with your favorite OnlyFans influencer (Bella).

"Alexa, schedule a coffee chat with my girlfriend? I bet you don't remember her name."

"It's Taylor, sir!"

"What does my calendar say for next month?" you enquire.

"She's not available that month and doesn't recall your name either. But wants to know about the month after."

Siri interrupts, "PayPal is requesting payment, and your Equifax score is down two points."

"Alert—Defcon 4—employer attempting neuro-link emo scan and direct brain computer interface. Stand-down, intercept successful. Pornhub is back online."

The real overarching theme of modernity is organizational complexity, and it is about to go exponential on us. Our wide and deep cognitive bandwidth is novel and will be tapped as fully as possible. While we may find relief in the simulation we are entering, we are now engaging a new level of complexity— and as stated here many times, it is complexity that is rapidly evolving, and not so much us—we are adapting. *How we adapt to complexity is driving our future and the single most important challenge facing the human condition.* Soon, two forms of absolute-mindedness will clash, human and machine. And only one outcome leads to the future.

The real question before us is: What forms will machine absolutism take? Technological intrusion will scale down to nano-CRISPR'd pluripotent stem cells, transcranial penetrating mind control and scale up to every networked sphere of human activity. It will operate at the direction and behest of corporations and governments around the world. The body will no longer be imperious but rather a harmonic bandwidth instrument. The reality is the world is neither rich enough nor sapiens smart enough for any other alternative.

Because change is a universal imperative, we must move beyond crisis intervention to technological redundancy to mitigate all possible contingencies. (Just recently, sapiens nudged an asteroid from its collision path with the Earth—that's what we are talking about!). The power of machine intelligence will be to ensure that our simulated networks are resilient to the extraordinary reach of small unpredictable events and their potentially catastrophic consequences.

And the problem with this strategy is, most small, unpredictable events have relatively little or no impact. This will require broad levels of control and suppression to mitigate low probability events. AI prediction will help, but it is not going to be Nostradamus.

In the pre-Singularity future, if machine intelligence has one overriding responsibility, one overarching directive, it will be to mitigate and tamp down the amplification of small changes on complex social networks. That also means you and me. We will not be the first priority; network reliability is machine priority for now. We will be straightened out later, which could put us at risk.

Do we fantasize a future without problems or struggle? A world free of sorrow and despair—one without disappointment—where happiness and contentment are mandatory? Are we constructing a future free of the unexpected and unpredictable? One where we believe all our needs will be met—as if we could possibly know what we will want and need in the future. Maybe Garrison Keillor's Lake Wobegon was prescient—*where all the women are strong, all the men are good-looking, and all the children are above average.*

Daydreaming after Work

He slumped into his sofa exhausted from sitting all day at his computer. Finally, in the shadow of night he watches the ballgame, snacks on chips, drinks beer while checking for text messages. Falling asleep, he dreamt that 21 million days ago (give or take a few)—a hunting party sprints along a ridge above the Olduvai Gorge (they didn't know it by that name, but it was vast and amazing). Later, a hunter squatting alone in silence, stares down a steep precipice at a herd of gazelles grazing below the winding, catastrophic geology a world away. Dazed on wild berries and seeds he fantasizes in confusion: *How many more precipices are there?* And we want to know the future (insert maniacal laughter here).

Will we ever agree what the future should look like? Perhaps the more fundamental question we are faced with is, What is the future going to impose on us and how much influence will we exert? And can AI, rationalists, and absolutists live together, or will they self-select into diverging species continually competing for the same eco-niche, not unlike *Homo sapiens* and Neanderthals? One a marvel of technological hybridization and the other strutting 4 million years of tribal surety.

If the only choice is between the dystopian and the utopian, then any rationalist would have to lean toward the probability of a dystopian future. There are simply more darkened paths to the future than positive ones. The positive path is narrower and more treacherous. In contrast, the dark paths have many readily discernable threads (pandemic, meteoroid strike, nuclear mishap, climate change, ecological collapse, super-volcano, humans). On the other hand, here we are, which is sort of a miracle in itself—on a 13.5-billion-year cosmic roll.

Our long transition from a physical to a simulated reality is accelerating, seriously disrupting identity formation (Who am I? Who are we?), a unique characteristic that is defining of the human experience. Only this time, our ever, ongoing conflict will be to assert the uniqueness of humanity in the face of rising AI.

Going forward, it seems likely that there will be great struggle and risk, and catastrophic failure will continually haunt us. Most sapiens will live disappointing and tragic lives. The loss of human potential will be extraordinary and grievous. There will be many different perilous futures, all fragile and utterly unknown to us. And there will be endless speculation about them as well.

Summary

- We are random and not that special. What might make us unique among species is our cognitive complexity. We should proceed cautiously. We need all the other species more than they need us.

- It turns out that innocuous and inconsequential changes in our dynamically networked systems can result in profound shifts in the most elementary aspects of our world. This should give us pause going forward.

- While our shifting perspectives have led to unending dispute, the question arises: What is the essence of being human and the case for our existence? We will enter this debate for the very first time with the rise of machine intelligence.

- With the advent of the internet, it was inevitable that conflict would jump track and achieve many new conflicted forms online, including all manner of mischief, deviance, and antisocial behavior. The real question before us is: How will conflict re-enter the world through the coming simulation?

- The real power of e-technology is that it projects each of us out into the world. What was once internal to each of us, with limited scope, is now external with unlimited reach for nearly everyone. Based on our conflicted and disruptive inner lives, do you see any potential problems here?

- Due to the rapid evolutionary development of complex social networks, sapiens have lapsed cognitively and emotionally, unable to keep up with the speed of change. If we are to survive, we will require immediate upgrades. Let's hope it's not painful.

- There are probably no circumstances in which broad and deep social changes did not lead to civil disruption—not unlike European colonialism. Who would have predicted that e-technology would extend the grip of authoritarian regimes, when its aspirational business model was to make us more communicative and connected?

- Initially, the unprecedented data haul by technology companies began as a benign commercial effort to monetize services, but quickly morphed into the political arena and comprehensive efforts to spread disinformation, influence and suppress voters, undermine democratic norms and surveil and control large populations. This is the new colonialism—now is not the time to become mesmerized by *data illusion*.

- Over time, each of us will have voluntarily sacrificed increments of freedom for convenience and security. This trade-off is built into our

DNA presets. As we voluntarily reduce ourselves to essential data—for security, health, convenience, relevance, and entertainment—we are exposing ourselves without caution to the world. There will be consequences.

- Many of us we will fall in love with our more perfect synthetic-selves and synth-partners because we are lonely and desperate to anthropomorphize an empty emotional life.

- In the pre-Singularity future, machine intelligence's one overriding responsibility will be to mitigate and tamp down the amplification of small changes on complex social networks.

- Any competitive scenario that is arbitrarily unfair and ends in gross advantages for some and few for others, but always in death—*life*—for instance, will always result in chaotic consequences. That is the future.

- Sapiens' ongoing conflict will be to assert the uniqueness of humanity in the face of rising AI.

11.0 – No Plan for the Future Either!

Attracted by a beauty I have not yet experienced.
—D. Deutsch, *The Beginning of Infinity*

Not only is there no plan for the future, there never was one, and there is no alternative to the future either. We need to get over the fact that this defeats one of the fundamental drivers of consciousness, to predict the future. As a result, it is fair to conjecture that chaos is bound to ensue in all its unexpected forms. Because the futurists, the TED talk influencers, and technologists have no clue what is in store for us, we should probably give the science fiction writers greater latitude on discovering the future.

With consciousness having outsourced evolution through our dynamically networked world, it is now advancing so rapidly that it is beyond prediction. Everything we have heard of or read on the topic is imaginative, but probably not in any substantive way.

Tens of thousands of experiments are being conducted across dozens of technology fields, each making advances that none of us can fully understand. Many times, not even the researchers conducting these experiments (chemistry, biology, material sciences, engineering, medicine, computer sciences, robotics, and the many dozens of subfields within them) completely understand them and certainly not the potential outcomes and consequences. Understanding what is transpiring in even one obscure subfield is beyond our comprehension, let alone hundreds of research areas.

Regardless, we are rapidly moving forward with innovation. This is all being driven by knowledge creators, as 2.27 percent of the bell curve are hell-bent on moving forward. We are now at a survival tipping point that should lead us to cheer them on. This world will dramatically shift and change in ways that will lead us to judge the past 100 years as relatively static. Mostly, we won't know it because we will be too busy.

To date, our technological transformation has been slow but is picking up speed. If you wear contacts, use a hearing aid, underwent Lasik eye surgery, joint or hip replacement, gastric sleeve, have been aided by a prosthetic limb, stent, pacemaker, artificial heart valve, underwent a heart or liver transplant, or submitted to cosmetic surgery—you are participating in the future. We are biochemically experimenting as well—birth control, in vitro fertilization, Botox, human growth hormones, and sexual and cognitive enhancers.

There are experiments at the genetic level—GMOs, gene editing, immune-system-targeted therapeutics, cloning, artificially grown human organs. There are also evolving minimally invasive treatments such as electrical and magnetic stimulation of brain cells to reduce seizures, enhance memory, and relieve depression. And soon, there will be algorithms that will read your mind and manipulate your brain waves into contented placidness.

Simultaneous with the rise of AI will be increased manipulation of the world through knowledge creation. The potential impact on human biology is beyond our imagination—disease control, increased longevity, cognitive enhancements, genetic advancements. We will begin the genetic human augmentation of our species and change the course of natural evolution, bending it to our imagination. AI will begin to displace the ordinary course of human social interaction and become our first interface with another species since Neanderthals.

We will see the world through many new lenses, interactive screens, and heads-up displays, uploading and downloading data as we physically navigate an altered reality. This will change how we interact and come to understand the world we live in, and reality itself.

But wait! There's considerable speculation that we will extend our evolutionary timeline due to the creation of a race of technologically superior sapiens. We will get upgraded immune systems, cognitive enhancements, and extended life spans due to nanotechnologies and gene editing. Coevolving with us will be synthetic life on the verge of displacing humans for most tasks, developing their own inter-subjective existence, and seeing and understanding the world in ways we don't or can't. Two competing species inhabiting the same ecological niche; what could possibly go wrong here? Evolutionary biologists suggest that the least adaptive species will disappear after a brief merger. Wonder who that will be? Yes, there will be an integrative phase, until our aging genetic programming no longer justifies the investment.

The reality may be that we are nothing more than a trivial evolutionary dead end, an experiment in consciousness and its adaptive possibilities lost due to global warming. Nothing personal here, nothing uniquely adaptive; it's just business—didn't work, didn't survive, let's move on, next—techno-intelligence. Wonder if there's anything uniquely adaptive here? Fewer programming bugs, better integration with fewer lines of code, longer lifespan and infinitely easier to reproduce and upgrade. Ours will have been a brief but spectacular evolutionary moment—consciousness—a darting firefly in a universe lit by stars.

As it has arisen over the past two centuries, technology constitutes nothing less than an effort to make humans function more machine-like. That, of course, was not the goal; it was the opposite. The irony is both goals have been accomplished, but at a significant cost. This quest is likely to continue exponentially, while we give lip service to making machines more human-like. And there's considerable speculation that we will be functionally more machine-like and technologically hybrid in the coming future. We may not be able to survive without making this transition.

As machines rise, humans will become a redundancy that requires reformulation. This is not only the task before all of us to reach the future, but also one with great risk and consequences. We all need to understand that our electronic interface is altering our identity, a necessary precondition for the rise of machine intelligence and the coming Singularity (S2). This is not a coincidence—as only AI will be able to manage the complexity of our simulated reality.

Futurists and thought influencers are continually speculating about the future, not unlike ancient Greek oracles. The range of speculation is expansive across many planes: dystopian-to-utopian, extinction-to-immortality, hedonism-to-transcendence. Many questions abound. Will we be better off? How different will we be? And will we survive? The answer is always the same—no one knows the future.

The game's cheat codes are not available, no matter how many levels we have advanced. There also has been considerable speculation that nothing has significantly changed with the advent of our electronic interface. Certainly nothing as obviously life-changing as electricity or the internal combustion engine. However, a case could be made that the entire world is currently being reconfigured, only from the inside out. That's why it is not only so obvious, but also more significant. While we are all being sold the elixir of technological salvation, the science fiction writers are at least honest enough to explore all the alternatives. And utopia, correctly, is not one of them. The future, without a doubt, will also be one of *sorrow*.

Perhaps we should all step back for a moment and contemplate the wisdom of Ernest Becker in his insightful book, *Denial of Death*. Here, he conjectures—"How do we know ... that part of the meaning of the universe might not be a rhythm in sorrow?" We seldom contemplate a future in which sorrow is a critical element of our destiny. Why is that? Becker then adds somewhat hopefully—"The most that any one of us can do is fashion something—an object or ourselves ... and drop it into the confusion...."

Electronic Bliss or Heroic Transcendence? Your Choice

So, what does all this portend? You are now only a neuro-upgrade from controlling all those undesirable thoughts and impulses. Besides, it will create enough pleasure and reward that you will not only enjoy it but also appreciate all the added benefits you gain from it.

Soon you will no longer be fully sapiens but a new and better adaptive variant. Inevitably, it will become simpler and cheaper to turn you into a bio-engineered hybrid, once everyone is on board with the *surveillance pleasure continuum*. Thriving in a data-rich, programmable cyber reality driven by endless sources of energy. You will not be able to resist it because it will be so much more fun and exciting (and much less stressful and worrisome). "No data-dump this time, bitch!"

We will embrace a modern electronic symbiosis that we can all get on board with—so long as you can afford the really massive data plan required to upgrade to all the good stuff; beginning with immortality (who can resist this upgrade), unlimited deep-consciousness and a hyperbolic pleasure-loop without induced resistance to ecstasy.

You can live out your existence fighting off "paperclips" in a never-ending combat for supremacy of the universe—and keep the Earth from being turned into a mining slurry pit. Or deep in the *Matrix*, you will deny insurance claims for Tesla owners for 100 million years and enjoy every moment of it—trapped in an infinity-loop, while algorithms work out the bugs.

What happens when we begin eliminating the random exigencies of life? We are about to find out. And more importantly, what happens if we like it? It might be wise to ask if there is going to be a future, with the realization that we will sacrifice it for the present—it's our nature, unfortunately. What technology has given us more than anything else is a glimpse of one potential future that we can only project our hopes and fears.

However, we are going forward, ready or not, toward every possibility we can imagine. That's our future. Do our actions today shape the future? Absolutely, but in the long term, we cannot know how or why. We might reasonably understand how tomorrow or the day after are affected—but not the destiny of a nation, culture or species. We face the black box riddle of the algorithmic future. Philosophic speculation is now giving voice to what is being termed Dadaism or "data-centric worldview," whereby, humans and all forms of life are cast as "data processing systems"—and death is the failure of information to flow. Culture is enhanced connectivity that expands data flows. What does this tell us about the future? We do not know.

Three hundred thousand years ago, there evolved a unique evolutionary experiment, when the human brain hit the 1400 cm^3 mark. This was an advance that paired higher intelligence with consciousness for the first time, resulting in two significant events: The development in humans of a vast intersubjective reality, capable of shaping the imagined world we live in today, and the unique pairing of intelligence in a symbiotic relationship with technology, of which the computer and its ability to network are the current apex.

The unanswered quandary in all of this, once we got the big brain, is why did it take so long for consciousness to fully ascend? What has been so unique about the past 400+ years? And why didn't all this happen sooner? Suspicions are that consciousness evolved slowly, even after we reached big brain status. Technological advancement likely required not only a density tipping point of exceptional people, but also an external means of information storage and retrieval as predicate to dynamically evolving networks.

It would also be reasonable to speculate that we wasted many thousands of years suppressing change as the safest adaptation. This effort is still ongoing and may limit the future, bringing the Anthropocene to an abrupt halt.

Species have come and gone through a multitude of extinction events, and most times, something equally profound has arisen in their place—that's how we got here in the first place. The dinosaurs had to go—all of them—after 500 million years of relative success. Maybe arising AI this time. Maybe not. Who could know? Currently, our future has many human drivers—empathy, creativity, knowledge formation, and the ubiquitous ones of greed, fear, and ambition—along with the primary ones of safety and security, and, of course, reproduction.

How does one begin to countenance the physics of small changes across complex and dynamical social networks—every person who is alive today and who will ever live, every thought and action in all the times to come? This is our unpredictable, chaotic future. This doesn't even begin to comprehend the eternal drivers of change—serendipity and stupidity!

The universe is an infinite probability machine. What percentage is in our favor, given we know how it ends every time? No one knows. Hey, this time it's a plasma flare. Didn't see that one coming! As current apostates of a dystopian future (Gates, Hawking, and Musk) have strongly hinted, AI poses many challenges and is potentially an existential threat.

While everyone anxiously anticipates the future, the reality is we are not getting to the future without advanced technology. We require technology to survive and will have to seriously worry about the consequences later. That is our current paradox. And, yes, this type of contingency planning has pretty much gotten us to where we are today, which is another problem—"Houston!"

The question is, Can cautionary measures forestall potentially devastating consequences? The answer is probably not, because we cannot predict the future, even a few years in advance (that's how fast we are moving now). Technology is exploding in unpredictable and unforeseen ways in the known present and coming future, and beyond conventional wisdom to fully comprehend or thwart. This is what I have termed the E-technology Anthropocene Explosion.

Initially, we will face existential risk from many unknown-unknowns, and, beyond that, the truly unknowable. We should do something—but I seriously doubt we know what to do, and even if we did, that we could agree on anything. Which means we are going to do something; we just don't know what. My guess is that we blunder forward and hope for the best.

We have any number of candidates for salvation going forward—the capacity for love and empathy; we are highly spiritual creatures and can serve a greater good, one that transcends the *self*; we can organize and solve problems in a crisis; serendipity, we could get cosmically lucky and, of course, the ever-popular, we are really, really smart. If you could bunch them all together, I would opt for a recessive quality all these traits share—imagination, the ability to create, and see beyond the obvious.

Evolution has always been a collective bargaining agreement and not an individual negotiation. It is also important to understand that it is the *wave-drive* or networked complexity that is rapidly evolving, independently of you, me, and all of us. How much complexity can we undertake? We are at the beginning of stress-testing this. What will become of all this is unknown. We don't get to choose, despite all the optimistic predictions of transcendent possibilities.

As an artist, I am betting on an outlier—creativity—because artists are prone to the inherent optimism of the creative process. Artists are always dropping "stuff" into the confusion to see what happens, and that's probably what we need to do. And as a result, I believe our evolving technology potentially represents the use of human imagination to disrupt the fundamental constant in the universe—entropy—and extend consciousness beyond its expiration date.

Imagination and its clever child, creativity, residing on the cusp of consciousness, are mostly unknown to us. But I believe them to be the great disrupters, the antagonists of entropy. It is the force of imagination that has risen to form the modern world and hopefully worlds to come. Creativity is a statement to the universe that we are capable of creating unlimited knowledge through technology.

In the coming future, we will have hopefully achieved what physicist David Deutsch terms the "beginning of infinity" and the endless creation of knowledge, rendering us an essential constant in the coming Singularity (S3). Be creative, I exhort—but invest heavily in all the other options as well. We should wish our children well, wherever they may go or whomever they may become.

Tell me: What future do you hope for? And then list all the consequences and possibilities of your vision you foresee—and never stop striving to bring them into clarity, then into reality—that's the only future there is—until there isn't.

…artists may be the most ruthless and persistent…they issue worlds of their own…for the entire cosmos to admire.

—A. Harrington, *The Immortalist*

References

Aggarwal, N. (7-9-2020) "Parents Make 1,750 Tough Decisions in Baby's First Year, Survey Say," the bump.com.

American Psychiatric Association. (2013) *Diagnostic and Statistical Manual of Mental Disorders* (DSM-5).

Andersen, R. (09/2020) 'The Panopticon is already here,' *The Atlantic.*

Andrews, B. (12/28/2020) 'Mind-controlling rats are now a thing,' *Discover Magazine.*

Arendt, H. (03/21/1973) *The Origins of Totalitarianism*, San Diego, CA: Harcourt, Brace, Jovanovich.

Barrat, J. (10/01/2013) *Artificial Intelligence and The End of The Human Era: Our Final Invention*, New York, NY: Griffin.

Beck, J. (12/18/2015) 'The Christmas the aliens didn't come,' *The Atlantic.*

Beck, J. (03/23/2016) 'Less than 3 percent of Americans live a 'healthy lifestyle,' *The Atlantic.*

Becker, E. (05/08/1997) *The Denial of Death*, New York, NY: Free Press.

Bell, J. (04/26/2017) 'Talking about periods beyond gender,' [Web log post]. Retrieved from https://helloclue.com/articles/cycle-a-z/talking-about-periods-beyond-gender.

Bennett, J. (01/30/2016) 'She? Ze? They? What's in a gender pronoun?' *New York Times.* Retrieved from https://www.nytimes.com/2016/01/31/fashion/pronoun-confusion-sexual-fluidity.html.

Bernstein, J. (12/17/2019) 'Alienated, alone and angry: What the digital revolution really did to us,' *Buzzfeed.* Retrieved from https://www.buzzfeednews.com/article/josephbernstein/in-the-2010s-decade-we-became-alienated-by-technology.

Bixler, E. O., Kales, J. D., and Healey, S. (1979) 'Prevalence of sleep disorders in the Los Angeles Metropolitan area,' *The American Journal of Psychiatry*, **136**, 10, 1257-62.

Bogost, I. (01/16/2020) 'Every place is the same now,' *The Atlantic.* Retrieved from https://www.theatlantic.com/technology/archive/2020/01/smartphone-has-ruined-space/605077/.

Bologna, M. and Aquino, G. (05/06/2020) 'Deforestation and world population sustainability: a quantitative analysis,' *Nature.*

Bostock, B. (03/02/2020) 'China enacted a sweeping new law that bars people from posting negative content online, ant it could be used to suppress coronavirus news,' *Business Insider.* Retrieved from https://www.businessinsider.com/china-internet-ban-criticism-could-suppress-coronavirus-news-2020-3.

Boyers, R. (09/24/2019) *The Tyranny of Virtue: Identity, the Academy, and the Hunt for Political Heresies*, Scribner.

Brockman, J. (02/19/2019) *Possible Minds: Twenty-Five Ways of Looking at AI*, London, England: Penguin Press.

Brooks, D. (10/5/2020) 'America is having a moral convulsion,' *The Atlantic.*

Bushwick, S. (04/30/2020) 'Step spy: New sensors pick up gait patterns remotely to identify people and monitor health,' *Scientific American.* Retrieved from https://www.scientificamerican.com/article/footstep-sensors-identify-people-by-gait/.

Chan, J. (12/20/2019) 'Amazon Echo speaker goes "rogue"; tells scared mom to "stab yourself",' *AOL.* Retrieved from https://www.aol.com/article/news/2019/12/20/.

Chayon, M. M. (31 August 2007) 'Prevalence and comorbidity of sleep disorders in general population,' *La Revue du Practicien*, **57**, 14, 1521-8.

Cherry, K. (09/29/2019) 'The trait theory of personality,' *Very Well Mind.* Retrieved from https://www.verywellmind.com/trait-theory-of-personality-2795955.

'Chinese smartphone health code rules post-virus life,' (04/01/2020) *Associated Press.* Retrieved from https://apnews.com/88f837f24461c6e40480c96b55a4b6db.

Chua, A. (02/20/2018) *Political Tribes: Group Instinct and the Fate of Nations*, London, England: Penguin Press.

Cobb, M. (02/27/2020) 'Why your brain is not a computer,' *The Guardian.* Retrieved from https://www.theguardian.com/science/2020/feb/27/why-your-brain-is-not-a-computer-neuroscience-neural-networks-consciousness.

'Code duello: The rules of dueling,' (n.d.) *PBS.* Retrieved from https://www.pbs.org/wgbh/americanexperience/features/duel-code-duello-rules-dueling/.

'Cognitive Dissonance,' Wikipedia. Wikimedia Foundation. (08/09/2020) Retrieved from https://en.wikipedia.org/wiki/Cognitive_dissonance.

Condemi, S. and Savatier, F. (10/03/2018) *A Pocket History of Human Evolution: How We Became Sapiens*, New York, NY: The Experiment, LLC.

Cornell University (01/27/2020) 'Profound evolution: wasps learn to recognize faces,' *Phys.org*. Retrieved from https://phys.org/news/2020-01-profound-evolution-wasps.

Courthouse News (5/4/22) 'Tiger Widows Shunned as Bad Luck in Rural Bangladesh,' courthousenew.com

Crossman, A. (01/30/2020) 'What is symbolic interactionism?,' *ThoughtCo*. Retrieved from https://www.thoughtco.com/symbolic-interaction-theory-3026633.

Culver, J. (05/21/2020) 'A Canadian teenager has been charged with terrorism inspired by the online 'incel' movement. What is an incel?,' *USA Today*. Retrieved from https://www.usatoday.com/story/news/world/2020/05/21/.

Cuncic, A. (07/19/2019) 'Coping with existential anxiety,' *Very Well Mind*. Retrieved from https://www.nybooks.com/articles/2020/04/09/bigger-brother-surveillance-capitalism/.

Cyphers, B. and Gullo, K. (06/30/2020) 'Inside the invasive, secretive "bossware" tracking workers' [Web log post]. Retrieved from https://www.eff.org/deeplinks/2020/06/.

Davidson, J. (08/03/2020) 'Physicists: 90% chance of human society collapsing within decades,' *EcoWatch*.

Dengler, R. (12/31/2019) 'A million species in danger,' *Discover Magazine*.

Deutsch, D. (03/31/2011) *The Beginning of Infinity: Explanations That Transform the World*, London, England: Penguin Press.

"Dox" (n.d.) In *Merriam-Webster.com Dictionary*. Retrieved from https://www.merriam-webster.com/dictionary/dox.

Eadicicco, L. (05/07/2020) 'Elon Musk says there's a chance his AI-brain-chip company will be putting implants in humans within a year,' *Pulse*. Retrieved from https://www.pulse.ng/bi/tech/elon-musk-says-theres-a-chance-his-ai-brain-chip-company-will-be-putting-implants-in/zygp6fm.

Echard, S. (n.d.) 'The ruin.' Retrieved from https://faculty.arts.ubc.ca/sechard/oeruin.htm. "Epigenetics: Fundamentals" (n.d.) Retrieved from https://www.whatisepigenetics.com.

Epstein, R. H. (02/10/2020) 'Bruce McEwen, 81, is dead; Found stress can alter the brain,, *New York Times*. Retrieved from https://www.nytimes.com/2020/02/10/science/bruce-s-mcewen-dead.html.

Eveleth, R. (10/08/2019) 'The biggest lie tech people tell themselves—and the rest of us,' *Vox*. Retrieved from https://www.vox.com/the-highlight/2019/10/1/20887003/tech-technology-evolution-natural-inevitable-ethics.

Ferrie, J. E., Kumari, M., Salo, P., Singh-Manoux, A. and Kivimaki, M. (December 2011) 'Sleep epidemiology: a rapidly growing field,' *International Journal of Epidemiology*, **40**, 6, 1431-7.

Finga, J. (01/14/2020) 'Study finds Grindr, OKCupid, and Tinder sharing sensitive data' [Web log post]. Retrieved from https://www.engadget.com/2020-01-14-study-finds-grindr-okcupid-tinder-spreading-sensitive-data.html.

Fukuyama, F. (03/01/2006) *The End of History and the Last Man*, New York, NY: Free Press.

Gawande, A. (01/01/2015) *Being Mortal Illness, Medicine and What Matters in the End*, London, England: Picador.

Goodin, D. (07/01/2020) 'Uncovered: 1,000 phrases that incorrectly trigger Alexa, Siri, and Google Assistant' [Web log post]. Retrieved from https://arstechnica.com/information-technology/2020/07/uncovered-1000-phrases-that-incorrectly-trigger-alexa-siri-and-google-assistant/.

Grudniewicz, A., Moher, D., Cobey, K. D., et. al. (12/11/2019) 'Predatory journals: no definition, no defense,' *Nature*, **576**, 210-2. doi: 10.1038/d41586-019-03759-y.

Harari, Y. N. (2017) *Homo Deus: A Brief History of Tomorrow*, New York, NY: Harper.

Harrington, A. (1977) *The Immortalist*, Berkeley, CA: Celestial Arts.

Harwell, D. (04/30/2020) 'Managers turn to surveillance software, always-on webcams to ensure employees are (really) working from home,' *Washington Post*. Retrieved from https://www.washingtonpost.com/technology/2020/04/30/work-from-home-surveillance/.

Haynie, D. (09/11/2020) 'Report: American quality of life declines over past decade,' *US News*.

Heilweil, R. (01/01/2020) 'Illinois says you should know if AI is grading your online job interviews,' *Vox*. Retrieved from https://www.vox.com.

Hewitt, J. P. (03/15/2010) *Self and Society: A Symbolic Interactionist Social Psychology*, London, England: Pearson.

Houser, K. (01/14/2020) 'The ocean is warming at a rate of 5 atom bombs per second, scientists warn,' *Science Alert*. Retrieved from https://www.sciencealert.com/the-ocean-is-warming-at-a-rate-of-5-atom-bombs-per-second-says-study.

Huntington, S. P. (08/02/2011) *The Clash of Civilizations and the Remaking of World Order*, New York, NY: Simon & Schuster.

Hvistendahl, M. (05/10/2020) 'How a Chinese AI giant made chatting—and surveillance easy,' *Wired*. Retrieved from https://www.wired.com/story/iflytek-china-ai-giant-voice-chatting-surveillance/.

"I and Thou." Wikipedia. Wikimedia Foundation. (02/18/2020) Retrieved from https://en.wikipedia.org/wiki/I_and_Thou.

Inglehart, R. F. (03/22/2018) *Cultural Evolution*, Cambridge University Press.

Inglehart, R. F. (09/2020) 'Giving up on God: the global decline of religion,' *Foreign Affairs*.

Inovalon. (2020) 'Why AI is the game changer healthcare needs,' *New York Times*. Retrieved from https://www.nytimes.com/paidpost/inovalon/why-ai-is-the-game-changer-healthcare-needs.html?smid=em-share.

Isikoff, M. (03/02/2020) 'Did the CIA's notorious mind control program create an infamous killer?' *Yahoo*. Retrieved from https://news.yahoo.com/did-the-ci-as-notorious-mind-control-program-create-an-infamous-killer-145804316.html.

Kang, C. and Frenkel, S. (06/27/2020) 'PizzaGate conspiracy theory thrives anew in the TikTok era,' *New York Times*. Retrieved from https://www.nytimes.com/2020/06/27/technology/pizzagate-justin-bieber-qanon-tiktok.html.

Karnes, E. (08/13/2020) 'The South Korean YouTuber Burned His Dick Off During a Livestream,' *The Blemish*.

Kendall-Taylor, A., Frantz, E. and Wright, J. (03/2020) 'The digital dictators,' *Foreign Affairs*.

Klein, E. (01/01/2020) 'How technology literally changes our brains,' *Vox*.

Koestler, A. and Butterfield, H. (06/05/1990) *The Sleepwalkers: A History of Man's Changing Vision of the Universe*, London, England: Penguin Books.

Konkoly, et al. (2021) "Real-time dialogue between experimenters and dreamers during REM sleep," *Current Biology* 31, 1417-1427.

Krebbs, B. (05/19/2015) 'A tough week for IP address scammers.' [Web log post]. Retrieved from https://krebsonsecurity.com/2019/05/a-tough-week-for-ip-address-scammers/.

Kurzweil, R. (09/26/2006) *The Singularity Is Near: When Humans Transcend Biology*, London, England: Penguin Books.

Kwon, D. (11/2020) 'A disorder of the mind and brain,' *Scientific American.*

LaFrance, A. (06/2020) 'The prophecies of Q,' *The Atlantic.* Retrieved from https://www.theatlantic.com/magazine/archive/2020/06/qanon-nothing-can-stop-what-is-coming/610567/.

Lasch, C. (05/17/1991) *The Culture of Narcissism: American Life in An Age of Diminishing Expectations*, New York, NY: W. W. Norton & Company.

Lathan, C. E. and Ling, G. (07/01/2019) 'Social robots: Droid friends and assistants are penetrating deeper into our olives,' *Scientific American.*

Lathan, C. E., and Maynard, A. (07/01/2019) 'Collaborative telepresence: participants in virtual gatherings will feel like they are physically together,' *Scientific American.*

Lee, S. Y. (07/01/2019) 'DNA data storage: life's information-storage system is being adapted to handle massive amounts of information,' *Scientific American.*

Leger, D., Guilleminault, C. and Dreyfus, J. P. (2000, March) 'Prevalence of insomnia in a survey of 12,778 adults in France,' *Journal of Sleep Research*, **9**, 1, 35-42.

Legg, T. J. and Kandola, A. (04/18/2018) 'What does nonbinary mean?' [Web log post]. Retrieved from https://www.medicalnewstoday.com/articles/321529.

Lewis, R. (11/01/2017) *Under Surveillance: Being Watched in Modern America*, Austin, TX: University of Texas Press.

Longrich, N. (11/21/2019) 'Were other humans the first victims of the sixth mass extinction?,' *Yahoo*. Retrieved from https://news.yahoo.com/were-other-humans-first-victims-153310350.html.

Lopez, L. (12/15/2019) 'China's next gambit to save its economy will export dystopia worldwide,' *Business Insider*. Retrieved from https://www.businessinsider.com.

Macdonald, K. (06/02/2020) 'Stupidly dangerous things that used to be considered normal,' *Maternity Week*. Retrieved from https://maternityweek.com

"Magical Thinking", Wikipedia. Wikimedia Foundation. (08/06/2020) Retrieved from https://en.wikipedia.org/wiki/Magical_thinking.

Manskar, N. (06/11/2020) 'Zoom suspends US activists for commemorating Tiananmen Square massacre,' *NY Post*. Retrieved from https://nypost.com/2020/06/11/.

Martone, R. (10/29/2019) 'Scientists demonstrate direct brain-to-brain communication in humans,' *Scientific American*. Retrieved from https://www.scientificamerican.com.

Mayor, A. (11/27/2018) *Gods and the Robots*, Princeton, NJ: Princeton University Press.

Mazzetti, M., Perlroth, N., and Bergman, R. (12/22/2019) 'It seemed like a popular chat app. It's secretly a spy tool,' *New York Times*. Retrieved from https://www.nytimes.com.

McEwen, B. (2018) *The Hostage Brain*, Franklin Classics Trade Press, NY.

McLeod, S. (2017) 'Theories of personality,' *Simply Psychology.*

McLeod, S. A. (02/05/2018) 'Cognitive Dissonance,' *Simply Psychology.*

McNamee, R. (06/07/2020) 'Facebook cannot fix itself,' *TIME.*

McKinney, K. (08/24/2020) 'How to sleep better,' *TIME.*

Meerwijk, E. L. and Sevelius, J. M. (01/11/2017) 'Transgender size in the United States: A meta-regression of population-based probability samples,' *Am J Public Health*, **107**, 2, 1-8. doi: 10.2105/AJPH.2016.303578

Melby, P. (06/11/2012) 'Insatiable shipyards: The impact of the royal navy on the world's forests,' 1200-1850 (Master's thesis). Retrieved from Semantics Scholar database. (Corpus ID: 115676493).

Miller, K. (10/24/2019) 'The 2010s broke our sense of time,' *Buzzfeed.* Retrieved from https://www.buzzfeednews.com/article/katherinemiller/the-2010s-have-broken-our-sense-of-time.

Miller, K. (05/2020) 'This is your brain on tech,' *Discover Magazine.*

Mirsky, S. (11/2019) 'Chairman: cardiovascular disease's link to stress sat in plain sight,' *Scientific American.*

Mitchem, S. (05/26/2020) 'Novel insight reveals topological tangle in unexpected corner of the universe,' *Phys.org.* Retrieved from https://phys.org/news/2020-05.

Morrison, R. (12/27/2019) 'Information has been TELEPORTED simultaneously between two chips for the first time which could help 'protect the world's data' on superfast quantum computers,' *Daily Mail*. Retrieved from https://www.dailymail.co.uk.

Moskowitz, C. (04/07/2016) 'Are we living in a computer simulation?,' *Scientific American*. Retrieved from https://www.scientificamerican.com/article/are-we-living-in-a-computer-simulation/.

Muehlenkamp, R. (01/08/2017) 'How many people died in all the wars in the 20th century?' Retrieved from https://www.quora.com/How-many-people-died-in-all-the-wars-in-the-20th-century.

Murphy, C. (01/2020) 'Our predictions about the internet are probably wrong,' *The Atlantic*. Retrieved from https://www.theatlantic.com/magazine/archive/2020/01/.

Murphy, C. (07/2020) 'The man who sacked Rome,' *The Atlantic*. Retrieved from https://www.theatlantic.com/magazine/archive/2020/07/douglas-boin-alaric-the-goth/612268/.

Musser, G. (06/01/2018) 'What is Spacetime?,' *Scientific American*.

Nenquimo, N. (10/12/2020) 'This is my message to the western world - your civilization is killing life on Earth,' *The Guardian*.

Nuzzi, O. (06/2020) 'What it's like to get doxed for taking a bike ride,' *New York Magazine*. Retrieved from https://nymag.com/intelligencer/2020/06/what-its-like-to-get-doxed-for-taking-a-bike-ride.html.

Paisley, J. (12/05/2019) 'I documented every surveillance camera on my way to work in New York City, and it revealed a dystopian reality,' *Business Insider*. Retrieved from https://www.businessinsider.

"Panopticon", Wikipedia. Wikimedia Foundation. (06/15/2020) Retrieved from https://en.wikipedia.org/wiki/Panopticon.

Perlmutter, D. and Ganim, K. L. P. (04/28/2015) *Brain Maker: The Power of Gut Microbes to Heal and Protect Your Brain for Life*, New York, NY: Little, Brown Spark.

Priest, D. (06/21/2020) 'Spyware technology found on phone of Moroccan journalist, report says,' *The Washington Post.* Retrieved from https://www.washingtonpost.com.

Qiang, X. (01/2019) 'The road to digital unfreedom,' *Journal of Democracy*, **30**, 1. Retrieved from https://muse.jhu.edu/article713722.

Qmechanic (11/14/2014) 'Can quantum entanglement and quantum superposition be considered the same phenomenon?' [Web log post] Retrieved from https://physics.stackexchange.com.

Reese, B. (04/28/2018) *The Fourth Age: Smart Robots, Conscious Computers, and the Future of Humanity*, New York, NY: Atria Books.

Reynolds, G. (09/09/2020) 'Exercise may make it easier to bounce back from stress,' *The New York Times.*

Rieff, P. (11/20/2006) *The Triumph of the Therapeutic: Uses of Faith after Freud*, Chicago, IL: The University of Chicago Press.

Robson, D. (08/17/2020) 'The "Batman Effect": how having an alter ego empowers you,' *BBC.*

Romano, A. (06/22/2020) 'How K-pop fans are weaponizing the internet for Black Lives Matter,' *Vox.* Retrieved from https://www.vox.com

Rosenberger, L. (05/2020) 'Making cyberspace safe for democracy,' *Foreign Affairs.*

Rovelli, C. (05/08/2018) *The Order of Time*, New York, NY: Riverhead Books.

Sadik-Khan, J. and Solomonow, S. (03/2020) 'Mean streets: the global traffic death crisis,' *Foreign Affairs.*

Samuel, S. (09/09/2020) 'You can get a robot to keep your lonely grandparents company. Should You?,' *Vox.*

Scott, S. (n. d.) '"Martin Buber." In Internet Encyclopedia of Philosophy,' Retrieved from https://www.iep.utm.edu/buber/.

Shankland, S. (2019) 'Elon Musk says Neuralink plans 2020 human test of brain-computer interface,' *Cnet.*

Shulevitz, J. (11/2019) 'Why you never see your friends anymore,' *The Atlantic.* Retrieved from
https://www.theatlantic.com/magazine/archive/2019/11/why-dont-i-see-you-anymore/598336/.

Sitaraman, G. (03/2020) 'Too big to prevail,' *Foreign Affairs.* "Sitting vs smoking: What's the scale of the risk?" *The One Brief.* Retrieved from https://theonebrief.com/sitting-vs-smoking-whats-the-scale-of-the-risk/.

Smith, D. (02/17/2009) *The Most Dangerous Animal,* New York, NY: St. Martin's Griffin.

Snouwaert, J. (05/08/2020) 'Elon Musk predicts people won't have to talk in 10 years because they'll be able to use an alien-like mind language to communicate without words.' [Web log post] Retrieved from
https://www.msn.com/en-us/money/other/elon-musk-predicts-people-wont-have-to-talk-in-10-years-because-theyll-be-able-to-use-an-alien-like-mind-language-to-communicate-without-words/ar-BB13NAib.

Southworth, P. (09/20/2020) 'Anglo-Saxon skull found with nose and lips cut off is first physical evidence of brutal punishment for adultery,' *Yahoo.*

Spataro, J. (04/08/2020) 'The future of work - the good, the challenging, and the unknown,' *Microsoft.*

Statt, N. (12/29/2017) 'Swatting over Call of Duty game results in deadly police shooting of Kansas man,' *The Verge.* Retrieved from https://www.theverge.com/2017/12/29/16830626/call-of-duty-swatting-prank-kansas-man-dead-police-shooting.

Stetka, B. (10/31/2020) 'How humans domesticated themselves,' *NPR.*

Stossel, S. and Knopf, A. A. (12/09/2014) 'What are you worried about? The fascinating history of anxiety' [Web log post]. Retrieved from https://www.alternet.org/2014/12/.

Sullivan, A. (06/12/2020) 'Is there still room for debate?,' *New York Magazine.* Retrieved from https://nymag.com/intelligencer/2020/06/andrew-sullivan-is-there-still-room-for-debate.html.

Sutter, P. (10/29/2019) 'An unpredictable universe: a deep dive into chaos theory,' *Space.* Retrieved from https://www.space.com/chaos-theory-explainer-unpredictable-systems.

Swales, V. (12/15/2019) 'When the O.K. sign is no longer O.K.,' *New York Times.* Retrieved from https://www.nytimes.com/2019/12/15/us/ok-sign-white-power.html.

"Synapses" (04/17/2004) *Biology Mad.* Retrieved from https://biologymad.com.

Tainter, J. (03/29/1990) *The Collapse of Complex Societies,* New York, NY: Cambridge University Press.

Tarlach, G. (01/2020) 'An old tooth and a new view of evolution,' *Discover Magazine.*

Tashea, J. (05/01/2017) 'Inaccurate leads from IP addresses prompt police to serve warrants on innocent people,' *ABA Journal.* Retrieved from https://www.abajournal.com/magazine/article/tor_technology_police_warrants_innocent.

Tau, B. (06/19/2020) 'IRS used cellphone location data to try to find suspects,' *The Wall Street Journal*. Retrieved from https://www.wsj.com/articles.

Tegmark, M. (08/23/2017) *Life 3.0: Being Human in the Age of Artificial Intelligence*, New York, NY: Vintage.

"The blogger who hit back against a hammer-wielding Russian 'assassin,'" (06/17/2020) *BBC News*. Retrieved from https://www.bbc.com/news/stories-53066537.

The Editorial Board. (12/21/2019) 'Total surveillance is not what America signed up for,' *New York Times*. Retrieved from https://www.nytimes.com.

"The founder of cosmic inflation theory on cosmology's next big ideas." (n. d.) *Scientific American*. Retrieved from https://www.scientificamerican.com.

"The lines of code that changed everything." (10/14/2009) *Slate*. Retrieved from https://slate.com/technology/2019/10/.

Thompson, D. (01/2020) 'The real trouble with Silicon Valley,' *The Atlantic*. Retrieved from https://www.theatlantic.com/magazine/archive/2020/01/wheres-my-flying-car.

Toews, R. (05/25/2020) 'Deepfakes are going to wreak havoc on society. We are not prepared,' *Forbes*. Retrieved from https://www.forbes.com.

Tolstoy, L., Solotaroff, L. and Blythe, R. (03/01/1981) *The Death of Ivan Ilyich*, New York, NY: Bantam Classicals.

Velasquez-Manoff, M. (08/28/2020) 'The brain implants that could change humanity,' *The New York Times*.

Vijayan, J. (12/26/2019) 'Ransomware situation goes from bad to worse,' *Dark Reading*. Retrieved from https://www.darkreading.com/attacks-breaches/ransomware-sitation-goes-from-bad-to-worse.

Virk, R. (03/31/2019) *The Simulation Hypothesis*, Baywood Books, LLC.

Wadhwa, V. (09/11/2020) 'The genetic engineering genie is out of the bottle,' *Voice.*

Wadman, M. (06/05/2020) 'Abortion opponents protest COVID-19 vaccines' use of fetal cells,' *Science Mag.* Retrieved from https://www.sciencemag.org/news/2020/06.

Walter, J. (12/17/2019) 'Elon Musk wants to put computers in people's heads,' *Discover Magazine.*

Watercutter, A. (06/25/2020) 'Doomscrolling is slowly eroding your mental health' [Web log post]. Retrieved from https://www.wired.com/story/stop-doomscrolling/.

Wee, S. (06/17/2020) 'China is collecting DNA from tens of millions of men and boys, using U.S. equipment,' *New York Times.* Retrieved from https://www.nytimes.com.

Weisberger, M. (07/31/2020) 'Mind-controlling fungus makes zombie cicadas lure other cicadas to a zombie fate,' *Live Science.*

Wong, M. and Bartlett, S. (5/4/22) 'Asymptotic burnout and homeostatic awakening: a possible solution to the Fermi paradox,' *Journal of the Royal Society Interface*, Vol 19, No 196.

Wu, T. (04/09/2020) 'Bigger brother,' *New York Books.* Retrieved from https://www.nybooks.com

Yonck, R. (03/07/2017) *Heart of the Machine: Our Future in a World of Artificial Emotional Intelligence*, New York, NY: Arcade.

"40 worrisome hacking statistics that concern us all in 2020." (n.d.) Retrieved from https://hostingtribunal.com/blog/hacking-statistics/#gref.